PRINCIPLES OF
FOREST ENTOMOLOGY

THE AMERICAN FORESTRY SERIES

HENRY J. VAUX, CONSULTING EDITOR

Allen and Sharpe • An Introduction to American Forestry
Baker • Principles of Silviculture
Boyce • Forest Pathology
Brockman • Recreational Use of Wild Lands
Brown, Panshin, and Forsaith • Textbook of Wood Technology
    Volume II—The Physical, Mechanical, and Chemical Properties
    of the Commercial Woods of the United States
Bruce and Schumacher • Forest Mensuration
Chapman and Meyer • Forest Mensuration
Chapman and Meyer • Forest Valuation
Dana • Forest and Range Policy
Davis • American Forest Management
Davis • Forest Fire: Control and Use
Duerr • Fundamentals of Forestry Economics
Graham and Knight • Principles of Forest Entomology
Guise • The Management of Farm Woodlands
Harlow and Harrar • Textbook of Dendrology
Hunt and Garratt • Wood Preservation
Panshin, de Zeeuw, and Brown • Textbook of Wood Technology
    Volume I—Structure, Identification, Uses, and Properties of the
    Commercial Woods of the United States
Panshin, Harrar, and Bethel • Forest Products
Preston • Farm Wood Crops
Shirley • Forestry and Its Career Opportunities
Stoddart and Smith • Range Management
Trippensee • Wildlife Management
    Volume I—Upland Game and General Principles
    Volume II—Fur Bearers, Waterfowl, and Fish
Wackerman • Harvesting Timber Crops

WALTER MULFORD WAS CONSULTING EDITOR OF THIS SERIES
FROM ITS INCEPTION IN 1931 UNTIL JANUARY 1, 1952.

FOURTH EDITION

PRINCIPLES
OF FOREST
ENTOMOLOGY

SAMUEL ALEXANDER GRAHAM

Professor Emeritus of Economic Zoology
School of Natural Resources
University of Michigan

FRED BARROWS KNIGHT

Associate Professor of Forest Entomology
School of Natural Resources
University of Michigan

McGRAW-HILL BOOK COMPANY

New York · St. Louis · San Francisco
Toronto · London · Sydney

FRONTISPIECE. These fine specimens of trembling aspen have grown to maturity. Meanwhile, a stand of balsam fir has grown beneath them. The firs, already approaching merchantable size, will be released over a period of years as the mature aspen become decadent and die one at a time. Once released, the fir will become suitable for a spruce budworm outbreak, whereas while growing under the aspen, it is safe from such injury. By prompt utilization of such stands of balsam fir when they reach merchantable maturity, outbreaks of the budworm can be avoided. If aspens and balsam firs are clear-cut simultaneously, a new stand of aspen will be established by root suckers and a new stand of balsam fir from small seedlings now on the ground will grow under them. (Courtesy of the Manistee News Advocate.)

TO OUR STUDENTS
on whose shoulders rests the responsibility of converting
into practice that which we teach, and

TO OUR RESPECTIVE WIVES
who have each contributed generously to this work

Since 1929, when this elementary textbook on forest entomology was published under the title "Principles of Forest Entomology," advances in the field have necessitated two revisions. This fourth edition begins a new phase. Now retired from the formal teaching of students, the senior author has been joined by a junior author, Dr. Fred B. Knight, whose writing, based upon his wide personal experience with recent developments, lends a fresh tone to this new edition.

By design, this is an introductory text on forest entomology for undergraduate forestry students, rather than a work on forest insects from the viewpoint of the entomologist. On this introduction the student can build his further training. As in previous editions, ecological matters are emphasized, and we attempt to show the place of forest entomology in the field of forest management and protection. Other books are now available that are especially suited to the needs of advanced students.

Because it is an elementary text, the authors feel that its length must be limited so that the contents can be covered in a single term. Therefore, many details have been left for later courses.

Selected species are used to illustrate principles or as examples of the various ecological groups of forest insects. The instructor may wish to substitute other species that are more appropriate for his special situation. With this in mind we have included in the bibliography references to important forest insects that are not considered in the text. In the selection of references we have kept three things in mind. We have, first of all, attempted to include references to new developments even though they are short papers likely to be expanded later. Second, we have selected publications that contain lists of references, many of which space limitation excluded from the text. Third, whenever possible, we have selected references that most adequately cover the subject discussed and are most likely to be available in libraries. Thus our bibliography, although incomplete in itself, can lead the student to an adequate coverage of literature in any forest-entomological subject that concerns him.

Forest entomology is a rapidly advancing field. Since the third edition appeared, control practices have been improved, survey procedures have become more precise, timesaving techniques have been developed, and biological studies have added information concerning many pests about which our knowledge was previously inadequate. In the future we may expect similar developments, especially along ecological lines.

Objections are being raised to the excessive use of pesticides, especially over large areas. Research efforts designed to develop new, more specific, and safer chemicals than are now available have been accelerated. Greater effort is being directed toward the development of preventive means of forest-insect control and the integration of direct chemical treatments with indirect preventive practices. These efforts will bear fruit in the near future, and the alert instructor must keep up to date on current developments and pass on new information to his students, even though they be beginners. The organization of "Principles of Forest Entomology" is such that current developments are easily fitted into the course.

During the preparation of this fourth edition, many foresters and entomologists have rendered valuable advice and assistance. They are too numerous to mention individually, but each has our sincere gratitude. Particular thanks are due to the forest entomologists associated with various forest experiment stations and laboratories in both the United States and Canada. These men have contributed information, often in advance of publication, and have freely expressed their ideas and given their advice. Their generosity has made possible the inclusion in the revision of materials that otherwise would not be published for some time. Illustrations have been made available from many sources. Each is acknowledged in the individual legends.

Finally, we thank our respective wives, Sybil Fleming Graham and Jane Wooster Knight, for their helpfulness, sympathy, and patience during the preparation of the manuscript and the later chores that are part of publication.

Samuel Alexander Graham
Fred Barrows Knight

CONTENTS

CHAPTER 1

INTRODUCTION

The field of forest entomology is concerned with both trees and insects. It deals with the effects of insects upon forests and forest products and how to prevent these effects from reaching serious proportions economically.

The forest entomologist studies the characteristics, the habits, and the physiological reactions of forest insects because by so doing he will be better able to regulate their activities. But also he must understand the forest: the life history and requirements of the individual tree species, their reactions to the habitat and to one another, and the characteristics that make some forest types either susceptible or resistant to insect injury. Thus the forest entomologist must be both a forester and an entomologist.

The majority of species treated in this book has a direct effect either upon the trees themselves or upon the products derived from the trees. Some, however, have an indirect effect in that they are predaceous or parasitic and prey upon the tree pests. In addition to these two types there is, entering into the forest economy, a multitude of insects that are neither pests of trees nor parasitic or predatory enemies of pests. Examples of these are insects that live upon the plants of the undergrowth, those that aid in the disintegration of waste wood in the forest, and those that feed upon the organic matter in the duff layer of forest soils. There can be no doubt that these insects play an important, if secondary, part in the forest. But they have received scant attention from entomologists, and relatively little is known of their activities.

FIGURE 1. The spiral gallery of *Agrilus horni* girdles a young aspen sucker. Such damage is common but is often overlooked. (Photograph by J. C. Nord.)

Importance of Forest Entomology in Forestry. It has been said that forestry is 90 percent protection. One may not accept this high percentage as a fair estimate of the importance of protection, but it must be admitted that, if our forests are not to be protected from the devastation of forest fire and the ravages of insects and fungous diseases, there will be little opportunity to practice forestry. Fire, fungi, and insects are the greatest agents of destruction in our forests. Any program of protection that ignores any one of this formidable triumvirate endangers our future timber supply and certainly invites disaster.

During every stage in the growth of wood, from the seed to the finished product, important insect problems are continuously presenting themselves. Even before the seeds are collected, they may be attacked and injured by certain insects. These are for the most part moths, beetles, and wasps. Although seeds of forest trees are produced in prolific quantities, often numbering millions per acre in a single season, the damage caused by seed-destroying insects is sometimes serious. In an oak-hickory woodland near Ann Arbor, Michigan, nut weevils destroyed such a large proportion of acorns that for many years little oak reproduction became established. Similarly in northern Michigan, the natural reproduction of white spruce that was expected from a moderately large crop of cones in 1948 failed to materialize because of the effects of cone moths, which had increased to outbreak proportions in the unusually large crop of cones of 1947. Even after the cones are gathered and the seed extracted

FIGURE 2. Longisection of a pine cone showing the galleries and larvae of a buprestid cone borer, *Chrysophana placida*. (U.S. Forest Service.)

and stored, deterioration of the seed, due to the activities of these insects, may continue.

In the nursery, the seedlings or transplants may be injured by such defoliators as climbing cutworms or by root-eating insects, such as white grubs and wireworms. Bark beetles, leaf or bud miners, plant lice, and scale insects all take their toll from the trees in the forest nursery and also from the advance growth of young trees under natural conditions.

Trees in the sapling stage are sometimes attacked and severely injured by defoliators, phloem insects, and sucking insects. The vigorous period between the sapling stage and commercial maturity is, as a rule, the stage most resistant to insect attack. However, even in this period, the trees may occasionally succumb to the attack of defoliators or primary bark beetles. With approaching maturity, vitality is reduced and the trees become increasingly susceptible to insect injury. Bark beetles that cannot kill vigorous young trees may breed successfully in the trees of the mature forest, and defoliators become much more dangerous than they were when the trees were in the full vigor of youth.

Later, when the trees die or are cut, they promptly become subject to the attack of the many kinds of wood-deteriorating insects. Bark beetles, ambrosia beetles, roundheaded borers, and flatheaded borers all attack and injure dying or recently killed trees and freshly cut wood. Not only do these insects injure the wood directly by their borings, but they are

FIGURE 3. Adult and larval galleries of the fir engraver, *Scolytus ventralis*, Le Conte, Dixie National Forest, Utah. (U.S. Dept. Agr. Forest Service.)

often responsible for the introduction of wood-staining and wood-rotting organisms. As the wood seasons or decays, it becomes subject to the attack of numerous other insects.

With such a multiplicity of insect species attacking trees and wood products, it is difficult, indeed, for a forester to find any line of forestry work in which he is not faced by some insect problem. Even the lumber salesman may be called upon to pacify a customer who finds powderpost beetles emerging from a newly laid hardwood floor. Also, in lumber manufacturing, in the pulp and paper industry, in forest by-product industries, and in the more technical phases of forestry work, entomological problems are forever intruding.

In the past, in spite of the tremendous losses caused by insects of forests and forest products, entomology has often been looked upon in forestry as something to be ignored whenever possible. This was due, in part at least, to the feeling among foresters and lumbermen that insects in the forest could not be controlled, and therefore they were given scant attention. But this point of view is rapidly changing, and forest entomology is now properly considered to be an integral and important part of forest protection. Forest insects are no longer disregarded. Forest man-

FIGURE 4. Pitch mass on pine caused by the attack of a small midge. The larvae feed upon the phloem, breathing through the anal spiracle extruding from the mass of pitch surrounding them. As a general rule these insects are scarce, but outbreaks have followed spraying to control the jackpine budworm.

agers are facing their insect problems with much the same attitude that they exhibit toward their problems in silviculture, management, and utilization.

Therefore, every forester should be able to recognize evidences of possibly dangerous insect activities and know enough about insects and their control to act intelligently. He should know how and where to obtain information about insects and should be able to apply the necessary remedies. A person totally ignorant of insects and their ways cannot hope to get the best results, any more than an inadequately trained physician can hope to give as good service as one who is well acquainted with the disease he is called upon to cure.

Losses Due to Forest Insects. It is undoubtedly true that in North America more wood has been destroyed by insects, fungi, and fire than

FIGURE 5. Flathead galleries in a decadent ponderosa pine produced by the second-year larvae of *Melanophila californica.* This insect is on the borderline between the primary and secondary species. (U.S. Dept. Agr. Forest Service.)

has ever been cut and used. Of the various wood destroyers, insects are by no means the least important.

Accurate estimates of losses due to forest insects are very difficult to obtain. In only a few instances have systematic loss records been made year after year, and even these are relatively fragmentary. The records of losses in the West due to bark beetles are perhaps the best available. They are based on records made annually on a considerable series of sample areas and assume that similar damage occurs on other similar areas.

Injury to trees by forest insects may result in their death, reduction of growth rate of injured trees, or degrading wood products. These effects combined represent the total damage. A new term used to describe this damage is *growth impact*. As defined, growth impact does not include *defects* caused by insects. In the *Timber Resources for America's Future* (Crafts, 1958) nationwide estimates of growth impact have been made for the first time for insects, diseases, fire, and other decimating agencies.

According to this review insects kill twice as much timber as do disease-causing organisms and seven times the amount killed by fire. However, where decay and growth losses and defect are added, the prevalence of stem rots changes the ratio, so that greater damage is said to be caused by diseases when expressed in terms of the broader definition of growth impact. The total yearly losses due to insects for the United States including coastal Alaska is estimated to be 8.6 billion board feet. Table 1 shows the estimated distribution of these losses in saw timber for the year of 1952.

TABLE 1   Loss in Saw Timber in the United States in 1952

CAUSE	MORTALITY, MILLION BD FT	GROWTH IMPACT, MILLION BD FT
Bark beetles	4,530	5,410
Defoliators	30	1,310
Other insects	480	1,900
All insects	5,040	8,620

However, deviations from the estimates in Table 1 may be expected to be great. In some years the mortality of trees from bark beetles is heavy, whereas in others it is very light. These fluctuations may be due to weather variations or other conditions that will be discussed later. Even greater than these yearly fluctuations are those which occur over longer periods of time. Between 1915 and 1936 on the West Coast, injury by bark beetles was higher than normal, owing in part to the large bodies of over-mature timber in the forest and in part to precipitation deficiency (Keen, 1952). After 1937 bark-beetle infestations declined. According to Keen, this decline can be correlated with an upward trend of precipitation, but in part, at least, it is attributable to improved forest practices. Partial cuttings made in areas of high beetle risk have removed most of the hazardous trees. As a result, the amount of timber that is favorable for the beetles has been greatly reduced. Similar injury by defoliators occurs periodically, so that in some years losses are severe, in others light.

For example, during the half century between 1910 and 1964 a series of outbreaks of the spruce budworm has occurred in eastern United States and Canada. The outbreaks of this insect that resulted in the greatest volume loss were between 1910 and 1920 in Quebec and the Maritime Provinces of Canada, and in Maine and Minnesota in the United States. An estimated total of 225 million cords of balsam fir died. No estimate of growth loss in surviving trees was made. Most of the survivors were either black or white spruce, and these grew at a sharply reduced rate during the period of defoliation, the annual rings averaging less than one quarter of the width of rings laid down in previous years.

Between 1935 and 1955 a number of severe outbreaks developed and declined in Ontario, Canada. In New Brunswick and eastern Quebec an outbreak covering 18 million acres started in 1949 and ended by 1958. Application of insecticides kept a large proportion of the trees alive. According to Macdonald (1962), in an unsprayed check area approximately 60 percent of the balsam fir had died by 1961.

Beginning also around 1949 a number of budworm outbreaks appeared in Douglas-fir and true fir stands in Oregon, Washington, and British Columbia. Between 1949 and 1955, 3,840,000 acres of Douglas-fir forest were sprayed to control the insect.

The recent outbreak of the budworm in New Brunswick covered approximately the same areas as the one that began 40 years earlier. Other things being equal, we may expect the period that will elapse between uncontrolled outbreaks of such an insect will correspond to the time required for advance reproduction to grow to pole size.

Thus the period between outbreaks of the spruce budworm, the larch sawfly, the hemlock looper, and others will depend upon the length of time required to replace the trees destroyed and bring the forest to a condition favorable for an outbreak. Thus the approximate annual loss will be the loss sustained during an outbreak divided by the number of years between the beginnings of outbreaks. On this basis the annual loss caused by the spruce budworm to eastern balsam fir, assuming a period of 50 years between outbreaks, is in the neighborhood of 4,700,000 cords, and that caused by the larch sawfly 400 million board feet.

Even the foregoing estimates, based as they are upon field observations, cannot be considered as very exact. They must, of necessity, rest on a comparatively small number of accurate measurements and a great deal of general observation, with the result that the probable error is high. It must also be kept in mind that a considerable portion of the timber killed by the spruce budworm, the larch sawfly, and even the hemlock looper, was located in areas that were and still are inaccessible for logging. In many instances, by the time some of these forests are needed to supply our demands for this kind of timber, a new crop of merchantable trees will have replaced those killed. As a matter of fact, after 40 to 50 years, many areas that were severely damaged by the budworm between 1909 and 1915 have been reoccupied by a merchantable forest. Thus, although the destruction of timber by insects has been almost beyond human comprehension, the actual economic loss is somewhat less than it might at first appear to be. The destruction of this timber, therefore, was not nearly so serious a matter as will be similar outbreaks in the future when these formerly inaccessible areas are needed to supply the demand for wood.

From the above it becomes evident that the economic loss from outbreaks cannot always be expressed fairly in terms of volume, because the actual monetary losses for the same volume vary inversely with the distance from the point of utilization. Protection of raw materials close to the point of utilization should, therefore, receive greater consideration than the protection of similar materials at a distance.

The losses resulting from such outbreaks of insects as those cited above represent only a part of the total damage for which forest insects are responsible. There must be added the less conspicuous but nonetheless real damage caused by insects present in normal numbers. No satisfactory estimates of these losses have ever been made, but in the aggregate they undoubtedly amount to millions of board feet annually. These unestimated losses should be added to the growth impact if loss estimates are to be realistic. But even without them, the damage caused annually by forest insects probably exceeds 5 billion board feet.

The destruction of manufactured wood products by insects amounts to a very high total, but no definite data are available at present on which to base an estimate. Termites, especially in tropical and subtropical regions, are particularly injurious to unprotected wooden structures. Even in the temperate regions of this country, particularly along the Atlantic and Pacific Coasts, termites are sufficiently numerous to cause injury to wooden structures. Other insects, such as the powderpost beetles and the pole borer, attack and destroy seasoned wood and finished products, but the data available are insufficient to form the bases for satisfactory damage estimates.

Incomplete and unsatisfactory as our statistics may be, they are, at least, sufficient to indicate that insects are an important economic factor in our forest industry and should receive a prominent place in our plans for the protection of forests and forest products.

Scope and Subdivisions of Forest Entomology. The scope of forest entomology is surprisingly wide. It includes a great variety of subject matter leading to the better understanding of the biological phenomena of forest life. The ultimate aim of forest entomology is to make possible the regulation, in the interest of man, of insect activities in forests and forest products. In the control of forest insects, the possibilities of using directly protective methods are limited because of the relatively high cost of such operations. Preventive rather than curative methods should be favored. This preventive entomology calls for a much more profound knowledge of both the insects and the forest environment than would be required if one could depend largely upon direct control. One of the first

FIGURE 6. Forest-insect research requires much specialized equipment. The research worker above is setting up a portable X ray used in studying cryptic insects in living twigs.

requisites for forest-insect work, therefore, is a sound basic knowledge of silvics and silviculture. Not until the forest entomologist knows trees is he in a position to apply his entomological knowledge to them.

In addition, anyone engaged in forest-insect work must know the insects. For this, he must be able not only to recognize the genus and species to which a specimen belongs but also to understand its functions, its reactions to its environment, and its physical limitations. Thus, all the major divisions of the science of entomology are needed in the solution of forest entomological problems. Taxonomy is needed in classifying insects and in indicating their relationships and origins. It not only aids the forester by providing names, but also, whenever a new forest entomological problem presents itself, it may actually furnish the key to satisfactory control measures, for closely related insects can often be controlled by similar means. Thus the service of taxonomy may often prove invaluable in showing relationships of new to old pests. Studies in morphology, histology, and physiology of forest insects lead to a more complete knowledge of the insects studied and aid directly or indirectly in the solution of forest entomological problems. Chemical entomology, which includes spraying, dusting, and fumigating, has its place in the control of insect pests, especially in emergencies. Ecological studies, including life-history investigations, the effect of climatic and other environmental factors upon forest insects, and the interrelation of parasites and predatory species with their hosts, are all of fundamental importance.

Obviously, no forest entomologist can be expected to have the detailed knowledge of taxonomy that is expected of a specialist in the subject and at the same time be a specialist in morphology, histology, physiology, ecology, and chemical entomology. The field is too large to permit such a wide scope of endeavor. The forest entomologist is, however, expected to have a general knowledge of each of these fields and to have a detailed knowledge of some of them.

With the advent of DDT and several other remarkable insecticides, the possibility of applying direct control to certain forest insects has been greatly increased. As a result, the emphasis in forest entomology has shifted toward chemical control. Forest entomologists in the United States are, therefore, devoting much time to the supervision of control projects and to research in the field of insecticides. Receiving correspondingly less attention is work leading to the prevention of outbreaks by cultural practices. In Canada, on the other hand, biological and ecological investigations which will lead to more effective control through silviculture and the use of natural control forces are receiving special emphasis while less emphasis is being placed on direct control procedures. A proper balance between these two approaches to forest-insect control is important and must be made the concern of administrative officers entrusted with the management of forests.

Doubtless the problems of forest-insect control will become more and more complex and will require the services of forest entomologists who have specialized in chemical control, insect pathology, ecology, physiology, and other specific fields. When such specialization comes to pass, let us hope that the workers will avoid the danger of overspecialization and will continue to maintain their grasp of the general field and thus keep a proper perspective of forest entomology as a whole.

Forest Entomological Literature.   Every worker must rely on the writings of others for a foundation of information in any given line. The ability to locate all available literature on any subject and to use that literature efficiently is essential for best results. The library is one of the most important tools. In the field of forest entomology there is particular need for training in the ways and means of locating information, because the writings in this field are so scattered that they are sometimes difficult to find and may easily be overlooked.

Fortunately there are valuable aids available. Among them are a series of indexed bibliographies published by the U.S. Department of Agriculture and a series of indexes published by the Entomological Society of America. Volumes I to V of the indexed work entitled "Bibliography of the More Important Contributions to American Economic Entomology" were compiled by Samuel Henshaw. The first three volumes were devoted to the writings of B. D. Walsh and C. V. Riley, two men who were perhaps the most prolific writers that entomology has ever known. Volumes IV and V cover the writings of other authors up to 1888. Volumes VI to VIII of this series were compiled by Nathan Banks and cover the period from 1888 to 1905. The series was then discontinued by the Department of Agriculture. The work was later taken up by the American Association of Economic Entomologists, now the Entomological Society of America, and the index portion continued. The next volume of this index was compiled by Banks and covers the years 1905 to 1914, inclusive. Thereafter, the tremendous increase in the quantity of published material has required reduction in the length of time covered in a single volume until in 1962, Vol. XVIII, covers the single year 1959.

These bibliographies and indexes provide a ready means of access to most of the important economic entomological literature of the United States and Canada, but they do not help where other literature is concerned. For this, one must go to other works, the most important of which is probably the *Zoological Record*. This record has been published annually since 1864 by the Zoological Society of London and aims to include all publications dealing with animals. A large part of each volume is devoted to entomological literature. Periodical index numbers are published. For information previous to 1864, one may go to the "Index Literaturae Entomologicae," compiled by Hagen, Horn, and Schenkling.

Owing to the fact that much forest entomological information has been published in forestry journals, trade journals, and other publications not ordinarily examined in the compilation of the bibliographical aids just mentioned, the forest entomologist should not neglect forestry literature or he may miss important contributions. This is particularly true of European literature. Beginning in 1902, the *Journal of Forestry* and its predecessor, the *Forestry Quarterly*, published monthly lists of literature which provided a readily accessible reference to many forest entomological articles not included in entomological bibliographies and indexes, but in recent years these lists have been discontinued.

The indexes and records mentioned above aid the student in his search into the past, but this is only a part of his problem. Often several years may pass between the date of publication of an article and the publication of an index referring thereto. Bridging this gap is no light task when one considers the scores of periodicals, bulletins, circulars, and books coming from the press each month that may contain forest entomological information. Even though each worker had access to all the articles in the mass of literature, he could scarcely take the time to examine each of them. As a timesaver and an aid to keeping in touch with recent progress, the reviewing and abstracting periodicals assist greatly. These publications are usually only a few months behind the publication of original papers.

One of the most important reviewing organs for the entomologist is the *Review of Applied Entomology*, published in London by the Commonwealth Institute of Entomology. This publication appears monthly and aims to review every article published in the field of economic entomology. It is world-wide in its scope and misses very few publications of importance. In the United States, the *Experiment Station Record*, published by the U.S. Department of Agriculture, covers a large part of the American literature. Beginning in 1928, the quarterly *Forstliche Rundschau; der Zeitschrift für Weltforstwirtschaft* covered the forestry literature of the world, including forest entomological titles.

Beginning in 1940 the Commonwealth Forestry Bureau, Oxford, has published *Forestry Abstracts, Compiled from World Literature.* Included are numerous reviews on forest entomological subjects. A still more recent series of volumes is the *Annual Review of Entomology*, Annual Reviews Inc., Palo Alto, California. Each volume includes papers reviewing advances in various entomological subjects, including forest entomological matters. Volume 9 of this series was printed in 1964.

Biological Abstracts, published since January, 1926, has superseded most of the older abstracting agencies in the United States because it covers the entire field of biology. By bringing together world-wide biological literature in this way, it greatly simplifies the problem of the individual worker in keeping abreast of the times.

Convenient and useful as they may be in helping workers in the various fields to keep up with scientific progress, there lies a danger in the use of these abstracting periodicals: the danger that one may neglect to read original articles. It must be remembered that an abstract does not take the place of the original but serves only to indicate whether or not the original is of sufficient importance to be read. The student of entomology must be familiar with all the original sources that apply to the work at hand.

Some of the sources in which one ordinarily expects to find the original publications dealing with American and Canadian forest entomology may be listed as follows:

1. U.S. Department of Agriculture:
Department bulletins and circulars
Yearbooks
Insect pest leaflets
Cooperative economic insect reports

Farmers' bulletins
Reports
U.S. Forest Experiment Station notes, papers, and reports
U.S. Forest Service separates
2. **State Publications:**
Experiment station bulletins, circulars, and reports
University bulletins and memoirs
State entomologist publications
3. **Canada, Division of Biology, Science Service to 1960. Later Forest Entomology and Pathology Branch, Canada Department of Forestry:**
Bulletins, circulars, and reports
4. **Periodicals:**
Journal of Economic Entomology
Journal of Forestry
Canadian Entomologist
Canadian Journal of Research
Canadian Journal of Zoology
Ecology
Forestry Chronicle
Forest Science
Journal of Insect Pathology
Proceedings of the Entomological Society of Ontario
Japanese Journal of Applied Entomology and Zoology
Trade journals

References to examples of these and other pamphlets and periodicals will be found in the bibliography.

In England, a considerable proportion of the forest entomological work is conducted by the Forestry Commission and is reported in its publications. Other articles appear from time to time in such periodicals as the *Journal of Ecology*. Still other articles on entomology are published in the *Indian Forester* and also in the official publications of the respective governments of Australia and South Africa. In addition to publications printed in English, there are many periodicals in foreign languages, particularly German and Swedish. Of these one of the most outstanding at the present time is the *Zeitschrift für angewandte Entomologie*; another is *Entomophaga*. Almost all the European forestry and entomological publications print occasional papers on forest insects.

An increasing amount of excellent forest entomological research is now being published in Russian. Much of this is unavailable at present.

Although the major portion of European forest entomological literature appears in the form of pamphlets and short articles, there are a number of important books on the subject. In America, however, forest entomological books are few. In fact, there are few general comprehensive works comparable with some of those that may be cited from European countries. American books that deal with forest insects are:

Packard, 1890. "Insects Injurious to Forest and Shade Trees." Fifth Report of the Entomological Commission, U.S. Department of Agriculture.
Felt, 1905. "Insects Affecting Park and Woodland Trees." *Mem.* 8, New York State Museum.
Felt, 1924. "Manual of Tree and Shrub Insects."
Essig, 1929. "Insects of Western North America."
Chamberlin, 1931. "An Introduction to Forest Entomology."
Felt and Rankin, 1932. "Insects and Diseases of Ornamental Trees and Shrubs."
Doane, Van Dyke, Chamberlin, and Burke, 1937. "Forest Insects."
Craighead, 1950. "Insect Enemies of Eastern Forests." *U.S. Dept. Agr. Misc. Publ.* 657.
Keen, 1952. "Insect Enemies of Western Forests." *U.S. Dept. Agr. Misc. Publ.* 273. Revised.
Anderson, 1962. "Forest and Shade Tree Entomology."
Graham, Kenneth, 1963. "Concepts of Forest Entomology."

There are several excellent general texts. Among them are:

Comstock, 1947. "An Introduction to Entomology."
Ross, 1956. "A Text Book of Entomology."
Borer and DeLong, 1964. "Introduction to the Study of Insects."

Some of the outstanding English and European texts are:

Escherich, 1914, 1923, and 1931. "Die Forstinsekten Mitteleuropas" (a revision of Judeich and Nitsche's "Lehrbuch der Mitteleuropäischen Forstinsektenkunde").
Trägårdh, 1914. "Sveriges Skogs Insekter."
Cecconi, 1922. "Manuale di Entomologia Forestale."
Nüsslin-Rhumbler, 1922. "Forstinsektenkunde."
Barbey, 1925. "Traité d'entomologie forestière."

Because forest entomological literature is so widely scattered in so many different publications, no local library can have on its shelves copies of all the publications. Even in some of our best entomological libraries, we cannot find every article on any one subject that may be pertinent. Fortunately, however, most of the local libraries have the privilege of borrowing from other libraries, or if the publications themselves cannot be loaned, photostatic copies of parts of articles or books can usually be obtained. Many foreign publications and doctoral theses from various universities and colleges are now being made available on microfilm. References to microfilms may be found in most university and many public libraries. Consequently, if we have a definite reference, it is usually possible to see a certain publication even though the facilities of our library are limited. The first and most important bibliographic aids are the indexes and the abstracting organs. With these at our command, literature can be searched effectively; without them, one is helpless. Therefore, every library should be equipped with at least these very necessary tools.

BIBLIOGRAPHY CHAPTER 1

Brooks, Fred E., and R. T. Cotton, 1929. Chestnut curculios, *U.S. Dept. Agr. Tech. Bull.* 130.

Crafts, Edward C., 1958. Timber resources for America's future, Forest Resource Report, *U.S. Dept. Agr. Forest Serv. Separate* No. 1.

Graham, S. A., and A. G. Ruggles, 1923. The obligation that economic entomology owes to forestry, *J. Econ. Entomol.,* **16:** 51–61.

Hagen, H. A., W. Horn, and S. Schenkling, 1928–1929. "Index Literaturae Entomologicae," 4 vols. to 1863.

Keen, F. P., 1952. "Insect Enemies of Western Forests," *U.S. Dept. Agr. Misc. Pub.* 273.

Macdonald, D. R., 1962. Studies of aerial spraying against the spruce budworm in New Brunswick. XVII, Mortality of fir and spruce in selected sprayed and unsprayed areas, *Can. Dept. Forestry, Forest Entomol. Pathol. Branch, Informa. Rept. Forest Entomol. Pathol. Lab.,* Fredericton, N.B.

Nelson, A. L., and N. D. Wygant, 1950. Beetles kill 4 billion board feet of Engelmann spruce in Colorado, *J. Forestry,* **48:** 182–183.

Packard, A. S., 1890. Insects injurious to forest and shade trees, *U.S. Entomol. Comm. Fifth Rept.*

Peirson, H. B., 1927. Manual of forest insects, *Maine Forest Serv. Bull.* 5.

Peterson, A., 1948. "Larvae of Insects."

Reiss, Donald, 1935. Biological study of the walnut husk fly, *Mich. Acad. Sci., Arts, Letters,* **20:** 717–723.

Rowher, S. A., 1949. The key to protection, *U.S. Dept. Agr. Yearbook,* 413–417.

Snyder, T. E., 1927. Defects in timber caused by insects, *U.S. Dept. Agr. Bull.* 1490.

Swaine, J. M., 1918. Canadian bark-beetles, *Can. Dept. Agr., Entomol. Branch, Tech. Bull.* 14.

Swaine, J. M., and C. B. Hutchings, 1926. The more important shade-tree insects of Eastern Canada, *Can. Dept. Agr., Entomol. Branch, n. s., Bull.* 63.

Wygant, N. D., 1938. Relation of insects to shelter-belt plantations, *J. Forestry,* **36:** 1011–1018.

Wygant, N. D., and A. L. Nelson, 1949. Four billion feet of beetle-killed spruce, *U.S. Dept. Agr. Yearbook,* pp. 417–422.

CHAPTER 2

HISTORICAL
REVIEW

The science of forest entomology, like the science of forestry of which it is a part, is relatively young. It had its beginning during the first part of the nineteenth century.

DEVELOPMENT IN EUROPE

Inasmuch as Germany was the first country to develop forestry, it is natural that forest entomology should have had its inception there. As the value of trees became more and more appreciated and as methods of silvicultural practice were developed, the necessity of protecting the trees from the ravages of insects became increasingly important.

Early Period. The outbreak of a forest pest was something with which the early foresters were unable to cope, and so they were forced to appeal to zoologists for help. As a result, a number of publications appeared that dealt with various individual forest-insect problems. For instance, one finds such treatises as that of Gmelin, "Abhandlung über die Wurm-trocknis," published in 1773, and that of Hennert, "Über der Raupenfrass und Windbruch," published in 1798.

The purpose behind most of these early studies of forest insects was the development of methods by which a certain pest or the pests of a certain tree might be controlled. It is true that this end was seldom accomplished and that the chief contribution of these studies to science was either taxonomic or biologic in character. Sometimes, however, effective measures were suggested and applied. For instance, Linnaeus is said to have recommended that freshly cut logs be floated in water to prevent injury by borers—a very effective method that is in use today.

Previous to 1800, forest entomology, as such, did not exist. There were no specialists in this subject, and the studies of tree insects were conducted by men whose primary interest was in other lines. The first attempt to gather all available information concerning forest insects was that of Beckstein and Scharfenberg who published, in 1804 and 1805, two volumes entitled, "Vollständige Naturgeschichte der für den Wald schädlichen und nützlichen Forstinsekten." This work was a pretentious compendium of forest-insect information and for a period of 30 years was the only general work available on the subject.

Natural-history Period. Then there appeared a monumental work which even today has never been surpassed in excellence and scope. This was Ratzeburg's "Die Forstinsekten." Ratzeburg, frequently called the Father of Forest Entomology, was the first man to devote all his energies to that field. He lived in an age when specialization was the exception rather than the rule. Even he attempted at first to cover forest pathology as well as forest entomology, but he soon found that these two subjects were too extensive to be handled effectively by any one man. His later work, therefore, was confined to the field of entomology.

The first volume of "Die Forstinsekten" appeared in 1837, the second in 1840, and the third in 1844. He also published a handbook, "Die Waldverderber und ihre Feinde," that summarized in more condensed form the material contained in "Die Forstinsekten." The demand for this handbook was so great that by 1869 it appeared in a sixth edition. After Ratzeburg's death in 1871, this book continued to appear in new editions edited by his successors. In 1885 Judeich and Nitsche published a book which purported to be a revision of Ratzeburg's work, in two volumes under the title "Lehrbuch der mitteleuropäischen Forstinsektenkunde." Still more recently, Escherich published a new edition, which is a masterpiece of its kind, under the title "Die Forstinsekten Mitteleuropas." Escherich added much new material and rewrote the older portion of the book, thus making a thoroughly modern presentation of the subject.

Ratzeburg published numerous other articles and books throughout his life. One of his best-known works is his "Ichneumoniden der Forstinsekten," published in three parts in 1844, 1848, and 1852. Ratzeburg dominated the period during which he lived. But although he stood head and shoulders above his contemporaries, there were other workers who made very valuable contributions to the science of forest entomology. Among them we find Kollar, Hartig, and Nordlinger in Germany and Perris in France. An important contribution by Kollar has been translated into English and is available under the title "Treatise on Insects Injurious to Gardens, Forests, and Farms." Perris is credited with the first experimental studies in forest entomology. He cut trees at different seasons and studied the life history and habits of the various insects that attacked them. His greatest contribution was the "Histoire des insectes du pin maritime," which appeared in ten parts between 1851 and 1870 in the *Annals of the Entomological Society of France.*

Taxonomic Biological Period. Up to the time of Ratzeburg's death, the chief emphasis in forest entomology was biological. These investigations were often in the nature of general natural-history studies and were usually not based upon controlled experimental evidence. The work of Eichhoff ushered in a new era that made of forest entomology a more exact science than it had previously been. By combining careful biological experiments and detailed taxonomic studies, he cleared up many misconceived notions concerning the biology of bark beetles and set up a model for other investigators to follow. His outstanding contribution, entitled "Europaischen Borkenkäfer," was published in 1881.

During the later part of the nineteenth century there were, particularly in Germany, many workers who devoted a part or all of their time to the study of forest insects. Among them was Altum, at Eberswalde, who did much to stimulate investigation and discussion as a result of his proposed theories and hypotheses. Nitsche at the Forstakademie in Tharand, and Henschel at the Agricultural College at Wien were both outstanding teachers and investigators.

Modern Period. From the very beginning until the end of the nineteenth century, European forest entomologists looked to Germany for leadership. This was the natural result of the tremendous amount of valuable pioneering work on forest insects produced by the entomologists of that country. Since the beginning of the twentieth century, however, a decided change has taken place until now, in the modern period, leaders in forest entomology instead of being centered in a single country are to be found throughout those parts of the Old World where forests are economically important. In Europe Escherich has perhaps exerted the greatest influence, and associated with him have been other capable forest entomologists too numerous to mention individually. Escherich's influence has been felt strongly through his editorship of the periodical *Zeitschrift für angewandte Entomologie.* Between the world wars the names of Rhumbler, Prell, Wellstein, Friedricks, Scharfenberg, Schadl, and more recently Schwertfeger, Voûte, Franz, and many others are frequently cited. Trägårdh and his successor Butovitch in Sweden have made outstanding contributions, especially to the analysis of forest-insect infestations, in both individual trees and forest areas, and to the development of methods for estimating accurately the population of bark beetles in a given unit of forest.

In still other countries forest entomological work is actively pursued as evidenced by the publications of Saalas in Finland; Munro, Fisher, and

Varley in England; Bovey in Switzerland; Inoye in Japan; and others too numerous to mention.

In Europe, the science of forest entomology has passed through several more or less definite periods. The first was the natural-history period, characterized and dominated by the work of Ratzeburg. The second was the period of great taxonomic activity supplemented by experimental life-history studies. Eichhoff characterizes this stage which was really the connecting link between the first period and the third. In the third, or modern, period the great emphasis is placed on experimental biology.

DEVELOPMENT IN AMERICA

During Ratzeburg's period of domination in Europe, an interest in tree insects was developing in America. Much of this work was prompted by an interest in ornamental trees.

The Natural-history Period. The early contributions in America, as in Europe, dealt largely with forest-insect biology from the natural-history viewpoint. These early writings are both useful and interesting to us today, but unfortunately they are so scattered in various publications that they are sometimes difficult to obtain. Most of this material, however, is referred to in the indexes already discussed. Many articles on tree insects are included in Harris's "Treatise on Some of the Insects Injurious to Vegetation" (1886) and in Fitch's reports on "Noxious, Beneficial and Other Insects of the State of New York" (1856 to 1870). The reports and articles of Walsh, Riley, Lintner, Comstock, and Forbes also contain much information concerning forest insects.

It was not until 1890 that the first compendium on American forest insects was published. At that time Packard brought together all the available material in the fifth report of the Entomological Commission of the U.S. Department of Agriculture entitled "Insects Injurious to Forest and Shade Trees." This report contains a mass of valuable information concerning tree insects and is well illustrated by numerous plates and figures. Packard included verbatim many of the important articles by other authors which were not easily accessible, thus adding materially to the value of his book for reference. His report was for years the only comprehensive work on American forest insects and still is an invaluable reference book. In 1905, *Memoir* 8 of the New York State Museum, a memoir by Felt entitled "Insects Affecting Park and Woodland Trees," added some new information not included in Packard's report, but its chief value was in its remarkably fine colored illustrations.

Taxonomic and Biological Period. Then followed a period when taxonomic-biological studies predominated in forest entomological work. This period, though coming later, was similar in character to the Eichhoff period in Europe, the influence of which was evident upon American work of the early part of the present century. Hopkins in his bark-beetle studies added much to our knowledge of that group of insects both biologically and taxonomically. He was able, as was Eichhoff, to dispel many incorrect views previously held concerning both the bark beetles and the bark weevils and to lay the foundation for modern control practices. He also made especially notable contributions to the subject of bioclimatology. Hopkins died in 1948.

Much of the work of both Swaine and Blackman belongs in the taxonomic-biological category, and some of the earlier work of Craighead was along similar lines; later all three of these men worked along the lines of experimental biology. Swaine shifted his activities from forest entomology and became director of research and then head of Science Service in the Department of Agriculture of Canada. After his retirement and until his death, he returned to the study of bark beetles.

During the early periods in America, the emphasis was placed on shade-tree insects. Virgin forests were still supplying an abundance of wood products, and the practice of forestry was practically unknown because it was unnecessary. The few methods of forest-insect control that were mentioned in the publications of that time were for the most part borrowed from continental Europe. This situation continued until recently. Today American forest entomology is developing independently, and methods of control are fitted to specific existing conditions.

Modern Period. Forest entomology in Europe has from early times emphasized the practical aspects. This has been the direct result of economic conditions in the densely populated Old World, where scarcity of wood has made the practice of forestry mandatory. Furthermore, in Europe, forest entomological investigations have been centered in schools of forestry. In America, on the other hand, wood has been abundant and, prior to 1915, owners of timberland paid little attention to insect damage. As a result, the insects have in the past been studied without considering seriously their ecological relations with the forest. Often these investigations have been conducted by entomologists whose training has in no way been connected with forests or forestry. As a result, the development of practical control measures has suffered.

Recently, however, the viewpoint has changed until today there are many workers devoting their entire time to practical forest entomology. This change has paralleled the development of forestry in America. Modern forest entomologists are interested both in the insects themselves and in the forest, but their primary concern is the influence of the insects upon the forest.

This modern point of view has resulted in the application of experimental biological methods to forest entomological problems. Purely observational methods of study have been largely abandoned, and in forest entomology taxonomy is no longer thought to be an end in itself but nevertheless is one of the useful tools of the science. Life-history studies are likewise regarded as means to an end rather than ends in themselves. The interrelation of insects with one another and with the various other elements of the forest environment is coming to be regarded as more and more important. Even the advent of new insecticides has not changed this trend entirely.

Thus the development of forest entomology in America has passed through stages that are comparable to those in Europe. The first or natural-history period was contemporaneous with a similar period in Europe. So also was the taxonomic-biological period contemporaneous with similar efforts in the Old World. The application of the methods of experimental biology, likewise, appeared in Europe and America at about the same time. These methods have led to the recent rapid development in the fields of ecology, physiology, genetics, and biometry. Forest entomology, like the other biological sciences, is now being developed on the basis of experimental work.

CONTEMPORARY WORK IN AMERICA

Students frequently ask where and by whom is forest entomological work being conducted. Because this information is not readily obtainable from current literature, a brief statement is introduced here, recognizing, of course, that the picture as it exists at present will soon change.

Federal Forest Insect Work. By far the greater part of the forest entomological work in the United States is carried on in the U.S. Department of Agriculture Forest Service. Previously these activities were in the former Bureau of Entomology and Plant Quarantine, Division of Forest Insect Investigations. Between 1921 and 1950, this division was headed by Dr. F. C. Craighead, later succeeded by Dr. J. A. Beal. In Craighead's administration, great strides were made in developing methods of forest-insect control, many of which were made possible by the sound foundation laid during the preceding administration of the late Dr. A. D. Hopkins. Before his retirement, Craighead, with the aid of other members of his organization, published a monumental book, "Insect Enemies of Eastern Forests."

In 1953 as the result of a reorganization of the U.S. Department of Agriculture all federal forest entomological research was transferred to the U.S. Department of Agriculture Forest Service and located in the regional forest experiment stations. Survey activities continued to be the responsibility of these stations until 1961, when this function was transferred to regional administrative offices.

Attached to each regional forest experiment station are subsidiary laboratories where special types of research are conducted. In addition laboratories for basic research in forestry in several regions have been constructed or are proposed. In each of these, forest entomological research constitutes an important part of the program. Thus, since 1950 the number of laboratories where forest entomological research is conducted has greatly increased. Also the diversity and complexity of the federally supported research program have grown correspondingly.

Some Eastern Forest-insect Laboratories. The oldest forest-insect laboratories in the East were located at Melrose Highlands, Massachusetts; New Haven, Connecticut; and Asheville, North Carolina. The laboratory at Melrose Highlands was known as the Gypsy Moth Laboratory. There pioneer studies of that introduced pest, its parasites, and predators were conducted for many years. Since its abandonment the New Haven laboratory has been the center of all forest-insect research in the New England and the North Atlantic states. For many years a special laboratory was maintained at Morristown, New Jersey. There intensive studies of the Japanese beetle were conducted. This work was later transferred to Columbus, Ohio, with the establishment there of the Central States Forest Experiment Station.

At the Asheville, North Carolina, laboratory, Craighead and his associates pioneered in the study of the southern pine beetle. There they determined the important relationship existing between the beetle and the fungi that cause blue staining of the wood. Also, important studies on tree medication were made at that laboratory.

The Asheville laboratory was closed for a time, but currently it is the administrative center for research in the Southeast with sublaboratories located at Raleigh, North Carolina; Lake City, Florida; and Athens, Georgia.

The Southern states are served by a laboratory located at New Orleans, Louisiana, at the Southern Forest Experiment Station. Work of that laboratory previously was concerned chiefly with wood-destroying insects. T. E. Snyder conducted much of his work on termites there. More recently the scope of the work has been broadened to include the study of bark beetles, insects injurious to hardwood trees, pests of forest reproduction both natural and planted, and other pests of the region. Field laboratories are located at Alexandria, Louisiana; Stoneville, Mississippi; Gulfport, Mississippi; and Nacogdoches, Texas.

The Lake States laboratory is located in St. Paul, Minnesota, at the Lake States Forest Experiment Station. There a variety of forest insect problems has been studied. Among these are several defoliators, root-eating scarabaeids, the hemlock borer, and insects injurious to coniferous forest plantations. A field laboratory is maintained at East Lansing, Michigan.

Western Forest-insect Laboratories. A forest-insect laboratory is located in Fort Collins, Colorado, at the Rocky Mountain Forest and Range Experiment Station, where work is conducted in cooperation with Colorado State University. That laboratory serves the southern and central Rocky Mountains and the central portion of the Great Plains. The study of bark beetles, especially the northwestern pine beetle[1] and the northern spruce beetle,[1] has required increasing attention. Studies have also been conducted on some defoliators of pine and Douglas fir and on pine tip

FIGURE 7. Pitch tubes produced by tree infested by the black turpentine beetle, *Dendroctonus terebrans.* This insect has increased greatly in importance throughout the South since 1945. Osceola National Forest. (U.S. Dept. Agr. Forest Service.)

moths. An important sublaboratory is located at Albuquerque, New Mexico, serving both New Mexico and Arizona.

One of the oldest forest-insect laboratories of the former Bureau of Entomology and Plant Quarantine, located for many years at Coeur d'Alene, Idaho, has been moved to Missoula, Montana, where it is a sublaboratory of the Intermountain Forest and Range Experiment Sta-

[1] Formerly the Black Hills beetle and the Engelmann spruce beetle, respectively.

tion. The headquarters of this station are in Ogden, Utah. The area covered by this forest experiment station includes Utah, the northern Rocky Mountain Region in Montana, Idaho, and parts of Wyoming and North Dakota. The work has been concerned especially with certain defoliators and bark beetles.

At the Pacific Northwest Forest and Range Experiment Station at Portland, Oregon, important studies are being conducted on bark beetles in ponderosa pine, sugar pine, and lodgepole pine. While in charge of the Portland laboratory, F. P. Keen (1943) developed his ponderosa pine tree classification used for the identification of trees that are susceptible or relatively resistant to bark-beetle attack. An interesting series of investigations concerned with the causes of bark-beetle outbreaks and the deterioration rate of fire-killed timber, especially Douglas fir, were conducted at this laboratory. Members of the Portland laboratory have been active in the investigation and control of the spruce budworm on Douglas fir, the hemlock looper, and other defoliators. Forest-insect work in Alaska is now separated from the Pacific Northwest Forest and Range Experiment Station.

The oldest forest-insect laboratory in the West is at Berkeley, California, now a division of the Pacific Southwest Forest and Range Experiment Station. Numerous important insects have been the subject of investigation, including the lodgepole pine-needle miner (Patterson, 1921) and the fir engraver beetle (Struble, 1937). Since about 1920, however, investigations have emphasized dendroctonus beetles, especially the western pine beetle, because of the tremendous losses they cause in mature stands of timber. For many years studies of the composition of insect populations in dying trees have also been conducted by members of the staff. These studies are leading to a better understanding of the relative importance of various insects as tree killers.

In addition to the field laboratories one important national laboratory should be mentioned. At the Beltsville, Maryland, Research Center near Washington, D.C., some very important studies are being conducted on insecticides and their application to forests and basic studies in physiology and behavior of forest insects.

The transfer in 1961 of forest-insect survey work from the forest experiment stations to the regional administative offices of the U.S. Forest Service has brought together in the same unit all activities concerned with evaluation of insect outbreaks and the application of control practices. Such an arrangement assumes that standard survey methods have been developed that can be used in a more or less routine manner. It also assumes that control practices have become standardized. Thus the administrative officers would be in a position to evaluate conditions and implement control procedures against forest insects just as a ranger might make a timber sale. Unfortunately neither survey nor control practices have been thus standardized. Therefore the closest cooperation on forest-insect problems between those conducting research and the administrative officials is still just as essential as ever.

Forest Entomology Outside the Federal Government. Outside the Federal laboratories organized programs in forest entomology have in the past been rare. Even in most forestry schools, forest entomology has often been taught by entomologists without special training in forest entomology. Since 1950 this situation has been changing rapidly until by 1962 forest entomology courses were taught by specialists in approximately one-fourth of our schools of forestry whereas in 1950 the proportion had been less than one-tenth. This trend has resulted in a corresponding increase in the scope of the research programs at the various schools.

With the increasing interest in forest management by wood-using industries a demand by industry for entomological services has increased. Some companies now employ full-time forest entomologists who are also professional foresters. Some of these are engaged in research, but as a rule their chief function is to apply the research findings of others to practical forest management.

Canadian Forest-insect Activities. In Canada the organization of forest-insect activities is very different from that in the United States. The biological, ecological, forest-insect survey and control programs of the dominion government are centered in the Forest Entomology and Pathology Branch of the Department of Forestry. Importation, propagation, and mass liberation of parasitic and predatory insects is the function of the Unit of Biological Control at Bellville, Ontario, under the Canada Department of Agriculture.

Most of the provinces cooperate closely with the Dominion in forest-insect activities, although in a few instances they may conduct independent projects. Also the educational institutions may from time to time conduct forest-insect investigations, but by far the major portion of the forest entomological activities is conducted either by or in cooperation with the dominion government.

The work in Canada, as in the United States, is carried on at regional laboratories, one being located in each of the principal forest regions of the country. The laboratories are, of course, responsible to and under the general direction of the central office in Ottawa. Each laboratory serves as the center of forest entomological work in its region, and each is a well-equipped and well-staffed center. Their program includes research, control, and survey projects.

The oldest laboratory is located at Fredericton, New Brunswick. There Tothill conducted his classic studies on the parasites of the spruce budworm and the fall webworm. In his report on the fall webworm he presented a mortality table that was similar to the more refined survival tabulations called by Morris and Miller (1954) life tables. To call both survival and mortality tables "life tables" would seem appropriate. Tothill's successors have continued work on the budworm at the New Brunswick station and in addition have contributed much to our knowledge of many other important species, among them the European spruce sawfly and the balsam woolly aphid.

In Ontario, at Sault Sainte Marie, the forest-insect laboratory is also concentrating much attention on the spruce-budworm problem. Workers there are studying this and other defoliators from various angles, special emphasis being placed on the ecological approach, including the study of both physical and biotic factors. Since 1946, special attention has been directed toward the use of disease-causing microorganisms for the control of forest insects, and a well-equipped laboratory for the study of insect pathology was opened in 1950 in association with the Ontario forest-insect laboratory. The Forest Entomology and Pathology Branch maintains other major laboratories where important forest entomological work is conducted.[1] These are located at Winnipeg, Manitoba; Indian Head, Saskatchewan; Calgary, Alberta; and Victoria, British Columbia. Shade-tree insects receive special attention at Maple, Ontario. At several sublaboratories outstanding work has been accomplished, two of the best known sublaboratories being at Vernon, British Columbia, in the West and at the Green River Experimental Management Area in New Brunswick. At Green River control of the spruce budworm by silvicultural means is being investigated.

The work of each laboratory is concerned with problems currently important in their respective localities. In the central provinces the larch sawfly and forest tent caterpillar have demanded special attention, while in the Far West dendroctonus beetles, the spruce budworm on Douglas fir, the hemlock looper, and certain sucking insects on conifers have been studied in considerable detail. There will be frequent occasion to refer to the work of the various Canadian laboratories in later chapters.

At the Dominion Parasite Laboratory in Bellville, Ontario, work is not limited to forest-insect problems. However, many parasites of forest insects have been studied there in the Unit of Biological Control, and a number of promising species have been released in places where their hosts are numerous. Several of these will be mentioned later.

FEDERAL AID FOR FOREST-INSECT CONTROL

The enactment of the Forest Pest Control Act by the U.S. Congress on June 25, 1947, marked an important milestone in the development of a nationwide forest-insect control program. This legislation was the culmination of a series of acts beginning with the establishment of the U.S.

[1] Reference to specific projects of these laboratories will be made at later points in this text.

Forest Service. To the Forest Service was delegated the responsibility for protecting federally controlled lands from fire, injurious insects, and disease. Since then the Federal responsibility for pest control has been broadened by each successive act of Congress.

The need for Federal leadership and aid in forest-insect control has been due in part to the widespread character of many insect outbreaks (Popham, 1950). Almost every important outbreak of forest insects in the United States has involved mixtures of landownership: Federal, state, and private. Attempts at control by individual owners seemed futile unless control was applied also to other adjacent infested lands. The need for one coordinating agency to assume leadership seemed essential.

1921 Deficiency Act. The first act to provide specifically for the control of a native forest pest was the Deficiency Act of December 15, 1921. It was aimed at the control of a bark-beetle outbreak in northern California and southern Oregon. It provided funds for the Secretary of Agriculture to "prevent further loss from beetle infestations on federally owned lands," in the designated area. Further, it provided for cooperation of the Department of Agriculture with the Indian Service and with state and private owners. In regard to cooperation with state and private owners, it stipulated that

> . . . no part of the appropriation, except necessary expenditures for preliminary investigations, shall be expended unless the States of Oregon and California, or the owners of pine timberlands adjacent to or intermingled with lands owned or administered by the United States, shall have satisfied the Secretary of Agriculture that the insect infestations on said adjacent and intermingled lands will be abated, in accordance with state law or voluntarily by owners of such lands.

Federal Cooperation Acts. Even though the Deficiency Act was an appropriation act and not basic law, it set the pattern for Federal aid to cooperative insect-control projects in which state, Federal, and private owners participated. This Federal-aid principle was established legally by the Clark-McNary Act of June 7, 1924, which was aimed at fire protection rather than at pest control. It provided for the protection of lands in state and private ownership with Federal and state funds in equal amounts. Appropriation for research on forest insects and diseases was specifically authorized by the McNary-McSweeney Act of May 22, 1928. At that time, however, there was no recognition of Federal obligation to aid in the control of insect pests when federally owned lands were not involved. It was not until 10 years later that this responsibility was recognized. Then Congress enacted the Joint Resolution of April 6, 1937.

Incipient and Emergency Pest Control Act. The Joint Resolution of 1937, usually called the "Incipient and Emergency Pest Control Act," authorized the Secretary of Agriculture to control ". . . incipient and emergency outbreaks of insects and diseases." Two million dollars was appropriated to the Bureau of Entomology and Plant Quarantine as a contingency fund for these purposes. This appropriation, unlike regular appropriations, could be carried over into the following fiscal year and remained available until spent. Authorization provided that, by subsequent appropriations, this fund be maintained at 2 million dollars so that prompt action might be taken to control dangerous pests. This was a most important step.

The Joint Resolution as enacted in 1937 applied only to specific agricultural pests, but in 1938 it was reenacted and broadened. This reenactment provided authority to the Secretary of Agriculture and directed him to apply methods of control to certain specific agricultural pests, and to ". . . all types of insects and diseases when they occur in emergency outbreaks or incipient infestations or infections." Furthermore, it required state cooperation. This was the first act to authorize the expenditure of Federal funds on private lands to control pests.

Agriculture Organic Act.   The Agriculture Organic Act in 1944 further defined the policy of cooperation and included provisions for cooperation with foreign governments. This act referred specifically to a stipulated list of pests, mostly agricultural. Only three forest pests were mentioned; the gypsy moth, the brown-tail moth, and the Dutch elm disease. The appropriation act of the same year was specifically restrictive, however, and provided that funds for the removal of trees infected with Dutch elm disease could be spent only on federally owned property. This action was contradictory to the Organic Act passed by the same Congress.

Ever since the Deficiency Act of 1921, there had been a strong trend in the direction of Federal participation in the control of both fire and pests. Nevertheless, there was an obvious need for general legislation that would make clearer the Federal obligations in pest control.

Forest Pest Control Act.   On June 25, 1947, legislation was enacted that established a definite pest control policy. This was the Forest Pest Control Act. Appropriations for a number of continuing projects were immediately made. The act provided that

> . . . it shall be the policy of the Government of the United States, independently and through cooperation with governments of states, territories, and possessions, and private timber owners to prevent, retard, control, suppress, or eradicate incipient, potential, or emergency outbreaks of destructive insects and diseases on, or threatening all forest land irrespective of ownership.

The Secretary of Agriculture is authorized either directly or in cooperation with other departments of the Federal government or with states or private interests (1) to conduct surveys of any forest lands to detect and appraise forest insects or diseases, (2) to determine the measures to be applied on such lands for control, and (3) to plan, organize, direct, and carry out control measures on state or private lands.

Provision was made for cooperation with other Federal agencies and with states to apply control on all lands, public or private. However, none of the funds appropriated under the act could be expended on state or private lands "until such contributions toward the work as the Secretary may require have been made or agreed upon in the form of funds, services, materials, or otherwise." Thus the act provided for cooperative action but left to the discretion of the Secretary of Agriculture the kind and amount of any contribution that would be required of state and private owners. The trend toward Federal leadership and aid in forest-insect control is clear. As a matter of fact, under the Forest Pest Control Act the Secretary of Agriculture, if he considers it to be in the public interest, may require little or no contribution from the state or from owners of private lands.

The act is especially significant because it applies to all forest lands and to all insects and diseases and because it recognizes the necessity for early detection and appraisal of dangerous insect conditions and provides for the control of outbreaks and the suppression of incipient and potentially dangerous situations.

The effective administration of this act should include, in every state where forests are an important resource, the establishment of (1) a detection service which will (*a*) continually collect information on insect population trends, (*b*) be ever alert for increases of potential pests, and (*c*) be prompt in reporting findings and (2) a control organization prepared to meet emergency control requirements and to aid forest operators in protective practices.

In recognition of the tremendous developments in the control of forest insects that were enabled by the Forest Pest Control Act a new official position was created. This official has the responsibility to coordinate the various activities under the act.

The application of the provisions of the Forest Pest Control Act has thus far been limited mostly to control projects involving the use of chemicals and generally to situations that have been considered emergencies. Under the wording of the act other forest-insect control practices appear to be included. Logically, thinnings, noncommercial cuttings designed to change stand composition, and even the regulated use of fires for insect control should be eligible for Federal aid under the Forest Pest Control Act.

The restriction of the law to chemical control is unfortunate in that it results in overemphasis of the importance of that type of control in the minds of foresters. As a result forest entomologists have sometimes been placed under pressure to use chemicals when other control practices would have been more appropriate.

No provision for research is included in the Forest Pest Control Act, but as a result of its implementation research has been stimulated. As the control program developed, the need for accurate information has become increasingly obvious—information about the pests themselves, their reactions to the trees on which they feed, and their reactions to one another. Only by a knowledge of facts can better control practices be devised. The need for such knowledge demonstrates the need for research.

The leadership exerted by the Federal government should stimulate state activities. As a matter of fact, the current policy appears to be directed more toward cooperation with state and private agencies than toward Federal domination. Thus the Forest Pest Control Act has stimulated tremendously the work on forest insects in both control and research.

STATE RESPONSIBILITY FOR FOREST-INSECT CONTROL

In most states there is some legal provision for the control by the state of insect pests that constitute a threat to the best interest of the public. Frequently statutes providing for this work supplement those providing for quarantines, embargoes, inspection, and certification. These laws and the control projects conducted under them are often administered by the state entomologist or other comparable official. In some states, however, special legislation provides for the control of forest insects by the state under the administrative direction of the state forester. Under such an arrangement, the control of forest insects is separated from the administration of regulations designed to check the spread of pests from one locality to another.

Oregon Forest Insect and Disease Act. Oregon is one of the states in which forest-insect control is set up under the state forester. The Forest Insect and Disease Act of Oregon is considered a model law, and although others might serve equally well, it is selected as an illustration. This law declares that forest-insect pests and forest-tree diseases constitute a public nuisance and orders every owner of timberlands to control, destroy, and eradicate them. It provides further that, in case of failure, neglect, or inability to do this, the state forester shall, with the approval of the State Board of Forestry, declare an infestation-control district and fix the boundaries within which the infested or threatened lands are situated.

The state forester is then instructed, under the act, to institute control measures within the control district. All monies appropriated by the state legislature, contributed by the Federal government, or received from any agency, corporation, or individual are deposited in the Forest Insect and Disease Control Fund and so made available for control work.

Under this act, all control activities, except those conducted independently by agencies, corporations, or individuals upon their own lands, must be administered by the state forester. Even though the Federal government is contributing to the project, its representatives act only in an advisory capacity. The final decision to apply or not to apply control measures, therefore, rests with the state. This is a logical responsibility for a state to assume, provided, of course, that the state forester is guided by the best advice available from state and Federal forest entomologists.

Problem of Mixed Ownership.   Mixed landownership, usually characterizing areas involved in forest-insect outbreaks, presents some difficult problems. With the adoption of the Forest Pest Control Act and state forest pest-control legislation, the problems are simplified. However, under the laws of most states, although the state authorities may enter upon private property to abate a nuisance, legislation fails to provide for any assessment against private property for insect control. As a result, some owners who refuse to participate voluntarily receive free benefits. The trend now seems to be in the direction of levying assessments for control against all property benefited.

In Oregon and other West Coast states, where the administrative responsibility is centered in the state, the lines of responsibility are simple and direct. The organization of the 1950 spruce-budworm control project in Oregon will serve as an illustration of this. In that project, 452,000 acres of forest were sprayed and five different bases were used. The following diagram, adapted from a report dated March, 1950, issued by

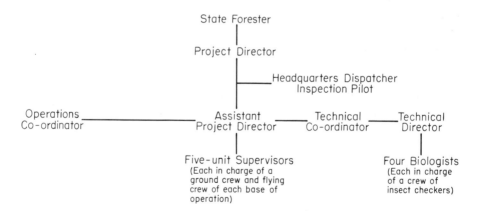

the State Board of Forestry, shows the lines of responsibility. The four biologists and the technical director acted in an advisory capacity but were closely coordinated with the administrative organization.

Under another situation, the administrative organization may be more scattered, with authority more divided between the various agencies concerned, and require more complex liaison and advisory arrangements. This sort of situation is illustrated by the organization of the northwestern pine beetle control project of 1948. The following diagram is adapted from the report of the U.S. Forest Service and the then Bureau of Entomology and Plant Quarantine on the above-mentioned project.

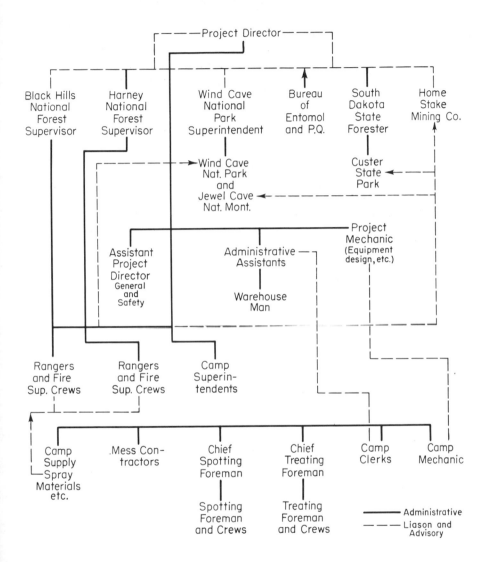

These two examples of project organization illustrate not only the diversity of arrangements that is required under the various state and Federal regulations but also the complexity of detail that must be considered in setting up a project. It must be realized that each agency, corporation, or individual entering into a control project must know his obligations and responsibilities in advance. To that end, cooperative agreements among the various parties concerned are absolutely necessary. Without them, confusion and misunderstandings are inevitable. From this we can see how important it is that the legislative provisions for forest-insect control be as simple and flexible as possible.

BIBLIOGRAPHY CHAPTER 2

Anon., 1947. Federal laws relating to forest insect and disease control, *U.S. Dept. Agr. Forest Serv., Reappraisal of Forest Situation, Rept.* 5.

Burke, H. E., 1950. "History of the Division of Forest Insects," unpublished manuscript.

Keen, F. P., 1943. Ponderosa pine tree classes redefined, *J. Forestry,* **41:** 249–253.

Miller, J. M., and F. P. Keen, 1960. Biology and control of the western pine beetle, *U.S. Dept. Agr. Misc. Publ.* 800.

Morris, R. F., and C. A. Miller, 1954. The development of life tables for the spruce budworm, *Can. J. Zool.,* **32:** 283–301.

Nusslin, O., and L. Rhumbler, 1922. "Forstinsektenkunde," pp. 1–9.

Patterson, J. E., 1921. Life history of *Recurvaria milleri,* the lodgepole needle miner, *J. Agr. Res.,* **21:** 127–142.

Popham, W. L., 1950. Development of co-operative effort in forest pest control, *J. Forestry,* **48:** 321–323.

Struble, G. R., 1937. The fir engraver beetle, a serious enemy of white fir and red fir, *U.S. Dept. Agr. Circ.* 419.

CHAPTER 3

REPRODUCTIVE POTENTIAL

The number of potentially injurious forest insects varies, as we have seen, from season to season and from locality to locality. These fluctuations are of major concern to the forest entomologist. If he can prevent insects from increasing above the level of economically serious damage, he will attain his ideal objective; if this is impossible, he may, at least, learn to anticipate outbreaks and be prepared to control them by direct means. In order to do either of these things, it is essential to know the capacity to increase that is characteristic of the more dangerous insect species and to understand the forces that operate in nature to prevent the attainment of these rates of increase.

The actual abundance of forest insects in general and of any one species in particular depends upon their ability to multiply and to live in spite of the various destructive forces in their environment. Before we can ascertain what will be the actual abundance of any insect, we must take into careful consideration (1) the ability of that insect to multiply in the absence of any destructive force and (2) the value of the sum total of all the environmental forces working toward its destruction. In other words, the rate of population growth is the result of a struggle between the forces of potential creation and potential destruction. Chapman (1925) has proposed apt terms for these two opposing forces: *reproductive potential* and *environmental resistance.*[1]

[1] Chapman proposed the terms *biotic potential, survival potential, reproductive potential,* and *environmental resistance.* These terms have been widely accepted, but un-

RATE OF MULTIPLICATION

The reproductive potential of an insect species, usually expressed in terms of a single individual, is its ability to multiply in a given time when relieved of all environmental resistance. The reproductive potential depends upon the female's fecundity, the length of the developmental period, and the sex ratio. The length of a developmental period is measured from one reproductive stage to the next. At this point we should

FIGURE 8. Lodgepole pine defoliated by the pandora moth, Arapahoe National Forest, Colorado. The pupae of this insect provided certain Indian tribes with a welcome source of nourishing food. (U.S. Dept. Agr. Forest Service.)

make clear that the force of reproductive potential alone does not determine the population level that a species will reach but merely the rate of increase that will occur in the absence of environmental resistance.

Fecundity.   The ability to produce young is one of the basic factors determining reproductive potential. Among insects there is a wide range

fortunately, the first two have not always been used consistently. On the other hand the latter two, *reproductive potential* and *environmental resistance*, are seldom misused. As originally defined by Chapman, these two terms adequately meet all the requirements in the following discussion. Therefore, in this text, the confusing terms *biotic potential* and *survival potential* will not be used.

of variation in this ability. The number of eggs that may be deposited by a single female may vary from a very few, as is the case with some wasps, to hundreds of thousands, as with the termites.

In general, the fecundity of insects is relatively high. Folsom and Wardle (1934) quote Mauw to the effect that two females of the broad-necked root borer, *Prionus laticollis*, were found to have in their ovaries 332 and 597 eggs. They further cite Girault as authority for the data in Table 2 concerning the fecundity of certain species.

TABLE 2   Fecundity of Insects

SPECIES	MAXIMUM	MINIMUM	AVERAGE
Evergreen bagworm, *Thyridopterix ephemerae-formis*	1,649	465	941
Eastern tent caterpillar, *Malacosoma america-num*	466	313	375.5
Scurfy scale, *Chionaspis furfura*	84	33	66.5

Other investigations have shown that the white-pine weevil, *Pissodes strobi*, lays on the average 115 eggs per female (Graham, 1926); the spruce budworm, *Choristoneura[1] fumiferana*, 316 (Graham, 1936); and the forest tent caterpillar, *Malacosoma disstria*, over 300. The author's class in forest entomology made counts showing that the scurfy scale, in the season of 1926 in Minnesota, laid an average of 25.6 eggs per female, with a maximum of 52 and a minimum of 6, a considerable variation from the figures cited above. In the same year the oystershell scale, *Lepidosaphes ulmi*, produced on the average 27.4 eggs per female, with a maximum of 68 and a minimum of 20; the white-marked tussock moth, *Hemerocampa leucostigma*, produced on the average 231.8 eggs per female, with a maximum of 467 and a minimum of 174. High as these figures are, it is improbable that in any of these cases the maximum possible number of eggs was deposited. For instance, dissection and examination of a series of tussock-moth females showed an average of 476 fully developed eggs per female, with a maximum of 764 and a minimum of 202—much higher figures than those based on counts of eggs actually deposited.

Polyembryony.   Some insects possess an ability that very materially increases their capacity to produce young. This is called *polyembryony*. Small hymenopterous parasites, notably the Braconidae and Procto-

[1] The generic name of this insect, like that of many other tortricid moths, has been changed a number of times since 1910. At various times it has been assigned to the genera *Tortrix, Archips, Harmaloga*, and *Cacoecia*. These changes are very confusing to the elementary student until he realizes that the group to which this insect belongs is a large and complex super family which has been in process of revision by taxonomists. Out of the apparent confusion will emerge a clear and stable classification.

trupidae, commonly possess this ability. A single egg deposited by a polyembryonic species produces from several to many individuals. Such a species, although it may produce comparatively few eggs, may still have a high rate of fecundity.

Length of Developmental Period. The rate of multiplication is dependent not only upon fecundity but also upon the length of time required for the completion of each generation. Many insects develop slowly. Certain species of Cerambycidae, for example, *Monochamus confusor*, the large pine sawyer, and *Monochamus scutellatus*, the white-spotted sawyer, require a full year to complete a generation under the most favorable conditions and as many as 4 years under adverse conditions. Some cerambycid beetles, such as *Hylotrupes bajulus*, the old-house borer, and *Eburia quadrigeminata*, the ivory-marked beetle, may live as larvae and pupae for as long as 18 to 20 years. It must be admitted that such extremely long developmental periods are unusual, even among wood borers, and are the result of unusually adverse conditions. A few insects, however, for example, the periodical cicada, *Magicicada septendecim*, have a normal life cycle almost as long as this.

On the other hand, some of the fruit flies of the genus *Drosophila*, under favorable conditions, may complete their development from egg to adult in less than 2 weeks and may, consequently, produce from 10 to 25 generations per year. Thus the short life cycle of such insects, coupled with the high fecundity of the individual insects, makes possible a rate of multiplication too great for the mind to comprehend. As an illustration of these tremendous possibilities, the calculation of LeFroy (1909) concerning the unrestricted multiplication of *Drosophila* may well be cited. He calculated that, if all the progeny lived and in turn reproduced themselves under favorable conditions, a single pair of fruit flies would in 1 year produce a mass of flies that, if packed 1,000 to the cubic inch, would cover the entire area of India to a depth of 100 million miles or would cover the earth to a depth of 1 million miles. Such a potential is difficult to imagine, because nothing like it has ever actually occurred. Nevertheless the immense possibilities of multiplication should not be overlooked.

SEX RATIO

The next important factor determining the reproductive potential of a species is the proportion of males and females characteristic of the species. This proportion is determined, in part at least, by the habits of reproduction.

Habits of Reproduction. Sexual reproduction is the type most commonly found among insects, although either partial or complete parthenogenesis is characteristic of many species. This latter habit of reproduction occurs very commonly among the Hymenoptera. For example, the larch sawfly, *Pristiphora erichsonii,* is partly parthenogenetic, and all the individuals of a form of the European spruce sawfly, *Diprion* (*Gilpina*) *polytomum,* are completely parthenogenetic (Smith, 1941). So also are the summer generations of plant lice, which give birth parthenogenetically to many generations of agamic females. In this way, many more individuals are produced during a season than would be possible with sexual reproduction.

Usually the females predominate in parthenogenetic species. This holds true in the case of the larch sawfly, which, under conditions observed during outbreaks, has as many as 96 females to 4 males. With such a high proportion of females, the number of progeny resulting from any one generation is much greater than would be the case with the usual half-and-half proportion of the sexes. Thus the sex ratio must be taken into consideration in calculating reproductive potential. The term *sex ratio* has been used in several ways. Frequently it indicates the ratio of males to females. More recent usage, where mathematical computations are involved, expresses it as the ratio between females and the total population. This latter expression should, for the sake of clarity, be called the sex factor. The sex factor of a species is determined by dividing the number of females in a given group by the total number of individuals in that group. Thus, if the sexes occur in equal numbers, the sex factor will be 0.5. In a purely parthenogenetic species, in which no males occur, it will be 1.0. In the case of the larch sawfly, mentioned above, the sex factor is 0.96.

Effect of Sex Factor. The important part that the sex factor plays in determining the reproductive potential of a species may be illustrated (see Table 3) by a simple calculation comparing two hypothetical insect

TABLE 3   Hypothetical Young Produced during Five Generations

GENERATIONS		FIRST	SECOND	THIRD	FOURTH	FIFTH
Species No. 1	Males 1	50	2,500	125,000	6,250,000	312,500,000
	Females 1	50	2,500	125,000	6,250,000	312,500,000
	Totals	100	5,000	250,000	12,500,000	625,000,000
Species No. 2	Males 0	0	0	0	0	0
	Females 2	200	20,000	2,000,000	200,000,000	20,000,000,000
	Totals	200	20,000	2,000,000	200,000,000	20,000,000,000

species, one of which produces equal numbers of males and females while the other produces only females. We shall assume that each of these species lays 100 eggs per female. If we start with two individuals of each species and calculate the rate of multiplication for each through five generations of progeny, assuming that each female lays her full quota of eggs and that every egg produces an adult individual, we shall see a great difference in the final numbers for each species.

In the fifth generation, it will be seen that species number 2 with the sex factor 1.0 has reached a total of more than 30 times the number of individuals in species number 1 with a sex factor of 0.5. Thus, we see that the sex factor is of vast importance in determining reproductive potential because it expresses the numbers of individuals in each generation of a species that are capable of producing new individuals.

CALCULATION OF REPRODUCTIVE POTENTIAL

Unless a specific numerical value for the reproductive potential of a species can be assigned, the term has little or no practical significance. Because the knowledge of the factors concerned has not been sufficient, it has often been impossible to arrive at such a value. In order to calculate the value of the reproductive potential of a species, all the factors that have just been discussed must be taken into consideration. The number of ovules that a single typical female is capable of producing, the number of generations that will be produced in a given time under optimum conditions, and the sex factor must all be known. The values for these factors are practically constant for any species of insect existing under ideal conditions, and they are sometimes called the constants for that species. If these constants are known, then the reproductive potential of any species may be calculated.

Values for Fecundity. According to the definition of reproductive potential, the constant values for fecundity can be observed only in the absence of environmental resistance. Therefore, the rate under ordinary natural conditions, when resistance is always more or less operative, cannot exactly indicate the potential value for fecundity. It is not the number of eggs which a typical female of a species actually lays that is the constant for that species, but the number she is capable of laying. To secure this potential number several methods may be used. The most accurate would be to rear a number of females from eggs to adults under ideal conditions, count the total egg production of each, and use the average production as the potential fecundity. Although this method has been used in several instances, it is both difficult and time-consuming; therefore, some easier way is desirable.

One method that is easier but, unfortunately, not so accurate is to count the fully developed eggs in the ovaries of gravid females that have never laid eggs and to assume the maximum number found in any one female to be the constant for that species. The reason for taking the maximum rather than the average is that in nature every individual is subject to the action of environmental resistance, including factors that might affect the fecundity of the individual. For example, a food shortage during the larval period for only a day or two can affect the number of eggs produced by the adult arising from such a larva. Therefore even the maximum number of eggs per female observed in nature is probably lower than the potential fecundity. This method of arriving at an approximation of potential fecundity cannot be used for species having a long oviposition period.

Counting the number of eggs laid under ideal conditions of confinement seems to be the only accurate method that can be used for determining the reproductive potential of an insect.

Values for Other Factors. The values for the other factors that enter into the calculation of reproductive potential are more easily obtained. For instance, the determination of the sex factor may be accomplished by rearing a large number of individuals and determining the number of each sex in the group. The number of generations in a given period and the number of individuals produced from a single egg may also be determined by simple rearing experiments. Chapman, in the calculation of reproductive potential, has used with adaptations a mathematical expression proposed by Thompson (1922) to express the number of progeny that will result from a given population in any number of generations. In this expression p represents the original population, which in the calculation of reproductive potential will be a single individual; z represents the product of the number of eggs per female and the sex factor; and n represents the number of generations in a given time. Then the number of progeny in n generations is pz^n. This expression is sound except when dealing with species that are polyembryonic, in which case it is necessary to include that factor also. For instance, if y represents the number of progeny arising from a single egg, the expression will then read $p(zy)^n$.

If it is assumed, for example, that the egg-laying capacity of the white-marked tussock moth is 764 eggs per female (the maximum number of fully developed eggs recorded as found in gravid females), the sex factor is 0.5, the number of individuals produced from an egg is 1, and the number of generations per year is 1; then the annual reproductive potential for the species expressed for a single insect is $1 \times (382 \times 1) = 382$. If, however, this were a polyembryonic species producing 4 individuals from a single egg and if it passed through two generations per season, the biotic potential would be $1 \times (382 \times 4)^2 = 2,334,784$.

This simple calculation demonstrates clearly the importance of each of the various factors of reproductive potential. Fortunately for man, this stupendous potential of creation is held in check by the forces of destruction that are analyzed in the following chapter.

BIBLIOGRAPHY CHAPTER 3

Chapman, R. N., 1925. "Animal Ecology with Special Reference to Insects," pp. 143–149.

Folsom, J. W., and R. A. Wardle, 1934. "Entomology with Special Reference to Its Ecological Aspects," pp. 123–126.

Graham, S. A., 1926. Biology and control of the white-pine weevil, *Cornell Agr. Expt. Sta. Bull.* 449.

———, 1936. The spruce budworm on Michigan pine, *Univ. Mich. School Forestry Conserv.* (now *Natural Resources*) *Bull.* 6.

LeFroy, H. M., 1909. "Indian Insect Life," p. 624.

Smith, S. G., 1941. Parthenogenetic form of European spruce sawfly, *Sci. Agr.,* **21:** 245–305.

Thompson, W. R., 1922. Étude de quelques cas simples de parasitisme cyclique chez les insectes entomophages, *Comp. Rend. Acad. Sci. Paris,* **174:** 1647–1649.

———, 1922. Théorie de l'action des parasites entomaphages, *Comp. Rend. Acad. Sci. Paris,* **175:** 65–68.

CHAPTER 4

ENVIRONMENTAL RESISTANCE

Environmental resistance is the sum of all the factors in an environment that tend to reduce the rate of multiplication of any organism. The factors that are combined to produce this force, as far as forest insects are concerned, may be divided into four principal groups: physical, nutritional, plant physiological, and biotic. These groups will be considered separately.

PHYSICAL FACTORS

Of all the limiting factors in the insect's environment, the physical factors have received the most intensive study and are best understood. But the knowledge of this group is still far from complete. Insects may change the physical conditions normally existing. For example, defoliators may change temperature and moisture within a forest stand by admitting unusual amounts of sunlight through the branches stripped of leaves. As a result conditions may become unfavorable for some insect inhabitants that are usually present (Turner, 1963).

Temperature plays an important role in determining both the rate of insect development and the distribution of all insects, geographically and locally. There are comparatively few species whose temperature reactions are definitely known. Likewise, the effects of light, moisture, air movement, and all the other factors that are thought of in connection with climate and weather are far from fully understood. Nevertheless much important progress has been made toward the understanding of these matters. In the following pages some of the more important effects of the action of these physical factors upon insect activities are discussed.

Temperature. One of the most important physical factors regulating insect activity is temperature. Each species of insect has a definite range of temperature within which it is able to live; temperatures above or below result in the insect's death. Near the upper and lower endurable limits are the dormant zones in which all external movement ceases. When an insect is in the lower of these zones, it is said to be in hibernation; when it is in the upper, it is said to be in estivation. Between these dormant zones lies the zone of activity or, as it is sometimes called, the zone of effective temperature.

As the temperature rises above the zone of hibernation in the effective zone, it becomes more and more favorable for insect development until an optimum point is reached. As the temperature rises above the optimum, conditions become less and less favorable until all activity ceases when the zone of estivation is reached.

The temperature requirements of insects vary with the species. Some species are active at a temperature only slightly above the freezing point of water, whereas most species are active only at temperatures above 15°C. The optimum temperature for most insects is in the neighborhood of 26°C, and estivation usually begins at 38 to 45°C. For many insects 48°C is the point of fatality at high temperatures, although some of the heat-resistant forms, for example, chrysobothris, can endure a temperature of 52°C for a short period (Graham, 1922). The low fatal temperature varies with both the species and the season. It has been shown that the same species is able to endure much more cold in the fall and winter than in the spring and summer (Payne, 1926). With each period of warmer than normal temperature during the winter, hibernating wood borers become less and less cold-hardy. As a result, in the spring the insects will be killed if exposed to subfreezing temperature which, in winter, they could have endured. The width of the zone of hibernation is so variable that no general statement regarding the usual point of fatality at low temperature can be made. All that can be said is that tropical species are, as a rule, much more susceptible to cold than are the temperate species.

This brings us to a consideration of the influence of temperature factors upon the distribution of insects. Several more or less successful attempts have been made to determine life zones on the basis of the sums of effective temperatures for different localities. Merriam (1898) used this basis for the construction of the life zones that are still widely used in biological work. Sanderson (1908) has shown, however, that insects do not always occur in every locality where the total of effective tempera-

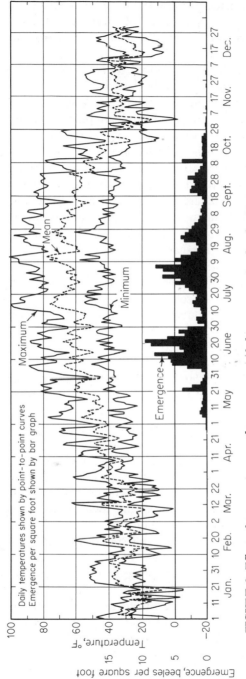

FIGURE 9. Effect of temperature on the emergence of the western pine beetle. (U.S. Department of Agriculture.)

45

ture is sufficient to make possible their complete development. Thus even though there may be a sufficiency of warm weather in the summer, a species may be kept out of a locality as a result of extremes of cold in the winter. For instance, the northward distribution of the gypsy and the brown-tail moths is definitely limited by low winter temperatures (Summers, 1922), and so it is probable that neither of these insects will ever reach the northernmost point at which summer temperatures are favorable. Similarly, the introduced European pine shoot moth, *Rhyacionia buoliana,* succumbs to temperatures of −18°F or lower and therefore cannot spread to the northern limits of its host species except when snow cover insulates the insects from low-temperature extremes. Such insulation by snow has permitted the European pine shoot moth to extend its range throughout Michigan, reaching and at least temporarily persisting in localities where temperatures of −18°F are frequently encountered. When a winter occurs when snow cover is absent and at the same time temperature is low, the northern range of this species may be expected to move southward.

In transition zones of temperature where fatal low temperatures occur only in certain especially cold winters, insects such as those mentioned above may temporarily move northward only to be extirpated during a cold year.

Some insects may be limited in their southward distribution by high temperature, but little positive evidence is available on this effect. We know, however, that the larch sawfly may pupate prematurely when exposed to excessively high temperature (Graham, 1956) and that animals other than insects are thus restricted in their southern distribution.

A very useful empirical law has been developed by Hopkins (1920 and 1938) which is known as Hopkins's bioclimatic law. By the use of this law, it is possible to prophesy from known conditions in one locality what conditions will exist at the same time in another locality. According to this law, any periodical biological phenomenon—such as the emergence of insects from hibernation, the spring awakening of vegetation, or the entrance of insects into hibernation—is correlated with latitude, longitude, and altitude. The law may be stated as follows: Other conditions being equal, the variation in time of any seasonal event in temperate North America occurring in the spring and early summer is at the general rate of 4 days later for each degree of latitude northward or 5° of longitude eastward or 400 feet of altitude upward. In the late summer and fall, conditions are reversed. This law appears to hold reasonably well for at least those portions of temperate North America east of the Rocky Mountains. Consideration of this law shows clearly why, on the basis of temperature alone, a high mountain range might prove an impassable geographical barrier to the spread of animals or plants from one region to another.

In the preceding discussion we have seen how temperature limits the geographical distribution of insects. It also limits with equal certainty the local distribution of these animals. The local temperature varies greatly within very short distances. For instance, on a bright day in summer the temperature at the surface of the ground may be as much as 50°C higher than the air temperature at breast height. A difference of 10 to 20°C between surface temperature and the temperature 1 foot above the surface is not at all uncommon. With such a wide range within such a limited space, it is possible for many insects to change their position so as to keep within a favorable zone (Chapman, 1925).

Some insects, those living in logs for instance, are unable to move quickly from place to place. If conditions become sufficiently unfavorable, the insects may be killed. In logs having comparatively thin dark-colored bark, the side exposed to direct solar radiation may reach 60°C or more (Graham, 1922 and 1924). Such temperatures are far above the fatal point for all insects, and so on the upper side of logs lying in the sun there is usually a sterile zone. On the sides where favorable temperatures prevail, the insects occur in greatest numbers; on the lower side, where uniformly cool conditions are found, there exist only those species that are able to live under cool conditions. As will be shown later, the fatal effect of high temperature upon log-inhabiting insects is made use of in insect control. Local distribution of insects can furnish highly useful information in evaluating forest-insect effects. For instance, from the facts of distribution it is possible to state whether or not a certain fallen tree was infested before or after its falling. If infestation came first, insects of the same species will be found on all sides of the log; if infestation followed falling, there will be a zone on the upper side devoid of insects and on the lower side a zone containing insects liking cool conditions. The reason for this lies in the fact that temperatures in standing trees never reach a point high enough to kill all insects while on the fallen tree trunk very high temperature may be reached on the top side. High subcortical temperatures can develop only where the sun's rays fall vertically and where they have the shortest atmospheric distance to travel. Since the latter condition exists only at midday, the rays will be falling vertically at that time only on trees in a horizontal position.

Temperature not only affects the geographical and local distribution of insects but also regulates the rate of insect development. In general, the rate of development increases in proportion to the increase in temperature until the point of optimum temperature is reached. The rate of this increase varies somewhat at different temperatures and with different species, but in general between the lowest effective temperature and the optimum point, an increase of 10°C doubles the rate of development. Sanderson and Peairs (1913), Peairs (1927), Krogh (1914), and other workers have expressed the increase in velocity of development more

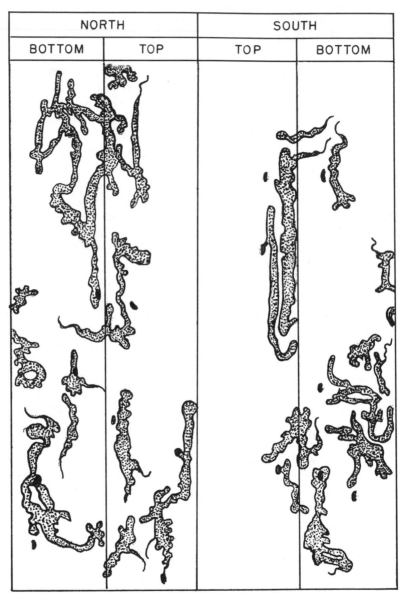

NORTH		SOUTH	
BOTTOM	TOP	TOP	BOTTOM

FIGURE 10. Distribution of hemlock borer tunnels under the bark of a hemlock log lying in an east-west direction. Observe the sterile zone on the upper-south side. Black spots represent emergence holes through the bark, sometimes at a distance from the subcortical feeding tunnels.

accurately, stating that the rate of development increases directly with the temperature, the developmental curve being a segment of a true mathematical hyperbola. Although this generalization is true only within certain limits, it is useful to the forest entomologist. Since, by definition, the reciprocals for the points on a hyperbola fall in a straight line, if we plot the reciprocals of two points and connect them by a straight line, it will be possible to compute the rate of development at any other temperature. Above the optimum point, a reduction in rate of development occurs with increasing temperature until at a high temperature the rate of development is reduced to zero. Thus a line through the points representing the reciprocals of the developmental rate will diverge from the straight line at high temperature. A similar divergence appears at low temperature, but the segment in which we are most interested follows the straight line.

The seasonal activities of many insects are definitely regulated by temperature. For instance, the Nantucket pine moth, *Rhyacionia frustrana,* has only one generation per year in Michigan and Minnesota and as many as five in the Southern states. Similarly the white-marked tussock moth, some bark beetles, and several of the giant silkworm moths have only one generation in the North and two or more in the South (Dawson, 1931). Both the number of generations and the time of emergence are correlated with temperature conditions. During a late spring, insects may be greatly retarded in emerging from hibernation; during cool summers, the length of the developmental stages may be greatly extended. For instance, during the spring of 1950 in Michigan, the European larch casebearer was at least 2 weeks later than usual in emerging from hibernation. An increase in the length of the larval stage usually affects an insect species adversely by exposing it longer than usual to predators and disease-causing organisms.

Light.   The reactions of insects to light are not very different from their reactions to temperature, and since these factors are usually closely associated with each other and since they generally vary synchronously, it is often difficult to determine whether the effects are produced by the one or by the other. Evidence indicates that temperature and light operating together may be necessary to produce certain reactions. Dickinson (1949) reports that diapause in the oriental fruit moth is induced by light and temperature combined when temperatures are median and when periods of light and darkness are about equal. Neither condition alone can produce this effect.

Theoretically, it seems possible to divide light, just as we do temperature, into optimum, effective, dormant, and lethal zones. Inasmuch as some insects respond positively and some negatively to light, it may be assumed that the optimum must vary greatly with different species. The stimulating effect of light on certain species is well illustrated by the reaction of chrysobothris adults. These beetles remain inactive on cloudy days when the air temperature may be as high as or higher than the temperature on some sunny days when they are active. Carpenter (1909) has shown that the convulsive motor reactions of drosophila that normally occur at a temperature of 39°C appear at 30°C under the rays of a strong light of 480 candlepower. Although certain insects are not able to endure strong light, it seems probable that light under natural conditions seldom goes beyond the limits of toleration of most species. It is true, however, that the presence or absence of light determines to a greater or lesser extent the local distribution of insects. Those that are positively phototropic or heliotropic will be found for the most part in the open, whereas those that respond negatively will be found during the day in the soil, under rocks or bark, or in some other dark location. In some instances, light appears to be an important factor in determining the place of oviposition of certain insects. For instance, Chapman (1915) has shown that the two-lined borer, *Agrilus bilineatus*, deposits its eggs by preference upon trees exposed to full sunlight. The oviposition niches of the poplar borer, *Saperda calcarata*, are most frequent on the south side of attacked trees (Harrison, 1959; Graham and Mason, 1958).

Insects do not react to light in the same manner at all stages of development or under all conditions. For instance, Wellington (1948), in a careful investigation of the photoresponses of the spruce budworm, points out that the first and second instars always react positively to light at room temperature whereas in other stages the light reaction is affected by feeding, except for the third, which is indifferent to light even when starved. The later instars react negatively when hungry, and all stages at ordinary temperatures react positively when not hungry. At excessively high temperatures, all stages react negatively. The results of these experiments demonstrate that caution must be exercised in drawing generalizations from field observations. From this discussion, we see that the effects of light are difficult to separate from those of temperature, but there is good evidence to indicate that light is important in the life of insects.

Moisture.   Another physical factor of the environment that plays an important part in insect activity is moisture. As with all other forms of life, so it is with insects: both their distribution and their development are dependent on the presence of water in the environment. The effectiveness of heat in stimulating or retarding the velocity of insect development is also influenced by the amount of moisture present. Under favorable moisture conditions, an insect is not so susceptible to extremes of temperature as it would be under unfavorable moisture conditions (Pierce, 1916).

With moisture, as well as with temperature, each species has definite requirements with optimum and effective zones. The extreme zones are less clearly marked than is the case with heat. Under ordinary conditions, an excess or deficiency of moisture does not result in an insect's immediate death but only in a disturbance of its activities. There are, however, certain outstanding instances of forest insects that are definitely limited in their activities by the moisture factor. The powderpost beetles, for instance, cannot live in moist wood (Snyder, 1926), whereas the ambrosia beetles cannot develop in dry wood. Bark beetles are definitely limited by moisture conditions in the phloem region. The northern spruce beetle,[1]

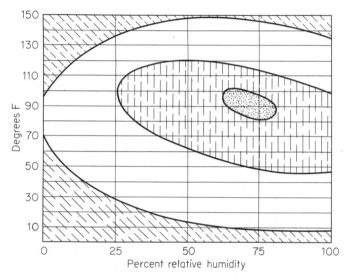

FIGURE 11. Combined effect of temperature and relative humidity on the rate of development of insects. Stippled area represents the most rapid development, vertical dashes show the favorable zone, the unshaded area is the zone within which growth is slow but conditions are tolerable, and the diagonal dashes represent the combinations within which no development is possible. The position of the zones on the temperature and humidity scales will vary with different species.

Dendroctonus obesus, is able to develop better under moist conditions than is its frequent associate *Ips perturbatus,* whereas the latter can live easily under conditions that are too dry for the dendroctonus (Denton, 1950). Also the smaller European elm bark beetle, *Scolytus multistriatus,* exhibits a marked preference for freshly cut logs and is unable to live in those that have dried to a point where the phloem is discolored (Martin, 1946). The rate of development of other wood-boring species may be

[1] Formerly known as the eastern spruce beetle, *Dendroctonus piceaperda.*

greatly reduced by the desiccation of the wood. In fact there are cases on record in which a wood borer having a normal life cycle of 1 or 2 years has required, because of unusually dry conditions, 20 years or more to reach maturity.

The activities of most insects are affected more or less by moisture extremes. For example, the spruce-budworm larvae cease feeding when the air becomes saturated with water. Thus, during periods of moist weather the larvae may be practically inactive, with the result that the length of the developmental period is extended.

Climate and Weather.   In view of the far-reaching effect that any one of these factors of temperature, light, and moisture may have on the life of forest insects, it is evident that, when all are combined and joined with still other factors, the resulting complex, which we call weather or climate, is fundamental in any consideration of forest-insect problems. Climate is the expression of the average physical conditions to be observed in a locality over many years. Climate may change, but such changes are slow. This climatic stability forms the basis of Hopkins's bioclimatic law and of Merriam's life zones. Observed climatic changes appear to be at the rate of about 1°F of mean temperature per century.

Weather, on the other hand, is the result of the combined action of all the physical factors of the environment at any given time and varies from hour to hour, day to day, and week to week. Weather influences the abundance of insects and the rate of development from year to year and from season to season in every locality. With insects of the forest, as well as with others, weather conditions are exceedingly important in regulating abundance. A late frost in the spring that kills the foliage on their host trees after the eggs of the forest tent caterpillar have hatched may result in the starvation of almost all the young larvae of that species (Blackman, 1918). The same situation may affect any leaf eater that feeds upon trees in early spring. Heavy rains during the larval stage of insects that feed on the exposed surfaces of trees may wash off and destroy large numbers of larvae and thus reduce the possibility of their becoming epidemic. During the spring of 1947, the number of pine sawflies in southern Michigan was materially reduced by heavy rains immediately following the hatching of the larvae. Cool weather during the developmental period may so lengthen the larval or nymphal stage that a much larger proportion of the species may fall prey to their enemies than would otherwise be the case. Moist warm weather also may make possible outbreaks of entomophagous organisms, such as disease-causing bacteria or fungi. Dry weather may so reduce the vegetative growth of trees on which certain species feed that great injury will result from the activities of only a normal number of pests. On the other hand, wet weather may produce an unusually luxuriant growth and overcome effects of an insect attack that might in the average season produce great injury to the trees. In the case of most defoliating insects, high temperatures combined with light rainfall tend to favor insect development and to encourage outbreaks. Soil-inhabiting insects are likely to be affected adversely by dry weather (Hawley, 1949).

Wellington and associates (1950) have studied the influence of weather upon the outbreaks of the spruce budworm. For his specific purpose, Wellington modified a method suggested by Kullmer (1933). By laying out a grid with north-south lines 5° of longitude apart and east-west lines 2.5° of latitude apart and recording the number of lows passing over each unit, Kullmer was able to draw isometric lines connecting those parts of the grid experiencing the same number of low-pressure periods. Lines bounding the points with the greatest number of "lows" indicated the position of the so-called storm track. This track shifts from season to season. By applying the modification of Kullmer's method, Wellington determined that, in any area, outbreaks of the spruce budworm tend to follow a period when for 3 or 4 years the number of lows has been decreasing. "In other words, outbreaks occur following periods of decreasing or minimal storminess."

From the viewpoint of the forest entomologist this sort of information would have limited value were it not for long-range forecasting of weather. There is little doubt that in the near future general forecasts for any locality can and will be made several years in advance. Thus in areas that are otherwise suitable for the outbreak of an insect, we can anticipate by several years when an outbreak is likely to occur. Also we can, with considerable certainty, anticipate the years that will be relatively safe.

The assumption that all species of insects respond to the same or even similar weather conditions is unsafe. There is, however, a growing accumulation of data to indicate that outbreaks of numerous species occur in the same climatic area at about the same time. Carpenter (1940) summarized outbreak records for Europe and treated the data as if all species were part of a single population. He found a strong tendency for outbreaks of any group of species in the same vegetational formation to occur concurrently. He says, "Analysis of the records of insect outbreaks . . . suggests that, in the deciduous forest region at any rate, outbreaks tend strongly to occur in the same groups of years, or are nearer together than would be expected from chance."

Although no similar study has been made in America, experience indicates that a comparable situation exists. In the Lake States, outbreaks of the spruce budworm and larch sawfly occurred simultaneously between 1910 and 1920. At about the same time, the pine tussock moth and the hemlock looper were abundant in Wisconsin. From the study of tree rings, it appears that both a budworm outbreak and a larch-sawfly outbreak occurred about 1880 in parts of Michigan; again in the middle twenties, local outbreaks of larch sawfly and spruce budworm occurred simultaneously in the Tahquamenon Swamp and adjacent areas.

Thus we are encouraged to hope that studies of the ways in which physical factors of environmental resistance affect various species of forest insects, coupled with long-range forecasting, may lead to better preparedness for outbreaks.

Indirect Effects of Weather.   In preceding sections the emphasis has been on the effects of physical factors upon the insects themselves. But often the effects of weather conditions on the infested trees may be equally significant.

Bark-beetle outbreaks are frequently associated with periods of drought, during which the trees are weakened from lack of water (Vite, 1961). Hetrick (1949) reports, however, that conditions were made more favorable for the southern pine beetle by excessive precipitation, because pines growing on low-lying areas were injured by high water. Apparently any force that reduces the vitality of the trees renders them subject to attack.

Wind and fire, the latter a reflection of weather conditions, kill and damage trees, thus encouraging the increase of bark insects and wood borers. Similarly winter injury is often a means of encouraging insect outbreaks. Widespread winter injury in the winter of 1947–1948 occurred from the Black Hills to New York State. An abnormally dry autumn was followed by an acute condition in February. In northern Wisconsin and Michigan high thawing temperature occurred on February 17 and was followed the next day by subzero temperatures. Many pines and hemlocks were defoliated as a result of desiccation at a time when the water loss could not be replaced through the frozen sapwood. This resulted in a marked increase in the abundance of the hemlock borer in 1949.

The close association of insect outbreaks with weather fluctuations stimulates interest among forest entomologists in the so-called climatic cycles. Long-term records and evidence in tree rings provide considerable information on these trends (Keen, 1937). Alternating wet and dry periods occur and with them alternating periods when certain insects are sometimes abundant and other times scarce. Although neither the time between wet and dry periods nor the amplitude of the variations appears to be uniform, there is a certain amount of consistency that is useful for general forecasts.

The various physical factors discussed above may be much better understood than any of the other limiting factors of the insect environment, but it is erroneous to assume that there are not other factors equally important entering into environmental resistance. These will be discussed under the headings of nutritional, plant-physiological, and biotic factors.

NUTRITIONAL FACTORS

The physical factors of the environment do not lend themselves to regulation, whereas the nutritional factors may often be controlled with a reasonable degree of exactness. If the food conditions can be so controlled that outbreaks of pests are improbable even in weather favorable for insects, we shall be less concerned about the effects of weather upon the rate of insect multiplication. For this reason, we should be particularly interested in the nutritional factors.

Quantity of Food. It is an accepted biologic law that, other things being favorable, an organism will eventually multiply to the limit of its food supply. As a rule, the more numerous the individuals of a tree species, the more abundant are its insect enemies. When there is an unlimited and convenient supply of a certain species of trees, the stage is set for an outbreak of the insect pests of that tree.

The spruce-budworm outbreaks in eastern United States and Canada, as will be shown later, are associated with an overabundance of mature balsam fir and possibly white spruce. Similarly, the larch-sawfly outbreaks have undoubtedly been stimulated by large volumes of tamarack, and the forest-tent-caterpillar outbreaks by extensive stands of poplar or other suitable food trees. Our forest and ornamental trees are often listed according to their susceptibility to insect attack. On examination of these lists it is found, with rare exceptions, that the species listed as insect-resistant are those which do not occur commonly in large masses. Red pine has in the past been classed as insect-resistant, but accurately speaking, it cannot be said that this and similar species are any more resistant than other species. Their apparent resistance was due to their relative scarcity in the forest. The validity of this statement is supported by experience following the widespread planting of red pine during the years after 1933. These plantations are being attacked by the Saratoga spittlebug, by several sawflies—especially the red-headed pine sawfly—and in the more southerly plantations by the European pine shoot moth. Now, in the nineteen sixties when they are reaching middle age, bark-beetle outbreaks are imminent.

At one time, jack pine, like red pine, was regarded as an insect-resistant species, but later it was seriously attacked by a number of dangerous pests. The reason for this apparent change in susceptibility can probably be explained by the fact that in the range of the jack pine this species has largely replaced the other pines that once formed the major portion of the virgin forest in the Lake States. Instead of scattered blocks of jack pine on lands too poor to support other species, we now have vast areas over which this species is predominant. Thus the quantity of food available becomes an important factor in regulating insect abundance. This, of course, has an important bearing on control (Chap. 5).

Kind and Quality of Food. The abundance of forest insects and the length of the developmental period are both limited by the kind and quality of food that the insects are able to use. An insect species, for instance, that feeds only on the succulent tissues of the phloem must complete its feeding period quickly while the perishable material which it eats is still in usable condition. Although perishable, this food is comparatively high in nutritional value. We should expect, therefore, that the phloem region would be filled with many kinds of insects, each with a short developmental period. This is exactly the condition that exists.

By the nature of their food, the development of almost all leaf-eating species is limited to a single season or even to a short part of one season. Few leaf eaters can pass the winter as partly grown larvae; consequently they must complete their development before the leaves drop in the autumn. In some cases, the length of the developmental period is limited to a few weeks during which the foliage is soft and succulent.

Wood borers, on the other hand, feed upon a medium that changes very slowly. It is therefore not at all uncommon for their life cycle to extend over several years. Many of the wood-boring species, such as some of Cerambycidae and Buprestidae, feed for a time in the phloem before entering the solid wood. In this way the young larvae are provided with more nourishing and more easily digestible food than are the larger larvae. This suggests that the powers of digestion of these species are better in the later than in the earlier stages. Other insects, such as the Siricidae, are able to digest solid wood from the earliest stages and are exclusively eaters of wood.

On the basis of these facts, we see that all tree insects do not have the same food requirements: some require leaves, some find the phloem region to their liking, and still others are able to wrest their living from the solid wood. As the wood is worked over by insects and fungi, its chemical and physical characters change, and with this change come new species of insects to replace those which attacked the living tree or recently cut log. These in turn are replaced by others until in the last stage of decomposition the population is identical with that of the duff stratum of forest soils. Thus there is a continuous succession of insect species inhabiting the tree from the fresh green condition of the newly felled or killed tree to the completely decomposed condition.

During the process of disintegration there is, in many instances, a close relationship between fungi and insects. In some cases, particularly in the early stages, a true symbiotic relationship can be demonstrated (Baumberger, 1919). Just as the fruit flies can develop normally only where bacteria or fungi are present to aid in the elaboration of raw food, so, in the case of many wood borers, fungi must be present to alter the character of the wood, thereby making the food materials available for the insects. In some cases, such as that of the ambrosia beetles, the fungus furnishes the entire food for the insect, and the galleries that are cut into the wood by the insects serve only for shelter and a place for the food fungus to grow.

The success of an insect species is determined not only by the kind of food available when it is needed and by the presence of symbiotic organisms but also by the quality of food as affected by soil nutrients. The lack of some element in the soil may affect the plants adversely but at the same time improve nutritional conditions for some insects, such as aphids (Haseman, 1950).

Host Selection.   Most species of forest insects are limited in their feeding either to one species of tree or to a more or less prescribed group of species. The locust borer, for example, feeds only on the black locust, the sugar-maple borer attacks only maples, the larch sawfly defoliates only larch, the Nantucket pine moth infests only pines, and the spruce budworm is confined to a comparatively limited group of conifers.

When an insect attacks only one species of tree, its control presents a comparatively simple problem; when it is a general feeder, like the gypsy moth, the problem becomes more complex. Fortunately with many species that feed on a variety of hosts the problem is simplified by the fact that there is a strong tendency for an insect to oviposit on the host upon which it was reared. This is called Hopkins's host-selection principle (Craighead, 1921; Wood, 1963), and it apparently holds true for many of the Cerambycidae, for some Scolytidae, and within certain limits for the spruce budworm. Further work along this line may show that this principle may be applied much more generally than is now known to be the case.

Perhaps the operation of this principle has in the past ages given rise to new species by developing first biologic varieties limited to a single host and later to forms distinct morphologically as well. However this may be, whenever host selection occurs, control measures are simplified thereby because each biologic variety may then be treated as if it were an individual species.

PLANT-PHYSIOLOGICAL FACTORS

Trees possess certain physiological characteristics which result in producing, in varying degree, a certain real ability to resist insect attack. These characteristics, by making environmental conditions less favorable for the insect than would otherwise be the case, increase the force of environmental resistance working against the insect.

Rapidity of Growth.   Vigorous rapidly growing trees suffer less from insect injury than do trees of the same species that are growing more slowly. Rapid growth has a double effect: (1) It produces in the tree more resistance, both to attack and to injury, and (2) it shortens each developmental stage of the tree, thereby reducing the period of susceptibility to the insects attacking each stage.

Another characteristic that is often associated with rapid growth and serves as a protection against insect attack is the copious flow of resin and sap. This flow will drive out or overwhelm and kill almost any of the phloem borers before they can become established in the tree. Only when an especially vigorous tree is attacked simultaneously by large numbers of these insects is it unable to resist attack. Illustrations of resistance through vigor may be seen in any forest where dendroctonus beetles are working. When resistant trees are attacked, they usually become covered at each point of attack with pitch tubes, formed by hardened resin. Examination of these trees will show some beetles entombed in their resin-filled galleries whereas other tunnels are deserted.

FIGURE 12. Trees are not always killed when attacked by bark beetles. Sometimes the tree recovers and overgrows the injury as illustrated above, in this case only to be killed later by another attack. (U.S. Dept. Agr. Forest Service.)

Other interesting examples of resistance to attack by vigorous growth may be cited. For instance, some of the buprestids, such as several species of the genus *Melanophila,* may deposit their eggs upon trees that are fairly thrifty. These eggs will hatch, and the larvae will penetrate into the bark. In order to develop, these larvae must feed for a period of time in the inner phloem and cambium, but they can feed only on the phloem of decrepit trees or freshly cut logs. Therefore when they reach the inner phloem of a healthy tree, they either die immediately or are forced to turn back into the bark, where they die a lingering death. These small buprestid larvae frequently have been found starving in the bark of healthy jack pine, hemlock, or ponderosa pine. The galleries of phloem insects are often found overgrown by many years of woody growth, indicating that an old attack has been outgrown. Galleries of the two-lined borer; the bronze birch borer; the poplar agrilus, *Agrilus liragus;* and *Melanophila californica* are frequently thus overgrown.

Foliage Characteristics. Sometimes a tree species may resist insect attack because of certain characteristics of its foliage. The lack of synchronization between the spruce budworm and the black spruce illustrates well this kind of resistance. A detailed discussion of this relationship will be taken up later, but it deserves mention here because it illustrates one type of physiological resistance. When the young budworms emerge from hibernation, they require tender fresh foliage for food. Their time of emergence is about 2 weeks prior to the opening of the black-spruce buds; consequently in a stand of black spruce the larvae are faced with a food shortage in the early part of the season. Some of them find the green tissues that they require by boring into a bud or by mining a needle, but many of them fail to do this and perish. Thus the presence of black spruce in a forest reduces budworm abundance.

The white spruce also has a means of reducing the number of budworm larvae feeding upon it. Unlike the black spruce, the buds of the white spruce open at a time suitable for the budworm, but the white-spruce needles harden and become unpalatable before all the larvae can reach full growth. Many of them perish when they are forced to leave the trees on which they have been feeding to seek more suitable food. Still another illustration of how a foliage characteristic may prevent the attack of an insect is the way in which the European elm leaf miner, *Fenusa ulmi,* is prevented from attacking American elm. The leaves of our native elms are much thinner than the European species and do not provide sufficient space to accommodate the full-grown miner.

Distasteful Characteristics. Certain trees apparently possess immunity from insects because they are unattractive or actually distasteful to the insects. Exactly what these characteristics are is not known, but their existence cannot be doubted. They are often not possessed by all the individuals of a species to the same degree. Some trees may be immune to attack while a neighboring tree is highly susceptible.

A striking example of the variation in this respect is to be observed in a certain plantation of Norway spruce on one of the forest properties of The University of Michigan. This plantation has been severely attacked by the eastern spruce gall aphid, *Chermes abietis.* Most of the trees are heavily infested, but others are absolutely untouched. Even when the branches of an immune tree interlock with those of a heavily infested one, the immune tree will remain uninfested.

Certain individual spruce trees in Europe exhibit a decided resistance to the attack of that much dreaded forest defoliator, the nun moth. The larvae refuse to feed upon the needles of these resistant trees, but when branches are cut and placed in water for 24 hours, they will then be accepted as food. This may indicate that some volatile repellent substance not present in other trees of the same species constitutes the active agency that prevents the insects from attacking the resistant individuals.

BIOTIC FACTORS

Biotic factors are the last of the limiting environmenal factors to be discussed. In this group are included all interactions among organisms that result in the limitation of insect multiplication. The biotic factors that play important roles in environmental resistance are competition, parasites, and predators.

Competition. Competition may occur either among the individuals of the same species or among different species. In either case the result is a reduction in the rate of increase of the competing organisms. Competition occurs *only* when something desired or needed is in short supply: food, space, or shelter, for example. Thus, under normal conditions when forest insects are present in moderate numbers, the things they need are in excess of their demands. As a result there can be no competition. Take food for example. In order that a continuous supply of food be available, only a small part of that which is in existence at any one time can be used. Food must be produced more rapidly than it is consumed, or the supply will eventually be cut off. This means that the forest trees can afford to supply other organisms with only that amount of food which they are able to produce in excess of their own requirements for maintenance and growth. Thus when other environmental forces are holding down the insects to normal numbers, the insects are using only this surplus or less. Therefore, there is no scarcity of food.

At a time when some insect species temporarily increases in number to a point where an outbreak may be said to exist, the situation is changed. Then the insects are no longer feeding only on the surplus but are actually using up the capital. Under such conditions keen competition occurs, not only among the insects of the species that is in the outbreak state but also with other species that require the same food. There can be only one result: Sooner or later, if the outbreak is not checked by the action of some outside controlling influence, the entire supply of food will become exhausted. The insects dependent upon it will either starve or be forced to migrate to new locations. Thus competition for food has reduced the number of the excessively abundant species and possibly some other species dependent on the same kind of food.

Similarly two different species of bark beetles may compete directly with each other for the same food. Recent studies in Michigan have shown that, when wind-fallen spruce trees or spruce logs are attacked simultaneously by the northern spruce beetle, *Dendroctonus obesus* and *Ips perturbatus,* direct competition results. Since ips beetles develop more rapidly, they soon destroy the dendroctonous brood. Only in trees or logs too moist for ips can the dendroctonus succeed. Evidence is plentiful in support of the contention that species with *identical* needs and habits cannot live together indefinitely.

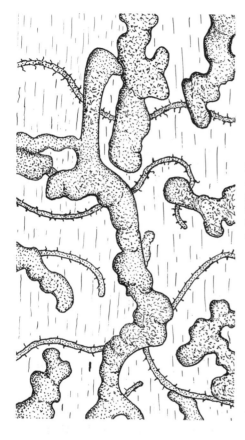

FIGURE 13. Cerambycid and dendroctonus tunnels in the phloem of pine illustrating competition between these insects. Increase of dendroctonus beetles is often prevented by their competitors.

Competition for space is an important limiting factor among some groups of forest insects. Competition of this type is sometimes very keen among the phloem insects and also among the wood borers. For instance, the number of white-pine weevils that can reach maturity in a terminal shoot of a pine sapling is directly proportional to the circumference of the shoot (Fig. 14). This is due to the habits of the insect. The eggs are laid near the top of the leading shoot, and the larvae work downward side by side in the phloem, encircling the shoot. If a single larva works ahead of the others, it is quickly overwhelmed and killed by the resin exuded into its tunnel. As the larvae increase in size, they become more and more crowded, are finally forced out of line, and are left to starve. Thus only those that remain in line can survive. The number of larvae maturing cannot be greater than the number that can lie side by side around the shoot. Many bark beetles of the family Scolytidae are limited in a similar way. Usually competition is among larvae, but occasionally in cases where all stages of an insect are living in a limited environment—

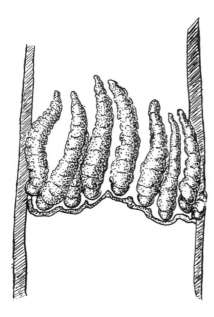

FIGURE 14. Arrangement characteristic of the larvae of the white-pine weevil as they work downward in the terminal shoot of white pine. This is the result of competition for space.

as do the bark beetles and ambrosia beetles—there may be competition for space between adults and immature stages.

In nature this competition for space is usually difficult to evaluate because other kinds of competition operate simultaneously. Only by carefully controlled experiments, in which space is the single limiting factor, can the true effects be demonstrated. Many such experiments have been made with insects and various other animals; the results of these all indicate that, whenever competing individuals are limited by restricted space, a definite population equilibrium develops. The population level is characteristic of the species and is attained regardless of the initial number of individuals (Crombie, 1946). If too numerous, the population will be reduced; if too few, the organisms will increase until the number characteristic of the species and the space is attained. In the case of forest insects, the number of young produced is usually in excess of the equilibrium number. Competition for space causes the elimination of part of the juvenile population.

Sometimes the abundance of forest insects is limited by competition for suitable shelter. The abundance of termites or of carpenter ants is definitely limited in certain instances by a scarcity of places in which to build their nests. With most forest insects, however, if food is sufficient, shelter is also available, for the insect's shelter is usually made from the same material that is used for food, from the bodily secretions of the insect, or from a combination of both.

Predators and Parasites. The effect of predators and of parasites in producing environmental resistance is so nearly identical that it seems advisable to discuss them together in order to avoid repetition. These two closely allied factors constitute an important part of environmental resistance. In fact, some authorities feel that they are more important than all other factors combined. Most authorities, however, do not agree with this estimate of their importance (Howard, 1926), but all admit that, without the control exercised by these beneficial insects, almost all insect pests would be more serious than they now are.

Both parasites and predators feed upon insects. According to common usage, a parasite obtains its food from its host without killing it directly; in entomological usage, however, the host is usually killed. Insectivorous parasites are found in many groups of organisms: fungi, bacteria, protozoa, nematodes, and various arthropods including insects. Of all these, the parasitic insects have received most attention from entomologists. However, the destructive effect on insects of the other parasitic forms is receiving increasing recognition.

Insectivorous predators are also found in many groups of animal life: birds, mammals, reptiles, amphibians, and most important of all, other insects. These insectivorous predators always kill their prey and are equal to the parasites in their importance as biotic factors of environmental resistance.

Between parasites and predators no stage in the development of an insect is free from attack. Even though the eggs of insects are generally very small objects, they have both their predaceous and parasitic enemies. No matter how carefully they are hidden, some of them are almost certain to be found and destroyed. Insect eggs furnish a staple article of diet for kinglets, nuthatches, and chickadees. After watching one of these insectivorous birds searching the trunk and branches of the trees in the winter, it is easy to believe that they are extremely effective in reducing the number of insects that pass the winter in the egg stage. Insect eggs are attacked by parasites as well as by predators. Even the eggs of small moths, such as the Nantucket pine moth, are large enough to provide sufficient food for the development of a tiny parasite. During 1926, in the Bessey Plantations at Halsey, Nebraska, about 60 percent of the summer-generation eggs of the Nantucket pine moth were parasitized. Careful examination of the eggs of aphids, tussock moths, tent caterpillars, or almost any other insect proves that many of those failing to hatch have been perforated with the exit hole of one or more parasites.

In spite of the activities of both predators and parasites in destroying the eggs of insects, there is usually an ample supply of larvae produced to cause a decided increase in the insect abundance. But predators and parasites also attack the larval stage. Even the larvae of wood borers are not entirely safe, well protected though they are by the wood in which they are tunneling. Woodpeckers dig them from their tunnels; some of the ichneumon flies, by inserting their long ovipositors through the wood, succeed in parasitizing them; some of the predaceous beetles follow them into their tunnels and destroy them there.

Larvae of defoliating insects and other insects exposed on the surface of plants are attacked by a host of enemies too numerous to mention. Insect parasites, predaceous insects, and birds all take their toll. When the larvae drop to the ground either accidentally or, as many do, to prepare for the pupal stage, they expose themselves to the attack of the terrestrial predators. Shrews, mice, skunks, ants, and ground beetles are all very fond of insect food and seize hungrily upon any larvae they find.

Insects usually seek secluded places for pupation, many spinning cocoons to protect themselves during this quiescent period. But well protected as they may be, many of them are killed. Parasites of the pupal stage are not common, although many larval parasites emerge as adults while their hosts are in the pupal stage. Predators of this stage, however, are plentiful. Insectivorous birds and insects feed upon the pupae aboveground, and small mammals, for example, shrews, mice, and skunks, dig up and eat those in the ground.

After insects have passed through all the developmental stages and become adult, they are still subject to attack by both parasites and predators. The parasites of adults are common enough but seldom kill the host. Those most frequently observed are mites and nematodes. Predators of this stage, on the other hand, are most important. Birds, shrews, voles and other vertebrates; predatory insects; and spiders all feed upon the adult stage.

BIBLIOGRAPHY CHAPTER 4

Baumberger, J. P., 1919. A nutritional study of insects with special reference to micro-organisms and their substrata, *J. Exptl. Zool.*, **28:** 1–81.

Blackman, M. W., 1918. The American tent-caterpillar, *J. Econ. Entomol.*, **9:** 432.

Carpenter, F. W., 1909. Some reactions of Drosophila, *J. Comp. Neurol. Psych.*, **18:** 483–491.

Carpenter, J. R., 1940. Insect outbreaks in Europe, *J. Animal Ecol.*, **4:** 108–147.

Chapman, R. N., 1915. Observations on the life history of *Agrilus bilineatus*, *J. Agr. Res.*, **3**: 283–294.

———, 1925. "Animal Ecology with Special Reference to Insects."

Craighead, F. C., 1921. Hopkins' host-selection principle as related to certain cerambycid beetles, *J. Agr. Res.*, **22**: 189–220.

Crombie, A. C., 1946. Interspecific competition. *J. Animal Ecol.*, **16**: 44–73. (Rev. of Lit.)

Dawson, R. W., 1931. The problem of voltinism and dormancy in the polyphemus moth, *J. Exptl. Zool.*, **59**: 87–131.

Denton, R. E., 1950. "Ecology of *Ips perturbatus* on White Spruce," unpublished thesis on file in library of The University of Michigan.

Dickinson, R. C., 1949. Light and temperature on diapause, *Ann. Entomol. Soc. Am.*, **42**: 511–537.

Graham, S. A., 1920. Factors influencing the subcortical temperature of logs, *Minn. State Entomol. Rept.* 18, pp. 26–42.

———, 1922. Effect of physical factors in the ecology of certain insects in logs, *Minn. State Entomol. Rept.* 19, pp. 22–40.

———, 1924. Temperature as a limiting factor in the life of subcortical insects, *J. Econ. Entomol.*, **17**: 377–383.

———, 1956. The larch sawfly in the Lake States, *Forest Sci.*, **2**: 132–160.

———, and R. R. Mason, 1958. Influence of weather on poplar borer numbers. *Mich. Forestry* No. 20, The University of Michigan.

Harrison, R. P., 1959. The insects and diseases of aspens, microfilmed, University Microfilms, Ann Arbor, Mich.

Haseman, L., 1950. Controlling insect pests through their nutritional requirements, *J. Econ. Entomol.*, **43**: 399–401.

Hawley, I. M., 1949. The effect of summer rainfall on Japanese beetle populations, *N.Y. Entomol. Soc.*, **57**: 167–176.

Hetrick, L. A., 1949. Moisture relationships of the southern pine beetle, *J. Econ. Entomol.*, **42**: 466–469.

Hopkins, A. D., 1920. The bioclimatic law, *J. Wash. Acad. Sci.*, **10**: 34–40.

———, 1938. Bioclimatics, *U.S. Dept. Agr. Misc. Publ.* 280.

Howard, L. O., 1926. The parasite element of natural control of injurious insects and its control by man, *J. Econ. Entomol.*, **19**: 271–282.

Keen, F. P., 1937. Climatic cycles in eastern Oregon as indicated by tree rings, *U.S. Dept. Agr. Weather Bur., Weather Rev.*, **65**: 175–188.

Krogh, A., 1914. The quantitative relation between temperature and standard metabolism in animals, *Intern. Z. Physik-chem. Biol.*, **1**: 491–508.

———, 1914. On the influence of temperature on the rate of embryonic development, *Z. Allgem. Physiol.*, **16**: 163–167.

———, 1914. On the rate of growth and CO_2 production of chrysalides of *Tenebrio molitor* at different temperatures, *Z. Allgem. Physiol.*, **16**: 178–190.

Kullmer, C. J., 1933. The latitude shift of the storm track in the 11-year solar period, *Smithsonian Inst. Misc. Collections*, **892** (2).

Martin, C. H., 1946. Effect of condition of phloem moisture on the entry of *Scolytus multistriatus*, *J. Econ. Entomol.*, **39**: 481–486.

Merriam, C. H., 1898. Life zones and crop zones in the United States, *U.S. Dept. Agr. Biol. Survey Bull.* 10.

Payne, N. M., 1926. Freezing and survival at low temperatures, *Quart. Rev. Biol.,* 1: 270–282.

———, 1926. Environmental temperatures and insect freezing points, *Ecology,* 7: 99–106.

Peairs, L. M., 1927. Relation of temperature to development ot insects, *W.Va. Agr. Expt. Sta. Bull.* 208.

Pierce, W. D., 1916. Relationship of temperature and humidity to insect development, *J. Agr. Res.,* 5: 1183–1191.

Salt, R. W., 1936. Freezing process in insects, *Univ. Minn. Agr. Expt. Sta. Tech. Bull.* 116.

Sanderson, E. D., 1908. Relation of temperature to hibernation, *J. Econ. Entomol.,* 1: 56–65.

———, and L. M. Peairs, 1913. Temperature and insect development, *New Hampshire Coll. Agr. Expt. Sta. Tech. Bull.* 7.

Snyder, T. E., 1926. Lyctus powder-post beetles, *U.S. Dept. Agr. Farmers' Bull.* 1477, pp. 1–13.

———, and R. A. St. George, 1924. Temperatures fatal to the powder-post beetle, *J. Agr. Res.,* 28: 1033–1038.

Summers, J. N., 1922. Low temperature and gypsy-moth eggs, *U.S. Dept. Agr. Bull.* 1080.

Turner, N., 1963. The gypsy moth problem, *Conn. Agr. Expt. Sta. Bull.* 655.

Uvarov, B. P., 1929. Weather and climate in their relation to insects, *Conf. Empire* (Gt. Brit.) *Meteorologists, Agr. Sect.,* 1929.

Vite, J. P., 1961. The influence of water supply on oleoresin exudation and resistance to bark beetle attack in *Pinus ponderosa, Contrib. Boyce Thompson Inst.,* 21: 37–66.

Wellington, W. G., 1948. Light and the spruce budworm, *Can. Entomologist,* 70: 56–82.

———, et al., 1950. Climate and spruce budworm outbreaks, *Can. J. Res.,* D28: 308–331.

Wood, D. L., 1963. Studies on host selection by *Ips confusus* (LeConte), *Univ. Calif. (Berkeley) Publ. Entomol.,* 27: 241–282.

CHAPTER 5

POPULATION LEVELS

The actual level of insect populations at any time or place is determined by the interaction of reproductive potential and environmental resistance. This chapter considers some of these interactions and their results. The importance of insect numbers lies in the fact that the capacity of an insect species to injure trees is in direct proportion to the number of that insect in the forest. When its population is low, a potential pest is innocuous, whereas the same insect may cause tremendous devastation when its population is high.

BIOTIC BALANCE

When the astonishing ability of insects to reproduce is considered, it is nothing short of amazing that our forests are not damaged far more than is actually the case. But the fact remains that our natural forests usually develop to maturity and are not destroyed by insects. This fact demonstrates that nature ordinarily maintains an equilibrium which, on the average, prevents insects from increasing to a destructive level. This condition of equilibrium is called the biotic balance.

Insect numbers fluctuate from year to year and from season to season, but their varying numbers and the elements of the environment are so equalized that survival of both trees and insects continues. Thus in the struggle for supremacy among different forms of life, there is a deadlock. The number of each insect species varies from year to year but usually within restricted limits. Biotic balance is, therefore, an oscillating and not a static equilibrium. It is a condition wherein, on the average, reproductive potential and environmental resistance are equal.

Weather conditions, the number of parasites and predators, and available food, all change continuously. As a result, the number of individuals in each forest species varies from time to time and from place to place, but usually the amplitude of the variations is not great as the numbers oscillate about a mean point. The importance of this oscillating equilibrium cannot be overemphasized. It is only under such a balanced state that long-lived organisms exist at all. The life of a tree extends over 100 years or more; sexual maturity is attained after many years of growth. Such long-time processes, obviously, presuppose generally favorable environmental conditions extending through centuries of time.

It should not be inferred from this discussion, however, that the same environmental conditions remain constant or even relatively constant throughout the life of any individual forest tree. Obviously the ecological picture gradually changes as the trees pass from infancy to old age. It has already been pointed out that trees of different ages are attacked by different insects. Likewise different plants and animals are associated with each age-class of trees. Thus, in considering any tree or small group of trees, we are dealing with only a segment of the complete environmental complex. Only on a large forest area, with a normal distribution of age-classes and their associated flora and fauna, is the environmental complex complete. Then each element of the complex is operative but in different spots at different times. As one factor ceases to operate in one spot, it is replaced by another. Thus the balance is maintained.

EFFECTS OF ENVIRONMENTAL RESISTANCE

In order to maintain a balanced condition, the force of environmental resistance must differ for insects with different reproductive potentials. For instance, if an insect produces 100 eggs per female and the sex factor is 0.5, then the reproductive potential of 50 must be matched by an environmental resistance of 50 if the population is to remain constant. Similarly, if a species has a reproductive potential of 200 individuals, the environmental resistance must be sufficient to destroy 200 individuals, including parents, for each individual of the parent generation. If the forces are not equal, it is apparent that the population will either increase or decrease. The difference between the number of individuals in one generation and the next, after the force of environmental resistance has taken its toll, determines the rate at which a species will increase or decrease. Thus the number of each succeeding generation will equal the number of individuals at the beginning of the generation times the reproductive potential minus the environmental resistance.

Compensation among Factors. If a species is to remain in relatively constant numbers in successive generations in spite of changes in the force of different factors of environmental resistance, it is apparent that the changes in resistance factors must be compensating (Graham, 1956). This is proved by the fact that more than 95 percent of the forest-insect species in a locality continue to be present year after year in relatively low numbers in spite of variations in the individual factors of environmental resistance.

An excellent specific illustration of this compensation of resistance factors was observed by one of the authors in studying the jack-pine sawfly, *Neodiprion banksiana*. For 6 years, under favorable food conditions the population remained approximately static. During two seasons there was a combination of unfavorably wet weather and a parasitic disease, another year there was little disease but a late frost killed a large proportion of the young larvae, and during three different years heavy storms washed many of the larvae from the trees. Thus there was no increase during the period in spite of the favorable food situation.

In the above example, the compensation among the environmental resistance factors occurred in the same locality but in different seasons. Similar compensatory effects are apparent when geographic areas are compared. For example, in the moist tropics, physical resistance is practically inoperative. There the increase of insects is prevented by the biotic factors—competition, predators, and parasites. In arctic and subarctic regions, on the other hand, physical resistance is high and biotic resistance is correspondingly low. In other words, increased biotic resistance compensates for lack of physical resistance in the tropics, while physical resistance compensates for biotic resistance in the colder localities (Voute, 1946).

Zones of Abundance. The physical factors in a locality follow a specific pattern. They act upon all the insects in a locality regardless of population density. Their chief effect is to determine whether or not an insect species can persist in an environment. Cook (1929) has analyzed the effect of physical factors on insects and divides the range of a species, theoretically, into several concentric zones. In the most favorable portion of the range lies the zone of normal abundance, within which physical conditions are invariably favorable for the species and within which outbreaks are controlled or prevented by the action of nutritional and biotic factors of environmental resistance.

Outside this zone lies the zone of occasional abundance, in which the physical conditions are always sufficiently favorable to permit the species to survive but only occasionally will favorable variations permit them to become abundant. Within such areas, continually favorable niches (Elton, 1927) occur in which the insects maintain themselves as they would in the zone of normal abundance. From these niches, they spread when favorable weather variations permit. In this zone, the abundance of the insects is regulated in the niches by biotic factors, and in the usually unfavorable part of the zone by weather conditions.

Next comes the zone of possible abundance in which conditions are usually so unfavorable that the insect cannot maintain itself except when favorable weather variations permit invasion from a more favorable zone. When weather conditions return to normal, the insects that have invaded the zone are destroyed. Another zone might well be added, called the zone of possible occurrence, within which physical conditions are never sufficiently favorable to permit the insect to become numerous but within which it might occasionally be found in favorable niches.

Physical factors are especially important in determining the distribution of a species by permitting it to occupy or by preventing it from occupying a given place. The success or failure of a species outside the zone of normal abundance depends on the distribution and size of the favorable niches, the physical environmental resistance being inversely proportional to the area occupied by the favorable niches. It is apparent that an insect is not likely to become economically important throughout its entire range and that outbreaks will seldom, if ever, occur outside the zones of normal and occasional abundance.

Density Dependence.   Frequently the value of a certain factor of environmental resistance may vary with the population density of the insect against which it is working. When the population of the insect is at one level, a factor of this kind may be relatively ineffective in reducing the insect's numbers, whereas, at another population level, it may be very effective. Smith (1935) has given the name density-dependent to such a factor in contrast to the physical factors previously discussed, which he terms density-independent. Density-dependent factors generally operate most effectively against relatively high populations and correspondingly less effectively against low populations. For instance, insect species that are parasitic or predaceous upon other insects and entomogenous disease-causing organisms usually increase their efficiency at high host density and decrease in efficiency at low host density. The rate at which this efficiency increases with host density determines the population level at which parasite and host will reach equilibrium. Thus a parasite that is able to produce a high rate of mortality in its host at low density will, if other things are equal, be economically effective, whereas another parasite that increases more slowly in efficiency with increased host density may be relatively ineffective.

Birds, as well as other vertebrate predators, are density-dependent. Unlike parasites and disease-causing organisms, birds are most efficient in retarding insect increase when the prey population is relatively low but still numerous enough to offer an attractive reward for hunting. This is especially true during the breeding period when the birds are confined to their breeding grounds, where their rate of increase is limited by their seasonal and spatial requirements. Territorial requirements limit to a certain number the nesting pairs that can live and breed in an area; during the breeding period, birds cannot increase their numbers at an unusually rapid rate to take advantage of an unusually abundant food supply. Therefore, birds are effective as resistance agencies up to the point at which their nutritional requirements are satisfied by the insect population on which they are feeding. When, however, the insect population exceeds that amount which the birds can eat, these vertebrates cease to exercise, during the breeding season, any important restrictive influence.

Insectivorous mammals, such as shrews, skunks, and voles, restricted as they are to limited areas, operate much as do birds. Although they eat more individuals of a certain prey when it is numerous than when it is not, their own population is relatively so limited that they are unable to exercise much influence when the insects are very abundant.

At different population levels of a certain insect, the effects of vertebrate predators would be as follows: At low levels the insect would not provide a satisfactory reward for hunting and would be taken only casually by birds and mammals on their breeding areas. At a somewhat higher population level, the insect would become sufficiently plentiful to reward the hunter sufficiently to encourage special attention, and predator pressure would increase in direct proportion to the insect population. The maximum resistance would prevail at the point where the nutritional requirements of the predatory species were satisfied. Above this point, the effect of vertebrate predator resistance would diminish with increased population of the insect. From this it is evident that within their breeding territory insectivorous birds and mammals, unable to increase their populations beyond a definite density, are most valuable in preventing low populations from growing to large proportions but are usually ineffective in reducing insect numbers once their prey has multiplied in excess of the predator's nutritional requirements (George, 1948).

At seasons other than the breeding period, birds show a density-dependent reaction by concentrating in areas where their prey is most numerous. A good example of this is the winter congregation of woodpeckers so common in localities where bark beetles are abundant. Similarly, chickadees, nuthatches, and kinglets exercise, during winter months, valuable environmental resistance functions. Webb (1953) found that small birds, operating in areas where the insects were abundant, destroyed as many as 70 percent of the overwintering larvae of the larch casebearer, *Coleophora laricella*.

OFFSETTING ENVIRONMENTAL RESISTANCE

Most insect species are provided with protective devices that assist them in overcoming the effects of excessive environmental resistance; thus they are able to maintain their level of population under temporarily adverse circumstances. The influence of these protective forces varies directly with environmental resistance. Under optimum conditions, when environmental resistance is inoperative, their value in maintaining numbers is zero; when the factor of environmental resistance against which the device is operative is at its peak, the protective value is also highest. The various protective factors are discussed individually in the following sections.

Insurance of Mating. It has previously been pointed out in our discussion of reproductive potential that the sexual type of reproduction is most commonly found among insects and that mating of the two sexes, therefore, is necessary to the survival of most species. It has also been shown that insects which reproduce sexually have a lower reproductive potential than equally fecund species that are parthenogenetic. Therefore, if the former type is to keep on any equality with the latter, mating must be assured. The very necessity for mating, demanding as it does close proximity of the sexes, means that the physical factor of space may result in raising the value of environmental resistance for a bisexual species more than for a parthenogenetic one. Consequently, insects reproducing sexually need something to offset their relatively low values for reproductive potential and high values for environmental resistance.

This they accomplish by means of a number of modifications and adaptations for bringing the sexes together. Many moths are attracted to the opposite sex by odors given off by that sex. A glandular structure on the back of the male tree cricket provides a delectable feast for the female, and its odor lures her to the male. Stridulation among the Orthoptera and other orders is frequently a means of attracting the opposite sex, and experiments have shown that the flashing of fireflies serves to aid the male in locating the female. All these adaptations tend to ensure mating with consequent reproduction of the species.

Care of the Young. After mating, insects continue their struggle against the forces of the environment. They have developed a number of devices for the protection of their eggs and young by which they offset to a certain extent the destructive forces of environmental resistance. Care of the eggs or young by the adults is one of the means by which this is accomplished. Care of the young is usually associated with the higher animals, but nevertheless it manifests itself in primitive ways among some insects. The highest development of this protective function in insects is usually found among the social forms, particularly among the Hymenoptera and the Isoptera; even among the solitary species, carpenter and leafcutter bees for example, it is strikingly developed.

When an adult insect selects and deposits eggs on the host tree upon which the larvae naturally feed, she is showing a primitive type of care for the young. Such care is exhibited by chrysobothris and other buprestids. In the cracks where they are placed, the eggs are inconspicuous and, therefore, not likely to be disturbed before they hatch. To this extent parental care is characteristic of most species, although there are some, such as walkingsticks, which drop their eggs without regard to location. Careless species such as these must have a very high reproductive potential if they are to survive because many of their young will almost certainly starve before finding suitable food. Such careless insects are very seldom serious pests.

Many moths, such as the gypsy moth and the tent caterpillar, cover their eggs with a protective material. This covering not only protects the eggs from excessive evaporation but, in some cases, also makes them unattractive to birds.

One effective device for protecting the welfare of the young is illustrated by some of the Diptera that are larviparous. These insects hold their eggs within their bodies until after they hatch. Then they deposit the larvae upon the host. This is true of some of the Tachinidae, many of which are parasitic upon the larvae of forest insects. The young of larviparous species have a much better chance of entering an active host than do the oviparous flies, since the eggs of the latter may be rubbed off or molted off the host's body before they have had time to hatch.

With the exception of the social species, parental protection of the young beyond the selection of a proper feeding place is rather rare among forest insects. In most instances the larvae, having been placed near a supply of food, must shift for themselves. The mother aphid and the mother tingitid are usually found near their young and are sometimes said to guard them, but it is doubtful if this proximity is an example of parental care. More likely it is a question of convenience. In social species, however, occur many striking examples of most meticulous care for all immature stages. It is not the mother but definitely designated workers that usually care for the young in these social groups. The mother, meanwhile, attends strictly to the process of oviposition. The young of both carpenter ants and termites are fed and cared for in this manner. In the ant nest, the young are carried from place to place in order to keep them under the most favorable conditions possible.

Defense. From the foregoing, it is evident that a primitive type of parental care is common among forest insects. It is also evident that the degree of care is not sufficient to ensure survival of the species. Other means of protection are, therefore, needed.

Some species are provided with disagreeable odors or flavors, making them distasteful to predaceous animals and serving as means of defense. The pentatomids and other plant bugs, certain beetles, and some butterflies are notable examples of insects possessing this means of defense.

Many insects are protected by their inconspicuous coloring or form. Few observers of nature have failed to notice how most insects blend into their background. Even some of the most gaudily colored species are comparatively inconspicuous in their natural surroundings. Protective coloring and protective form are so characteristic of insects as to be obvious to the most casual observer.

There are three types of protective appearance: (1) The color pattern of the insect's markings blends into the surroundings. Leafhoppers, aphids,

FIGURE 15. A larva of the Douglas-fir tussock moth is defended by poisonous hairs. (U.S. Dept. Agr. Forest Service.)

underwing moths, and many other insects exemplify this protective coloration. (2) The insect resembles some part of the plant on which it lives. There are many well-known examples of this sort of protective resemblance: treehoppers, walkingsticks, and spanworms. (3) The resemblance is to some other insect that is either distasteful or feared by insect predators. This last method of protective resemblance is known as mimicry (Gerould, 1916), one of the most common examples being that of the viceroy butterfly, which is almost a perfect replica of the monarch butterfly, a species that is said to be distasteful to birds.

In addition to the various means of defense already mentioned, many insects are provided with mechanical contrivances for defense. The heavy exoskeletons of many beetles make them less vulnerable than if their bodies were soft. The sharp and sometimes venomous spines possessed by many caterpillars serve as a defense against insectivorous birds. Other mechanical means of defense may be mentioned, for instance, the strong mandibles of many forest insects. These are ready weapons of defense and are frequently used effectively. Another powerful weapon with which some of the Hymenoptera are provided is the venomous sting. By means of the various methods of defense, insects are often able to prevent the normal reduction of their numbers resulting from the action of environmental resistance.

Use of Shelter. Some forest insects are able to evade at least partially the force of environmental resistance by retiring into shelters of various sorts. Shelter protects insects to some degree against changes of weather and also makes them less easily found by their enemies. These shelters may be constructed of silk or wax secreted by the insect itself or of other materials such as sticks, stones, wood, earth, or of combinations of these materials.

FIGURE 16. A single cocoon of the fir tussock moth. The silken cocoons are spun by the larvae to shelter the defenseless pupal stage from many potential enemies.

One type of insect shelter with which everyone is more or less familiar is the cocoon. By means of this structure, the pupa is protected during its period of quiescence. Some insects when in the larval stage build cases of silk and other materials for their protection throughout the developmental period. The bagworms, for instance, carry a case about with them from the time they hatch until they are fully grown. As the larva grows, the case is enlarged to accommodate it. The female bagworm never leaves the case but lays her eggs and dies therein.

The spruce budworm and some others of the same group construct another kind of shelter. During the larval period they work under a light web of silk that they spin. The tent caterpillars and the fall webworm build nests of silk into which the larvae retire. Other species, such as the armored scales and the woolly aphids, are sheltered by their own waxy secretions.

Some species of insects make use of their food material for shelter. Leaf miners are sheltered between the upper and lower cuticula of the leaves in which they feed. Cynipids, gall aphids, and gall mites find both food and shelter in the abnormal plant growth for which they are responsible. The bark-mining and wood-boring insects are well sheltered in their tunnels and galleries.

FIGURE 17. A case of the evergreen bagworm. The larva carried this case about through the feeding period, enlarging it from time to time and finally transforming to the pupa within it. Thus, throughout the developmental stages the insect provided its own shelter.

Certain insects, such as rhagium and pytho, construct pupal cells of frass and chips beneath the bark, thus forming an effective shelter for the pupae. From these examples, it becomes evident that insects make use of many different types of shelter to aid them in overcoming environmental resistance.

Locomotion. When an insect is threatened by a parasitic or predaceous insect or by unfavorable conditions of moisture or temperature, it has two choices: (1) It may remain quiescent, trusting that its enemy will not notice it or that the temperature or moisture conditions will remain within its range of tolerance, or (2) it may try to escape.

Adult insects are usually well provided with the necessary means of locomotion to permit escape. Most of them possess both legs and wings, which they use effectively. By means of these appendages, they are able to escape either from their enemies or from locally unfavorable physical conditions of the environment. Furthermore, the ability to move about quickly helps to bring together the sexes, thus ensuring successful mating. The power of locomotion also helps the insect in its search for food, often makes possible effective distribution, and helps the insect to place its eggs in a location favorable to the larvae.

Larvae, on the other hand, are generally much less able to move about from place to place. None of the immature stages of insects have functional wings with the exception of the May flies, which have a subimago winged stage. Larvae must, therefore, depend primarily upon their legs for locomotion except as they are carried by birds, other animals, vehicles, or wind. Some of them have well-developed legs and can move about rapidly, but others, the caterpillars and grubs, for instance, can move only slowly. Even this ability to move feebly makes it possible for many of them to secure more favorable conditions of moisture or temperature or to improve their food conditions. This is true of practically all insects that feed on the surfaces of plants.

In addition to the use of their legs, many lepidopterous larvae have another means of locomotion useful for protection. The larvae are able to spin very rapidly a thread of silk on which they can drop out of harm's way. A larva hanging by its thread can later, when it is safe to do so, return to its original position.

The miners and borers, on the other hand, are greatly restricted in their movements. Only a few species, such as the carpenter-moth larvae, can move back and forth in their galleries. The others must take what comes. Such insects, having a limited sphere of activity, are confined to those locations where the extremes of environmental conditions always lie within their zone of toleration. The motile species, because they are better able to adjust themselves to changing conditions, have a much wider range of activity, and when conditions become unfavorable in one place, they move to another.

Migration and Dissemination.   At some time during the year almost every insect species passes through a period of local dissemination. Then the individuals move out in various directions in search of favorable new locations. This movement usually occurs during the adult stage, but in some instances it may also occur during the larval stage. As a result of this movement from centers of concentration, almost every suitable breeding place will receive its share of insects. Sometimes this dissemination is very limited in distance. For instance, it has been found that the walkingstick, *Diapheromera femorata,* because it is wingless and not especially active, moves out from centers of infestation at the rate of only ⅛ mile per year (Graham, 1937) whereas the western pine beetle, *Dendroctonus brevicomis,* may fly miles from the trees in which it developed. In a few instances insects may migrate from north to south in the autumn, as do migratory birds. Also some insects move northward in the spring as the season advances and breed far north of the areas where they can winter.

The efficiency of insect distribution can well be illustrated in any large coniferous forest area that has been killed by fire in the spring of the year. Even though the area of killed trees may be 100 square miles or more, practically every suitable tree will be infested with its complement of borers; monochamus, ips, chrysobothris, certain siricids, and other subcortical and xylophagous insects. There could not possibly have been present before the fire enough adults to reproduce the multitude of borers found in the area after the fire. It is evident, therefore, that they flew in from surrounding territory. The omnipresence of certain leaf eaters in every suitable location is still further proof of the general distribution of at least the more common species. The search for food or for a suitable place for oviposition is the chief cause of dissemination, but apparently, even when food and places for oviposition are abundant, insects may still move about.

The desire to move to new locations seems to be inherent. Dissemination is a means by which the intensity of local environmental resistance may be reduced. The value to the species of the ability to move out from centers of concentration is inestimable because the more widely a species is distributed, the less likely it is to be wiped out by some local adversity. Some insects migrate, within the same locality, from one host to another. Frequently this involves the alternation of hosts, the insects transferring their activities from one host to another and later returning to the original host species. This sort of migration is common among aphids and chermes. Some insects, for example, some lady beetles, move from low to high altitudes in late summer and autumn, returning to lower elevations in the spring.

Dissemination of insects is often aided and directed by air movements. Winged insects may be carried upward by convection currents and drift for many miles before returning to the earth. The influence of the prevailing wind accounts for the more rapid spread of insects in North America from west to east than in other directions. The occasional flights of insects observed far from possible breeding centers are likely the result of air movements combined with peculiar atmospheric conditions which stimulate the insects to take wing.

Freeman (1945) points out that heavy winds are not likely to produce dissemination because the insects take shelter and refuse to fly under such conditions. Insects are likely to be most numerous in the air when the wind is under 12 miles per hour, the relative humidity above 54 percent, and the air temperature at least 64°F. As a result, dissemination occurs most frequently on warm summer evenings.

Ever-increasing amounts of evidence prove that many wingless insects are carried aloft in air currents and transported long distances. Many have special adaptations that aid in air transportation. For example, some young caterpillars are provided with long hairs that increase the surface exposed to air currents without materially increasing the weight. Others spin a free thread on which they are capable of ballooning for long distances.

Tropic Responses.   Some insects possess other characteristics that are advantageous in the struggle for existence. These abilities relate to re-actions, called *tropic responses,* that result in the orientation of the in-sect's body in relation to some physical or chemical stimulus. For instance, when one of the hover flies habitually heads into the wind, it is exhibiting a tropic response: anemotropism. Species living near the sea, by re-sponding anemotropically, may prevent themselves from being blown away from land and thus becoming reduced in numbers.

Examples of other types of tropic responses are numerous. Lady beetles, when seeking a place to hibernate, are positively thigmotropic; that is, they respond positively to the sense of touch and, by creeping into cracks where their bodies are in close contact with surrounding surfaces, they ensure their safety. Many insects respond either positively or negatively to chemical stimuli and are then said to be either positively or negatively chemotropic. Insects that turn toward the light are positively phototropic, whereas those that turn away are negatively phototropic. Those that seek out sunny places are positively heliotropic whereas those that shun the sun are negatively heliotropic.

These terms are descriptive of how insects respond to external stimuli. They do not in any way explain why insects react in certain ways. In order to avoid the common error of trying to explain the cause of certain reactions merely by giving those reactions a name, it must be kept clearly in mind that the terms are descriptive rather than explanatory.

Through many generations, natural selection has brought about a survival of those insects which have come to respond in ways that are favorable to the species. Thus it is that tropic responses have had, during the course of evolution, an important influence in determining how suc-cessful an insect will be in overcoming environmental resistance. The in-sect that orients itself to environmental forces so that it is most likely to be favored is much more likely to survive than one that is erratic in its re-actions or one that fails to react at all. Some authorities think that prac-tically all the activities of insects are the results of tropic responses; even if this is not entirely true, it cannot be doubted that tropisms play an exceedingly important part in the life of insects and that they determine to a large degree whether or not an insect will thrive.

Effect of These Protective Devices.   From the foregoing discussion, it is evident that an insect's abundance depends not only upon the reproductive potential of the species and the amount of environmental resistance but also upon the inherent ability of each insect species to meet and reduce in various ways the force of environmental resistance. Like other inherent qualities, this ability varies with different species. Its value also differs with varying conditions. Under optimum conditions, the ability of insects to overcome environmental resistance is not needed and is, therefore, inoperative. But when pressure is so increased that this ability is needed, its operation becomes more and more important until finally under conditions of extreme environmental pressure it may be so important as to determine whether or not a species may survive. Thus, by acting with increasing power as environmental resistance increases and with decreasing power when resistance is reduced, the ability to overcome environmental resistance tends to stabilize insect numbers and to reduce extreme fluctuations in abundance that otherwise might occur as a result of fluctuations in the environment.

HIGH POPULATION LEVELS

Damage by insects is almost always the result of excessively high population levels. Usually these are temporary in character, occurring for a season or a few seasons and then subsiding. When a decided upswing in population level of an insect occurs and injury to trees or products results, we say that outbreak conditions prevail. Very often an insect outbreak is referred to as an epidemic. Although that term should be applied only to human populations, its use has become so common in forest entomological literature that it seems permissible to apply the term to insect outbreaks.

Continuous Abundance.   Although damage by insects is usually associated with outbreaks, there are a few instances when injury is not associated with any marked upswing in abundance of the insect concerned. Such insects are always present in sufficient abundance to cause injury to any materials that are exposed to them. In instances of this sort, the biotic balance has been established above the point at which economically important damage will result.

Examples of continuous abundance are not common among insects that attack living trees, but they are not unusual among species that attack various kinds of wood products, freshly cut products, lumber or partially manufactured products, and wood in use. For instance, in the forest there is always an abundance of borers ready to attack any freshly cut green materials. Similarly, in localities where termites cause damage there are always enough of these insects present so that any susceptible piece of wood, left in contact with the ground, will almost certainly be attacked within a year.

Endemic Populations. In some forests, conditions are favorable for certain insect pests so that their activities are always evident, although their numbers are not increasing and are not sufficiently high to cause enough damage to justify the application of control measures. This situation is referred to by forest entomologists as being endemic. Endemic infestations are best illustrated in overmature pine stands in which a moderate number of trees are succumbing each year to bark-beetle attack. An endemic infestation has been defined as one in which the annual losses are less than the annual growth of the trees, as expressed in merchantable volume (Salman and Bongberg, 1942).

This definition is suitable when applied to bark-beetle infestations but will not fit some other conditions. For example, in pine plantations in the Lake States, when a few trees are infested with sawflies, an endemic condition is said to prevail. Or when any defoliating insect is present in usual numbers, the infestation is endemic. This situation should not be confused with incipient conditions which exist when the insect population is on the increase but is below the numbers required to cause economically serious injury.

Outbreak Conditions. An insect outbreak is a temporary condition characterized by excessive insect numbers and injury to valuable materials. Outbreaks may be either of two kinds: sporadic or periodic. A sporadic outbreak is one that appears suddenly in a small or restricted area, lasts a single season, and then subsides. Sporadic outbreaks are usually associated with changed conditions, often the result of man's activities. These changes are usually temporary in character and result in the brief flare-up of an insect population, followed by a return to normal. A good illustration of this type of outbreak may frequently be observed when coniferous trees are cut to clear a right of way or when logs are decked temporarily in the woods. Bark beetles will be attracted to the freshly cut material. If more are attracted than can find space in the cut wood, they may attack and kill nearby green trees. Also, beetles emerging from the cut materials may kill a few trees. Usually little or no brood is produced in the attacked trees, so the beetle population disappears.

Periodic outbreaks are far more serious. They are characteristic of many defoliating insects that become injuriously abundant at more or less regular intervals. Examples of these are the spruce budworm, the hemlock looper, and the tussock moths. These outbreaks may occur at susceptible stages as a result of certain weather conditions or as a result of changed biotic resistance. The length of time between periodic outbreaks is often determined by the time required for the forest to recover from a previous outbreak and develop once more to a susceptible stage. Periodic outbreaks are usually catastrophic in character and often result in the destruction of a considerable part of the attacked forest. They constitute some of the most important and difficult forest-insect problems. Their control, as we shall see later, depends on man's ability to maintain conditions in the forest that are, in general, unfavorable to large populations of harmful insects.

Causes of Outbreaks.   Outbreaks of insects are the result of some environmental condition that temporarily disturbs the biotic balance. If, instead of the usual compensatory fluctuations in the factors of environmental resistance, a change should occur that would lower the combined effect of the resistance factors for any insect, an outbreak of that insect would be inevitable. Relieved of the resistance pressure that had held its numbers down, the insect would reproduce rapidly and soon come to dominate its environment.

The numbers attained by insects when they reach outbreak proportions are almost beyond belief. For instance, the larvae of the forest tent caterpillar, *Malacosoma disstria,* were so abundant during an outbreak in Minnesota that they almost covered the ground when they dropped from the trees. Similarly in Michigan the same species wandering across a paved highway near Saint Ignace were crushed in such numbers by passing automobiles that the road became slippery and highly hazardous. Often thread-spinning caterpillars in outbreak numbers will cover ground, stumps, and trees with a mantle of silk built from the threads that the larvae spin as they move about. Once started, an outbreak will continue until the force of environmental resistance destroys the pest and the balance is restored at a low population level.

Usually the cause of an outbreak may be found within the forest where the epidemic occurs, but in rare instances circumstances in one locality may contribute to an outbreak in another. For instance, a disaster to migrating birds occurred in 1909 and again in 1910 in southern Minnesota, Wisconsin, and Iowa owing to an unseasonable late spring freeze. The birds, especially warblers, died by the thousands. Although no observations were made during the following years on the nesting grounds in the coniferous forests to the north, there must have been a material reduction in nesting birds for a season or more. It is significant that an outbreak of the spruce budworm occurred in the area of these nesting grounds in 1912.

Ecological Significance of Outbreaks.   In the following chapters the causes leading to the development of specific outbreaks will be discussed. We shall see that outbreaks are sometimes the result of overmaturity or decadence of the trees in the forest. Sometimes they are the result of our attempts to grow forests in a manner contrary to nature's laws. Sometimes they are the result of poor tree health due to excessive competition, poor site conditions, and various other undesirable situations too numerous to mention at this point. Almost invariably, outbreaks follow the development of unsteady environmental conditions. After the outbreak, when the excessive insect numbers have subsided, the environmental complex will have become more steady than it was immediately prior to the outbreak.

The outbreak of insects, therefore, is one of nature's means of restoring a temporarily disturbed biotic balance. Insects are useful, in the natural order of the forest, as a means of eliminating overmature or decadent trees, as a means of eliminating species from sites to which they are not suited, as a means of thinning stands that are too dense, and as a means of improving stand composition.

Unfortunately the actions of insects, in performing these functions, will often run contrary to the desires and needs of man. Nature's way may be good in the long run, but it is wasteful economically. The insect outbreak may be effective in correcting an undesirable condition, but it will be more sensible for foresters to manage the forest so that the undesirable conditions that lead to outbreaks will not develop. In the following chapters we shall show how this can often be accomplished and how losses occasioned by insect outbreaks can be avoided.

BIBLIOGRAPHY CHAPTER 5

Andrewortha, H. G., 1961. "Introduction to the Study of Animal Populations," University of Chicago Press, Chicago.

Chapman, R. N., K. M. King, A. E. Emerson, H. S. Smith, and S. A. Graham, 1939. Symposium on insect populations, *Ecol. Monographs,* 1939.

Cook, W. C., 1929. A bioclimatic zonation, *Ecology,* **10:** 282–293.

Elton, C. S., 1927. "Animal Ecology."

Freeman, J. A., 1945. Distribution of insects by aerial currents, *J. Animal Ecol.,* **14:** 128–154.

George, J. G., 1948. Spruce budworm control by insectivorous birds, *J. Forestry,* **46:** 444–445.

Gerould, J. H., 1916. Mimicry in butterflies, *Am. Naturalist,* **50:** 184–192.

Graham, S. A., 1937. The walkingstick as a forest defoliator, *Univ. Mich. School Forestry Conserv.* (now *Natural Resources*) *Circ.* 3.

————, 1956. Forest insects and the law of natural compensations, *Can. Entomologist,* **48:** 45–55.

Milne, A., 1957. Theories of natural control of insect populations, *Cold Spring Harbor Symp. Quant. Biol.,* **22:** 253–71.

Morris, R. F., 1963. The dynamics of epidemic spruce budworm populations, *Entomol. Soc. Can. Mem.* 31.

Nicholson, A. J., 1958. Dynamics of insect populations, *Ann. Rev. Entomol.,* **3:** 107–136.

Poulton, E. B., 1890. "The Colours of Animals."

Punnett, R. C., 1915. "Mimicry in Butterflies."

Salman, K. A., and J. W. Bongberg, 1942. Logging high risk trees to control insects in pine stands of northeastern California, *J. Forestry*, **40:** 533–539.

Smith, H. S., 1935. The role of biotic factors in population densities, *J. Econ. Entomol.*, **28:** 873–898.

Voute, A. D., 1946. Climate and insect outbreaks, *Arch. Neerl. Zool.*, **7:** 435–470.

Webb, F. E., 1953. An ecological study of the larch case bearer, Doctoral Dissertation, The Univ. of Michigan, Microfilmed, Univ. Microfilms, Ann Arbor, Mich.

CHAPTER 6

DETECTION
AND
EVALUATION

The adoption of the Forest Pest Control Act, with the general acceptance of the principles expressed or implied therein, has led to a marked increase in detection and evaluation[1] activities. Our success in preventing and controlling outbreaks will depend to a great extent on preparedness. If we are forewarned of an impending outbreak, it can often be checked in the incipient stage, whereas if an outbreak develops without warning, it may reach proportions beyond any practicable possibility of control. There are numerous cases on record in which easily obtainable information could have led to control measures and the prevention of major insect epidemics. In control of outbreaks, as in fire control, success depends, first of all, upon early detection. The reason for this is that an incipient condition can grow to serious proportions in only a season or two.

The task of guarding 460 million acres of commercial forests is a monumental one. Obviously it would be impossible to employ enough forest entomologists to carry out such a huge job. There must be aid by many

---

[1] The term *evaluation* is here used in a broad sense. It includes not only the evaluation of damage in terms of timber volume and monetary value but also the evaluation of the fluctuations in abundance of forest insects from time to time and place to place.

other men working in the forest who must be on the alert for the early detection of outbreak conditions.

Realization that prompt detection is an essential preliminary to effective control has led to the organization of systematic annual surveys to determine the population trends of potentially noxious forest insects. Some of these surveys have been organized and directed by local agencies such as state or provincial governments. Others are conducted by Federal agencies, the U.S. Forest Service in the United States and the Department of Forestry in Canada. Private agencies have seldom organized forest-insect detection under any formal administrative setup, but in numerous instances they have cooperated enthusiastically and have become an effective part of surveys directed by governmental agencies.

No matter what the administrative organization may be, the objectives of all forest-insect surveys are the same: the detection of outbreaks and the evaluation of both insect abundance and timber damage.

Although the objectives have been practically the same in all surveys, the procedures have varied considerably. Some surveys use relatively untrained observers almost exclusively, whereas others use trained personnel only; still others have used a combination of trained and untrained workers. Each of these methods has good points in its favor. With untrained observers, extensive coverage can be obtained but some inaccuracies are inevitable. With trained observers, accuracy will be high but so will costs, and in many cases it would be impossible to employ enough trained men for the job even if sufficient money were available. Since in most cases both effectiveness and cost must be given consideration, a combination of trained and untrained will prove most satisfactory.

SOME TYPICAL SURVEYS

In the following sections a brief description is presented of a number of typical surveys. They illustrate how the various agencies have approached the problem of forest-insect detection.

Insect-pest Survey, U.S. Department of Agriculture. A general insect-pest survey has been conducted since 1920 by the U.S. Department of Agriculture. This survey has included reports on all noxious species, among them forest pests. Monthly and annual reports have been published regularly, and from time to time special articles on insects of current interest have been prepared and distributed. Information for these reports comes from cooperators who send in statements of conditions in their localities each month. Most of these men are trained entomologists in the employ of the various states or the Federal government.

The various reports published by the survey provide a general picture concerning the annual abundance of important agricultural and forest pests. Usually the reports on forest insects are made only when outbreaks prevail, and therefore, they come too late for the initiation of preventive control measures.

U.S. Forest Service Surveys.   The detection of incipient outbreaks requires much more complete information than is provided by the insect-pest survey discussed in the preceding section. Therefore in the several regions of the U.S. Forest Service, more detailed information is collected on various important forest insects. Much of this information never finds its way into print but is used only to guide local insect-control activities. The survey work of the regions is conducted in very close cooperation with the Bureau of Land Management, the Indian Service, and the National Park Service. Close cooperation also exists with the various state and private agencies. In this way unnecessary duplication is avoided and coordinated plans are made for detection and later for control.

Unfortunately in some states little interest is shown by either the state agencies or private industry in cooperative forest-insect detection. Under such circumstances the regions concentrate their surveys and services upon federally owned land. Furthermore, limited resources often compel the regions to curtail their services to the states at a point below a desirable level. Limited resources also require the surveys to be restricted for the most part to those pests that seem most likely to become injurious and that can be easily controlled. Thus, instead of following the rise and fall of all potentially harmful species, the surveys in each region become specialized. The ideal coverage should include all species that are potentially dangerous and all lands that are heavily forested.

Canadian Forest Insect Survey.   Far more detailed and comprehensive than any survey thus far developed in the United States is the Forest Insect Survey of Canada made by the Forest Entomology and Pathology Branch, Canada Department of Forestry. Its keynote is cooperation, and most of the reports come from relatively untrained observers. Each cooperator, however, is carefully instructed in how to make and report observations, and each is provided with mailing containers and other supplies to facilitate collecting and shipping materials to the central laboratory in Ottawa or to the nearest field laboratory.

The Canadian survey is all-inclusive, as it attempts to obtain information on every species of forest insect that can be collected. Cooperators, usually employees of a forest industry, are scattered throughout Canada. As a result, their collections are representative of every forest condition. When the collections are received at the laboratories, the insects are counted, reared, and identified. Records are then published showing population trends and the proportion of the various stages that have been attacked by parasites or are diseased. Thus the collective activities of all cooperators provide information not only on pests that are known to be important but also on many other species.

Forest-insect rangers attached to each laboratory give instruction to cooperators and make intensive examinations of locations where infestation of important forest insects occur. A bimonthly report is published and distributed to all cooperators. At the end of each season a nontechnical report on forest insects is issued for general distribution. As a result of this survey, very complete information is obtained concerning the distribution and abundance of forest-insect pests in Canada.

State Forest-insect Surveys. In the United States forest-insect surveys are conducted by a number of states. The state of Maine conducts a survey of forest insects using cooperators to make observations and collect specimens. This survey is patterned somewhat after the Canadian plan. Specimens are sent to the office of the State Entomologist, where they are identified and the records tabulated. Annual reports indicating increase or decrease in the abundance of important forest insects are published.

Similarly, Wisconsin has undertaken a forest-insect survey through the office of the State Entomologist in cooperation with the State Department of Conservation and the University of Wisconsin. This survey, as in the case of Maine, depends chiefly upon the aid of cooperators to collect information, and an attempt is made to gather data on all forest insects. Likewise in Minnesota a survey is conducted through the Agricultural Experiment Station using cooperators. In California, Oregon, and several other Western states, the states conduct surveys in close cooperation with the Pest Control Branch of the U.S. Forest Service.

In Michigan, a forest-pest detection program is conducted by the Division of Forestry of the Michigan Department of Conservation. This survey illustrates a specialized type that has been developed through independent initiative of the state, but in close cooperation with the U.S. Forest Service. No attempt is made to observe all potentially injurious pests. Only certain critical species that may be expected to cause damage under existing conditions are reported on systematically. Others when they appear in abundance may, however, be reported incidentally. The program is built into the state forestry organization, with its districts, each manned by technical foresters. These foresters observe the relative abundance of critical species in their respective districts. For each species on the critical list, every district forester examines annually and reports on several sample areas in his district. To secure reliability of observations, each forester attends a training program where he is taught to recognize all the critical species. In addition to the regular reports on the critical species, each man is instructed to report on any pest not on the critical list if an unusual increase in numbers is observed. Also he is instructed to send specimens for identification to the central office whenever there is any doubt of the identity of any species.

In all these state surveys, the detection activities cover all forest lands regardless of ownership. However, the coverage of areas in state forests and parks is sometimes more complete than is the case on private lands. With increasing services by state employees on private lands and with increasing cooperation of private operators, more and more complete coverage will result.

DESIRABLE SURVEY PRACTICES

Each of the surveys discussed in the preceding sections possesses both good and bad features; the ideal procedure has still to be devised. There are, however, certain desirable practices that might well be incorporated into any survey.

Cooperation of Agencies.   The trend in the direction of cooperative programs is certainly desirable. By cooperation, the number of men watching forest-insect activities is multiplied many times. The effective use of cooperators, however, depends upon their ability to observe accurately and to report in a manner that will permit correct interpretation. Reports based only upon impressions of untrained men or even trained men, for that matter, are usually so inadequate that reexamination is necessary before conclusions may safely be drawn.

Training of Personnel.   One of the preliminary essentials for successful survey work, therefore, is an adequate training program for workers. This training cannot be expected to enable the average man to recognize all potentially dangerous pests, but it can teach him to recognize those species that he is most likely to encounter and to report on them in a standard manner. A printed description of the important insects and their work should be furnished each observer. Information should also be provided to him on such matters as how, when, and where to look for evidence of each important species. To encourage the making of observations at the proper time, workers should be sent various memoranda during the course of the season, advising appropriate action.

Observers who have had the benefit of such a training program are equipped to make reports that can be valuable and trustworthy. Their data will be reasonably accurate and inclusive. Inadequacy of data, due to the deficiencies in their knowledge of insects in general, can be remedied to a large extent if they are taught how to invoke expert aid when it is needed. After a proper training course, an observer who finds an unknown insect in large numbers will send not only specimens of the insect and its work to a central laboratory but also a report describing the abundance of the insect and the characteristics of the locale.

Standard Reporting Procedure.   The training of workers to become effective observers would be of little value if they were not trained also in the proper reporting of their observations. Ideally, reports should contain sufficient information about the conditions of site and type to permit correct interpretation by forest entomologists without the necessity of their

TABLE 4   Michigan Forest Pest Detection Program—Observation Report

Pest_____(Write in name if known)

Col. 3–4. Day_____	Col. 12–13. District_____	Col. 22. Ownership	Col. 23. Origin
Col. 5–6. Month_____	Col. 14–15. Town__N S	__1. Federal	__1. Seed
Col. 7–8. Year_____	Col. 16–17. Range_E W	__2. State	__2. Sprout
Col. 9–10–11. Sample	Col. 18–19. Section_____	__3. Coun. or Sch.	__3. Plantation
Area No,_____	Col. 20–21 Forty_____	__4. Private	

Col. 24. Fire Record	Col. 25. Cutting Record	Col. 26. Windfall	Col. 27. Grazing
__1. Unburned	__1. None within 5 yr.	__1. Normal or none	Record
__2. Current yr.	__2. Clearcut within 5 yr.	__2. Current yr.	__1. None
__3. Previous yr.	__3. Partial cut within 5 yr.	__3. Previous yr.	__2. Currently
__4. Past 2–5 yr.	__4. Thinned within 1 yr.	__4. Past 2–5 yr.	__3. Past 2–5 yr.
__5. Older	__5. Pruned within 5 yr.	__5. Older	__4. Older

Col. 28. Soil Groups	Tree Species Present in	Col. 39. % Ground	Col. 40. % Ground
__1. Porous	Order of Importance	Area Shaded	Covered by
__2. Nonporous			Overstory
__3. Rock outcrop	Col. 29–30. A_____	__1. 1–20	__1. 1–20
__4. Stagnant bog	Col. 31–32. B_____	__2. 21–40	__2. 21–40
__5. Stagnant marsh	Col. 33–34. C_____	__3. 41–60	__3. 41–60
__6. Seepage	Col. 35–36. D_____	__4. 61–80	__4. 61–80
__7. Flood plain	Col. 37–38. E_____	__5. 81–100	__5. 81–100

Col. 41. Attack			
Record	Host or Hosts		
__1. Started this yr.	under Attack	Col. 52. Attacked Trees Average Size	
__2. Started last yr.	Col. 42–43. A_____		
__3. Started earlier	Col. 44–45. B_____	__1. Under 2 ft.	__5. 6–12 in. diam.
__4. Old attack evident,	Col. 46–47. C_____	__2. 2–6 ft.	__6. 12–18 in. diam.
none now	Col. 48–49. D_____	__3. 6–15 ft.	__7. 18–24 in. diam.
__5. None evident	Col. 50–51. E_____	__4. 15–30 ft.	__8. Over 24 in. diam.

Col. 53. % Alternate	Col. 54. Host Health	Col. 55. % Stand	Col. 56. % Suscep-
Host Attacked	Classes	Composed of	tible Trees Attacked
__1. 1–10	__1. Good	Host Species	__1. 0–1
__2. 11–20	__2. Medium (dead twigs,	__1. 1–20	__2. 2–10
__3. 21–40	foliage faded)	__2. 21–40	__3. 11–20
__4. 41–60	__3. Poor (dead branches,	__3. 41–60	__4. 21–40
__5. 61–80	leaves small)	__4. 61–80	__5. 41–60
__6. 81–100	__4. Dying	__5. 81–100	__6. 61–80
	__5. Dead		__7. 81–100

Col. 57. Stage of Pest	Col. 58. Degree of Attack		
	Bark Beetles	Defoliation or	Number of
		Terminal Injury	Stem Cankers
__1. Egg	__1. One attack per sq. ft.	__1. 1–20 %	__1. One
__2. Larva or nymph	__2. Two attacks per sq. ft.	__2. 21–40 %	__2. Two
__3. Pupa	__3. Three attacks per sq. ft.	__3. 41–60 %	__3. Three
__4. Adult	__4. Four attacks per sq. ft.	__4. 61–80 %	__4. Four
	__5. Five or more per sq. ft.	__5. 81–100 %	__5. Five or more

Col. 59. Similar	Col. 60. Abundance of	
Stands in Area	Pest in Similar Stands	
__1. Predominant	__1. None	Observer_____
__2. Frequent	__2. Same	(Make sketch map on back of sheet to show local
__3. Scattered	__3. Lighter	distribution if this can be determined. Also indi-
__4. Scarce	__4. Heavier	cate under remarks any information which will
		give a more complete picture of the situation.)

Cols. 75–76–77. Species of Pest (to be entered by Ento-mologist after precise identification)

making many field examinations. This type of adequate reporting based on careful observation could easily consume more time than the observers have at their disposal. To conserve time and to produce uniform reporting, the use of well-planned report forms is highly desirable.

The observation report form used in the Michigan Forest Pest Detection Program will serve as an illustration (Table 4). This form is arranged in such a way that, after editing, the data can be punched on tabulating cards for mechanical analysis. To facilitate punching, the column and line numbers are indicated on the form. The chief advantages of this sort of form are: (1) Very little writing is necessary in the field, since most of the information is indicated by a check in the appropriate space. The form can be filled out in less than 5 minutes. (2) Sufficient detailed information is given about existing conditions so that fairly accurate interpretation can be made without further field inspections.

DEVICES FOR EVALUATING INFESTATIONS

By Using Evidences of Injury.   Since injury is in direct proportion to population, it is possible to express population trends in terms of injury. There are numerous examples that illustrate how these methods can be used to indicate the abundance of some forest insects. For instance, the rate of bark-beetle increase or decrease may be determined by comparing

FIGURE 18. Shapes characteristic of borer emergence holes of common borers. From left to right, round-headed borer; three flatheaded borers, *Chalcophora, Melanophila, Agrilus;* and a scolytid.

the number of entrance tunnels with the number of emergences, the latter being indicated by emergence holes or empty pupal cells. The abundance of a defoliator may be determined relatively by the percentage of defoliation. The numbers of sucking insects, such as the Saratoga spittlebug or some scale insects on pine, may be indicated by the number of "flags," that is, twigs on which the needles have turned red.

The method that expresses populations in relative terms based upon injury is quite satisfactory when the insects are present in large numbers. During periods between outbreaks when little or no damage is evident, this method cannot be used. Since it may be desirable to know when a population increase is starting, more intensive means must be used to determine the abundance of insects. Usually a trained forest entomologist will be required to do this, and the method must be adapted to the specific insect or group of insects.

By Trapping Insects. Adult insects are often attracted by lights or odors and so can be captured by traps and counted. Several of these trapping devices are mentioned in Chap. 8. As a means of estimating the abundance of species that are attracted to them, traps are a valuable aid.

With traps it has been possible, for instance, to detect the spread of some foreign insects from locality to locality. The presence of the Japanese beetle has often been detected by trapping in newly invaded localities before it has become sufficiently numerous to be detected by other means. Local control, applied promptly to eradicate the early invaders, retards the insect's rate of spread. Similarly, traps have been used to detect the spread of the introduced gypsy moth into new localities; by this means, its presence has been detected before it could otherwise have been found. As a result of this warning, several spot infestations have been eradicated by prompt application of control measures and general infestations thus prevented. Traps have also been used later to verify the success of control programs.

The chief objection to the trapping method for general survey work is the time required to operate the traps. The insects captured must be sorted, preserved, and counted, and the numbers tabulated. The operation

(a)

(b)

(c)

FIGURE 19. Increment cores illustrating three types of reduced radial growth are useful in evaluating conditions that have affected a tree. A wider-than-normal ring is often laid down on the lower part of the bole during the first year of very severe defoliation when translocation of food is disturbed, as illustrated in (a). Effect of unfavorable weather is illustrated in (b), where the effects are limited to the years during which the unfavorable conditions prevail. Suppression resulting from root and crown competition is illustrated by (c). Reduction of growth from year to year is gradual but recovery requires only a few years.

of traps will usually be limited to the detection of special insects. Occasionally they may be used for more general collecting, where they can be easily attended.

By Measuring Frass Drop. One example of the method of arriving at comparative data is through the evaluation of frass drop. Frass is a term applied to the waste materials produced by insects in feeding. Since its amount is in direct proportion to the amount of material eaten, the abundance of insects can be calculated by measurement of the resulting frass.

Morris (1949), collecting the frass on standard-size cloth-bottomed trays set out under given trees, was able to demonstrate a high degree of correlation between frass drop and spruce-sawfly populations. By collecting frass from under the same trees in successive years, Morris learned how great was the fluctuation of larvae from year to year.

By Counting Cocoons. Some insect populations may be measured relatively by means of cocoon counts. For instance, sawflies, such as the European spruce sawfly, the larch sawfly, and the jack-pine sawfly, spin cocoons beneath the trees on which they feed. These cocoons are not difficult to find if one knows how and where to look for them. By repeatedly examining selected areas where such cocoons are most likely to be found, one can determine the relative population of the insect (Prebble, 1943).

By Counting Infested Parts. In many instances the relative number of insects may be determined by counting those present on a certain unit of shoot, twig, or stem. The relative number of the larch casebearer may be expressed as the number per fascicle of leaves. The abundance of the spruce-gall aphids may be expressed in terms of the number of galls per branch. The abundance of the Saratoga spittlebug may be expressed as the number of infested sweetfern plants, the alternate host. Similar counts may be made in the case of numerous other insects.

METHODS FOR DETERMINING DEGREE OF HAZARD

In all surveys it is desirable to keep costs at a minimum without reducing effectiveness. One way to accomplish this is to concentrate efforts on potentially dangerous spots. Since some cover types are more subject to insect attack than others, areas of high hazard often follow cover-type lines. A good cover-type map, therefore, is a guide in planning surveys and is useful in reducing survey costs.

Cover-type Maps. Even the usual forest-type map that shows merely the location of commercial tree types and crown classes is of some aid because it shows where susceptible tree species and sizes are located. Forest entomologists know well, however, that this information is not always adequate. Some stands may be very susceptible to attack of a certain injurious insect, whereas other stands containing practically the same combination of species but in different proportions may be almost immune. Such differences are often related to soil conditions and to the stage of ecological succession of the stand. Therefore to be most useful, the type map should indicate soil and ecological stage as well as tree species.

Since the character of both woody and herbaceous vegetation is correlated directly with soil, it is possible to classify cover types in such a manner that site will be indicated. A classification of this sort has been devised for Michigan and, with minor modifications, has been widely adopted in other localities (Graham, 1945). It is based on the ecological successional stages that are characteristic of an area. A brief résumé of this classification is presented here to illustrate one approach to cover classification. The major divisions are based on the origin of the various successional series characteristic of a locality or climatic area; for example, bare soil, rock, semiaquatic, or aquatic situations. Each is given names indicative of these origins. The following are the names and letters used to designate each series in this classification:

A. **Nonporous Soils:**
   Clay and clay loams through which water does not readily percolate.
P. **Porous Soils:**
   Sands and sandy loams through which water percolates readily.
R. **Rock Outcrops:**
   Shallow soils built upon bedrock.
B. **Stagnant Bogs:**
   Water-holding depressions that have filled or are being filled by the thickening of a floating mat of vegetation, with water flowing through them only at times of flood.
M. **Marshes:**
   Shallow depressions holding water that have filled or are filling with organic material produced by plants rooted in the bottom.
S. **Seepages:**
   Wet areas covered with either bog or marsh plants, through which fresh water flows within a few feet of the surface.
F. **Flood Plains:**
   Alluvial deposits along streams with high water table and good drainage.
E. **Transition Belts:**
   Narrow strips between types that differ from both adjacent types.

The ecological stages in each of these series have been divided into 10 arbitrary divisions, starting with the substratum—open water, bare soil, or rock—and passing through six herbaceous stages and four woody plant stages. These last four are of chief concern to the forest entomologist.

They are the *shrub stage,* the *intolerant tree stage,* the *midtolerant tree stage,* and the *tolerant tree stage.* They are designated consecutively by the numbers 7, 8, 9, and 10. In type-mapping an area by this system, the type will be indicated by the appropriate letter and number representing the series and stage, followed by the symbols for the predominant trees or shrubs. Under certain conditions it may be necessary to modify the system. For instance, in dry climates, where stage 10 will never be attained, it may be necessary to subdivide stage 8 or 9 to show local variations within them. Modification of the system may also be necessary in mountainous localities, especially at high altitudes, where climatic changes occur within astonishingly short distances. In such localities exposure, variations in elevation, air drainage, and temperature inversion may require subdivision of the general climatic area. By the use of a good cover-type map extensive surveys can be concentrated on high-hazard types with full confidence that in such places trouble will appear first; low-risk types can be disregarded. Thus the total area to be examined and the cost of detection operations can be much lower than would otherwise be possible.

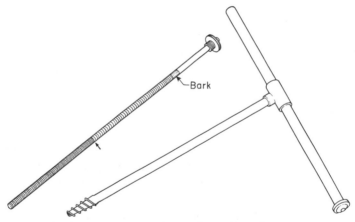

FIGURE 20. Increment borer, the tool used to remove a core from a tree, with extractor and core from a hemlock tree. The arrow indicates the ring laid down in 1895, one year after cutting of the virgin white pine that had previously suppressed the hemlock.

Hazard Rating of Areas. Economic conditions sometimes demand that mature or even overmature forests be utilized over an extended period. During this time, the risk of insect injury is great, and losses have often been so high that conservative practices have been abandoned in favor of destructive logging operations. This situation has been especially true in the east-slope ponderosa and Jeffrey pine types and in overmature inland types of ponderosa pine.

In these types, hazard surveys are regularly made to determine where the hazard is greatest and where conditions are relatively safe. On the basis of such a survey, maps are prepared to show hazard conditions in various places. With this information, operators can direct logging first into those areas that are most likely to suffer injury. These surveys have greatly reduced the trend toward rapid liquidation designed to save capital invested in overmature stands and have thus contributed to the greater stability of the forest industry. The degree of hazard in any area may change over a period of years. Therefore, repeated surveys are necessary.

Several methods have been used to determine hazard. For example, the number of trees dying in any one season or over a period of years indicates directly the degree of hazard. However, information based on mortality alone may become available too late to permit effective planning of operations. Research has indicated that individual high-risk trees can be recognized by definite characteristics. The proportion of high-risk trees in the stand can, therefore, be determined, and the relative degree of hazard evaluated.

Risk Rating.   Risk rating of individual trees is now applied generally in mature ponderosa and Jeffrey pine types in California and in Idaho and Montana ponderosa pine types (Johnson, 1949). The rating is used not only in connection with surveys but also in certain silvicultural practices that are discussed in Chap. 14.

The rating of trees is based upon the presence of symptoms indicating poor tree health. Arbitrary values have been given to the various symptoms, the combination of all indicating the risk rating for the tree. The trees are divided into four risk classes: (1) low risk, (2) moderate risk, (3) high risk, and (4) very high risk. In practical application, different individuals appear to assign different values to the various symptoms. As a result, personal variations in ratings may occur especially in groups 2 and 3.

Keen, by statistical analysis of data, has established definitely the relative values that should be assigned to the various symptoms. His conclusions indicate that the following symptoms are especially useful indicators of poor tree health: (1) fading or off color of foliage, (2) top dying, (3) thin, open crown throughout, (4) dying lateral twigs, (5) short needles above, longer below. Good tree health, associated with low risk, is indicated by crowns with full, dense foliage, long needles, dark-green foliage, and almost no dead twigs. With the collection and analysis of further information, the evaluation of risk symptoms will become more refined and the usefulness of risk rating for survey purposes will be increased.

From this discussion of forest-insect surveys, it is apparent that our initial concern in forest entomology is to detect promptly the presence of noxious insects whenever their populations are dangerously increasing. Detection and evaluation of populations are essential preliminaries to control. When we detect an increasing population, we must evaluate the significance of that increase. In order to do this, the forest entomologist must understand those forces that are operating to bring about the increase or decrease of insect numbers. In the following chapters these forces are discussed.

BIBLIOGRAPHY CHAPTER 6

Anon., 1950. Report of forest insect detection surveys in Oregon and Washington, Season 1950, *Oregon State Bd. Forestry* and *U.S. Dept. Agr. Bur. Entomol. P. Q., Forest Ins. Lab.*, Portland, Ore.

de Gryse, J. J., 1938. Canadian forest insect survey, *J. Forestry,* **36**: 983–986.

Graham, S. A., 1945. Ecological classification of cover types, *J. Wildlife Management,* **9**: 182–190.

Johnson, P. C., 1949. Determining the bark beetle hazard of pine stands in northeastern California, *J. Forestry,* **47**: 277–284.

McGugan, B. M., 1956. The Canadian forest insect survey, *Proc. 10th Intern. Congr. Entomol.,* **4**: 219–232.

Morris, R. F., 1949. Frass drop measurement, *Univ. Mich. School Forestry Conserv.* (now *Natural Resources*) *Bull.* 12.

Prebble, M. L., 1943. Statistical analysis of population counts, *Trans. Royal Soc. Can., Third Ser., Sect. 5,* **37**: 93–126.

Wear, J. F., and J. W. Bongberg, 1951. Uses of aerial photographs in control of forest insects, *J. Forestry,* **49**: 632–633.

———, and W. J. Buckhorn, 1955. Organization and conduct of forest insect aerial surveys in Oregon and Washington, *U.S. Dept. Agr. Forest Serv. Pacific Northwest Forest Range Expt. Sta.,* Processed Report.

CHAPTER 7

SPECIAL METHODS FOR DETECTION AND EVALUATION

In the previous chapter some general aspects of detection and evaluation have been considered. Now we shall proceed to a discussion of specific procedures and techniques that are used. In practice, detection and evaluation are closely related; from the time an outbreak is detected, the evaluations begin. Detection surveys are designed to locate threatening populations of forest insects before severe outbreaks can develop. Evaluations of detected infestations are made by observing either the insect population or the damage caused by the insects. Surveys of damage reflect the economic impact of outbreaks and generally must precede control operations. Evaluations of population trends are extremely useful in prediction of changes in an outbreak. Evaluations may be of an observational nature or may be extremely precise. The type of survey used depends on many factors including both biological and economic considerations.

EXTENSIVE SURVEYS FOR DETECTION

Detection of possible beginnings is a prime requisite. The first type of survey will, therefore, be extensive in nature and will stress detection, leaving until later the job of careful evaluation and appraisal. Extensive surveys have been conducted in various ways, but at present they are most frequently made either from the air or, where terrain permits, from lookout points. Their objective is to determine where damage caused by insects is located.

Surveys from Lookouts. In some mountainous regions it is possible to view large areas of forest from elevated points. When such lookouts are readily accessible, they make possible extensive surveys of insect injury at very low cost. From the combined observations made from a number of lookouts, reasonably good coverage of an area may often be obtained. Observations from lookouts are made with field glasses, infested areas are spotted on a map, and notes are made concerning the intensity of the

FIGURE 21. Severe blowdown in a stand of Engelmann spruce, Santa Fe National Forest, New Mexico. The northern spruce beetle often increases to outbreak numbers in such situations. (U.S. Dept. Agr. Forest Service.)

infestation. The results are comparable to those obtained from the aerial survey. Annual observations indicate whether spot infestations are increasing or decreasing and show whether or not intensive evaluation should be made.

Reconnaissance Surveys by Trained Personnel. Extensive observations are regularly made by trained personnel whenever such men travel from place to place. In the course of a season, these incidental observations by various observers may cover much of a locality. The combined reports of all trained men in a region will provide information on the more conspicuous species present and over a series of years will indicate trends.

Roadside Reconnaissance Plots.   The general reconnaissance becomes more specific when observations are made on a series of definite plots or areas within easy sight of a road. Conspicuous evidence of insect injury may be observed on these areas from the road; thus rapid coverage of extensive areas is obtained. Roadside observations are open to criticism because they are not always representative of conditions throughout a locality. Nevertheless they are useful extensive indicators of conditions. Through an examination of the same plots year after year, trends become evident.

Aerial Surveys.   The aircraft is a major means for planned detection surveys in the United States. Outbreaks of various kinds can be easily detected from the air, since excessive insect activity produces effects that are plainly discernible, such as defoliation or change of foliage color. An example of this is the yellow or reddish hue that characterizes coniferous trees attacked by most bark beetles. Survey by airplane for detection purposes is both rapid and effective over wide areas of forest.

FIGURE 22. Surveys may sometimes be accomplished by viewing from higher elevations. Groups of trees killed by the northwestern pine beetle as viewed from a hillside. (U.S. Dept. Agr. Forest Service.)

The usual procedure is for one or sometimes two observers to ride with the pilot so that during the flight the infested area can be spotted accurately on a map or aerial photographs and the nature and extent of the infestation recorded. The height at which the plane flies is determined by the character of the infestation and the ease with which it can be discerned.

Flights must be carefully timed to correspond to the period in which injury is the most conspicuous. Since some insects produce greatest injury only in the early spring, others in midsummer, and still others in the fall, flights must be made at different times of the year. Because of this seasonal nature of conspicuous injury, the observations during any flight are usually aimed at a single species of insect. This simplifies the problems for both pilot and observers, since it limits the examination to types highly susceptible to one specific insect. For instance, a survey for larch sawfly would be made in July and would concentrate on stands of pole-size or larger tamarack. For the detection of defoliation by the jack-pine budworm, flights would be made during July over mature or orchard-type jack pine; for the spruce budworm, a similar insect, flights would be concentrated over stands of predominately mature balsam fir. Flights in late June over aspen stands would disclose the presence of forest tent caterpillars. Bark-beetle outbreaks vary in their conspicuousness according to the species involved; damage by some species is most readily observed in the spring, whereas others are observed in late summer or fall. Some cannot be seen from the air before the beetles have emerged.

Improvements are being made continually in aerial survey procedures through the better timing of examinations, greater accuracy in observations, the use of photographic recording equipment, and improved flying techniques. In spite of all possible future improvements, it is unlikely that sufficient detail can be secured from the air to serve as a basis for the detailed planning of most control projects. Follow-up examinations from the ground will, therefore, be necessary in most cases. These will be considered in the following section.

INTENSIVE SURVEYS FOR EVALUATION

After the presence of a dangerous pest has been located, an evaluation of the situation becomes imperative. If the extensive surveys for detection have been conducted for a number of years general trends have usually become apparent. Then more intensive evaluations must be made.

Evaluation of Damage. Whenever an extensive survey of a forest area indicates a marked increase in insect population, detailed examinations of an intensive nature should immediately follow. These are best carried on by ground surveys. The specific object may vary in different surveys, but in general it is one of evaluation and appraisal of conditions with the damage done to the trees as the criterion.

The methods used in such intensive surveys are usually patterned along lines similar to those used in timber cruising. This is natural, since the objective is to determine the volume of timber, the number of trees, the acreage, and the value of the materials involved. On the basis of this information, control measures will be planned and the cost estimated. On small areas, a 100 percent cruise of damage is often made. If the infested areas are large, estimates are made by the use of either strips or sample plots. Damage on these sample areas is measured accurately, and the total damage to the entire area is assumed to be in the same proportion. The percentage of an area that must be examined in order to give an accurate average will vary with the degree of homogeneity characterizing the forest and with the size of the area involved. Ordinarily from 2.5 to 5 percent of the total area is included within the strips or plots.

In the use of either strips or plots, care must be taken to obtain representative samples of existing conditions. When strips are used, they are often run at 1/4-mile intervals and are usually 1/2 to 2 chains in width. Sample plots are laid out at regular intervals along a compass line, the size of the plot varying from one job to another, depending upon the insect involved, the size of the trees, and the density of the stand. In pole-size timber, for instance, 1/10 acre is a common size, whereas in saw timber 1/4 acre or even larger plots are advisable. If the samples are truly representative, they can serve as a basis for sound calculation of the total damage.

Quantitative Evaluation Data. Quantitative survey data may be expressed in one of two ways: (1) They may indicate absolute quantities for an area, for instance so many trees or so many board feet of timber per acre. (2) They may indicate relative quantities, for instance the ratio of entrance and emergence holes, the percentage of defoliation, the percentage of parasitism, or the proportion of larvae destroyed by a spraying operation. The relative quantities may make no reference to areas, or they may refer to a restricted or selected area that may or may not represent

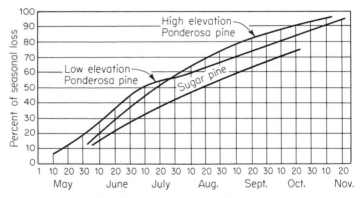

FIGURE 23. Appraisal of seasonal damage must usually be started before the insects complete their activity for the season. The figure above illustrates how the proportion of total seasonal damage observable on a certain date may vary with species and elevation. (Adapted from U.S. Dept. Agr. Forest Service.)

the forest type as a whole. When these relative observations are made through a season or from season to season, they show trends but cannot be used to show the absolute number of insects present or the absolute amount of foliage destroyed.

In the evaluation of damage for computing control costs, accurate figures are essential. These figures, as we have seen, are usually obtained by taking samples according to a systematic pattern. When a sufficient number of samples have been taken, the addition of more samples will not change the average. Thus, with an adequate number of systematically arranged samples, it may be assumed safely that the results will apply to the entire area in the same proportion.

There are a few control measures that demand more definite information on population than can be expressed by a relative quantity. For example, control of bark beetles by trap trees or logs is effective for a few species. These freshly cut materials are more attractive to these bark beetles than living trees and, therefore, are attacked first. After they are infested, the brood in them is destroyed. To use these devices effectively, the approximate number of bark beetles in an area must be known so that enough, but not too many, trap trees may be prepared (Trägårdh and Butovitch, 1938).

Similarly when parasites or predatory insects are liberated for the immediate suppression of noxious insects, the number to be released can be calculated accurately only if the population is known. As forest-insect control practices become more and more intensive, the need for absolute population data will doubtless increase. Under current conditions in America, however, we are not justified in directing a great deal of effort toward this end.

The mechanical and observational evaluations that have been described rest upon an understanding of the biological and ecological characteristics of the insects that are being surveyed. The characteristics of insect populations must be measured in terms of this biological knowledge and usually in successive generations. Only by reliable measurements can we determine with certainty whether we are dealing with increasing or declining numbers. The decision to use or not to use some direct control procedure is, or at least should be, based upon the facts thus disclosed. In the next section will be considered some specifications for making biological evaluations in such a manner that the results will command confidence.

BIOLOGICAL EVALUATIONS

Biological evaluations that we are about to describe are designed to measure and predict the trends in forest-insect populations. When such evaluations are being made, many interrelated factors must be known.

The insect population must be carefully measured and the susceptibility of the stand must be rated, with the recognition that two major biological organisms are involved: the insect and the host tree. Each is dependent upon the other. If the host is not susceptible, the insect will do no serious damage, and if the insect is not present in sufficient numbers, a susceptible host will remain practically undamaged.

FIGURE 24. Specialized equipment is often needed for forest-insect surveys and research. The sno-cat makes it possible to reach inaccessible areas during the winter. (U.S. Dept. Agr. Forest Service.)

Effective biological evaluation procedures have not been developed for most of the important forest insects because of the vast amount of information needed. This lack of technique does not mean that these evaluations are of minor importance. On the contrary, effective biological evaluations can help greatly in reducing the number of mistakes due either to failure to act when outbreaks are imminent or conducting needless control when outbreaks are subsiding.

Biological evaluations require a thorough understanding of the populations involved. Sampling procedures are required which measure the population and the interrelated organisms, such as parasites and predators. Also, the population numbers must be related to damage to the host trees.

Sampling Specifications. The procedure to use in sampling is suggested by the insect species and the intensity and size of the infestation. There is no standard procedure applicable to all species or situations; however, closely related species may require techniques which are similar.

Morris (1955) describes five ways in which population data may be expressed. This classification is helpful in understanding some of the problems involved. The first four expressions are based on direct population measurement: insects are located and counted. The fifth is a result of indirect observation based on measuring some index related to insect numbers. Morris's classification is as follows.

1. *Population Intensity* — Insect populations may be expressed in relation to the food supply available to them. A defoliator might be described as a certain number of individuals per shoot or leaf group or a bark beetle in terms of number of beetles per square foot of bark surface. Such an expression is perhaps the most useful for biological evaluations because the number of insects is described in relation to the host and can readily be subdivided into various degrees of damage.

2. *Absolute Population* — In this expression the insect counts are related to some absolute unit such as insects per acre. Such measurements can be very useful in expressing changes in total insect population from year to year or generation to generation. Because of changes in quantity of food available, the population-intensity expression may reveal only apparent trends that are not accompanied by absolute changes in insect numbers.

3. *Basic Population* — The insect population may be measured relative to some specific unit in the forest stand, an individual tree, for example. Such a unit then can be converted to absolute population if supporting data are known on the structure of the tree and the forest stand. Such measurements may be used as an indicator of absolute population if the normal characteristics of the forest stand are not disturbed. The important difference between basic population and population intensity is that an expression of basic population can be directly related to absolute population whereas population-intensity measurement may not represent valid expressions of change in absolute population.

4. *Relative Population* — Some surveys utilize gross measurements unrelated to any specific unit of the forest or tree as a means of expressing trends. Examples are the "beating" method used in forest-insect surveys and many of the "sweeping" procedures used in fields. These methods are useful in keeping track of presence or absence of insects but are not precise enough for use in accurate evaluations.

5. *Population Indexes* — In some situations an index can be used more effectively than a count of the insect population. In a survey of defoliators the index may be an ocular estimate of defoliation intensity, or in bark-beetle work the index may be the numbers of trees killed. Indexes are extremely useful in population evaluations and in many cases are the only feasible method because of the expense entailed in other more precise procedures.

The specifications for sampling must be based on a knowledge of statistics. There are numerous texts which cover the subject adequately. If all biological populations were distributed according to the normal curve, the development of biological evaluation procedures that are statistically sound would be relatively simple. Unfortunately among forest-insect populations other distributions are generally more common than the normal. Thus considerable statistical knowledge is required for measuring forest-insect populations or conditions. The forester or forest entomologist should actively seek the help of well-trained statisticians, but he himself should have a basic knowledge of the subject so that he can express his ideas clearly to the statistician and understand the advice he obtains.

Biological evaluations must be based on soundly conceived plans. Steele and Torrie (1960) list five basic steps in planning and execution of a sample survey. The steps are as follows:

1. The objectives must be clearly stated.
2. The sampling unit and sampling universe must be defined.
3. The sample must be chosen.
4. The survey must be conducted.
5. The data must be analyzed.

Most of the above steps are self-explanatory, but two terms should be defined. The *sampling universe* is chosen by the surveyor for his purposes. The universe may be in terms of trees or portions of trees, or it may be in acres or other portions of the forest floor. The *sampling unit* is selected as the basic unit within the universe on which the counts are made. The sampling unit should be such that all the units in the universe will have an equal chance of selection. It should be stable in number and size but should be small enough so that an ample number of samples can be taken to estimate variance adequately.

The method by which the sampling units are selected is important. Generally a random selection is advisable, although there are specific situations where other methods are more practicable. Stratification of samples into groups having some characteristic in common is often necessary to obtain the maximum information for the time available. Timing is a major problem in biological evaluations. The sampling period may be relatively short in duration. For example, the best time to sample the northwestern pine beetle in biological evaluations is immediately before emergence of adults. This is a relatively short period when most of the insects have reached the adult stage but before the first ones emerge.

Distributions. The thought presented previously that the distribution of data from biological populations does not generally approximate the normal curve should be considered further. Two questions arise: (1)

How can we analyze such data? (2) Are there mathematical distributions which do fit?

No set of biological data is likely to fit exactly any mathematical form. But the data may satisfactorily approximate one of several mathematical functions that may be represented by either a straight or a curved line. Discussions of the various types of distribution can be found in most statistics texts, and good discussions in relation to forest insects can be read in Waters's papers (1955, 1959). Insect data will often approximate one of the three following distributions:

1. *Binomial* — The binomial distribution may be applicable when the data concern merely "success" or "failure." In forest-insect work we might record only insects present or insects absent or damage present or absent. An assumption is made that every sample unit in a lot has an equal chance of containing insects or damage.

2. *Poisson* — The Poisson distribution is a random distribution which is often approximated when insect populations are at low levels. When the populations are higher, a binomial distribution either positive or negative is more likely. The Poisson is of doubtful reality in nature because the following basic assumptions are seldom met.

a. Each individual has the same chance of occurring on any unit.

b. Each sampling unit has the same chance of having an individual land on it.

c. The presence of an individual or individuals on a sampling unit neither attracts nor repels other individuals from the unit.

3. *Negative Binomial* — The negative binomial is one of several "contagious" distributions and is applicable to biological data of many types. This distribution is nonrandom. There is a definite tendency among biological organisms toward "clumping," i.e., if one insect of a species is present in a unit, there is an increased chance that others of the same species will be present in the same unit. This may happen in nature when larvae hatch from eggs laid in masses, when insects are attracted to especially favorable spots, or when they exhibit gregarious tendencies.

The three distributions as well as the normal and others which biological data may fit are discussed in books and journals on statistics. Our objective here is merely to impress upon the reader that there are many possible types of distributions and that biological populations do not always occur randomly.

Transformations may be effectively used on biological data to convert data to approximate a normal distribution. Once the transformation has been made, the transformed data may be analyzed using statistical procedures based on the normal curve. Transformations that are often effective are the log, the square root, the reciprocal, and the arc sine.

Nonparametric Statistics. The use of nonparametric statistics should be briefly mentioned because of the usefulness of the techniques. In insect surveys and in research as well, many data are collected for which the underlying distribution is not known. To handle such data, procedures are needed which are not dependent on a specific parent distribution. The nonparametric procedures supply ways in which such data can be analyzed. These procedures are not often used because of lack of knowledge of their usefulness. The individual should investigate the possibility of a nonparametric test before accepting parametric procedures based on weakly supported assumptions. Generally the procedures in such tests as "the sign test," "Wilcoxon's signed rank test," or the rank correlation tests are quick and easy to learn and apply. Those who desire to read a short discussion on nonparametric methods should consult a statistics text such as Steele and Torrie (1960), "Principles and Procedures of Statistics."

Sequential Sampling. Sequential-sampling procedures have been extremely useful in biological evaluations. The method involves a flexible sample size in contrast to the conventional methods, which utilize fixed numbers of sample units to be examined. In sequential sampling, the basic units are examined and cumulative counts are recorded until the sample total fits one of the classes defined in advance. The least sampling is required where the insect is very sparse or very abundant. The savings in sampling time can be considerable when using this method. Waters (1955) presents detailed procedures for computation of sequential plans for four mathematical distributions: binomial, negative binomial, Poisson, and normal.

The method is not useful in population work where counts consisting of numbers of insects are desired because it yields only classes by previously defined abundance groups. The development of a sequential plan requires a considerable knowledge about the insect. Its biology must be known. Also the mathematical distribution of counts for the basic sampling unit is needed, and the effects of the insects on the host trees must be known. If the sequential-sampling procedure is to be used to distinguish between light versus moderate defoliation, we need the class limits in terms of insect numbers. What is the maximum number of insects per sampling unit that will cause no more than light defoliation, and what is the minimum number that will cause no less than moderate defoliation? This information must be obtained through research before a sequential plan can be developed. Generally no more than three classes are needed and sometimes only two. A sequential system could be devised with two classes, for example treatment needed or treatment not needed. Confidence limits are a part of the equations for the sequential method, and in most forest-insect plans a 10 percent probability has been set.

There are numerous plans which could be used as examples. Here we will use one from Cole (1960) for the spruce budworm in Douglas fir. This plan was developed for use in postcontrol surveys to class the control as either satisfactory or unsatisfactory. Such a procedure is much more useful than conventional methods, which state merely that 95 percent or more mortality is satisfactory. Percentage mortality values are often misleading. In a very heavy infestation, 95 percent mortality could result in more survivors than are normally present in a light, increasing infestation. The sequential plan avoids this problem by basing success on the number of living insects remaining rather than the percentage surviving.

Postcontrol population data were found to approximate the Poisson distribution closely. Cole set the following class limits for the two classes.

M_0 (satisfactory) — that the average number of larvae per 15-inch twig is 0.35 or fewer.

M_1 (unsatisfactory) — that the average number of larvae per 15-inch twig is 0.50 or more.

TABLE 5   Sequential Table for Field Use in Postcontrol Sampling of Spruce-budworm Larval Populations*

NUMBER OF TWIGS EXAMINED	CUMULATIVE NUMBER OF BUDWORM LARVAE SATISFACTORY VS. UNSATISFACTORY		
15	— Satisfactory control	—	12 Unsatisfactory control
20		2	14
25		4	17
30		6	19
35		8	21
40		11	23
45		13	25
50		15 Continue sampling	27
55		17	29
60		19	31
65		21	34
70		24	36
75		26	38
80		28	40
85		30	42
90		32	44
95		34	46
100		36	48

* From Cole, 1960.

Cole's limit was set at 100 twigs. If, after 100 twigs had been sampled, the cumulative total was between 36 and 48, the statement was made that the control was "equal to 95 percent reduction." Thus, the maximum sampling for borderline cases is 100 twigs, but for clearly satisfactory or clearly unsatisfactory control far fewer samples would be examined. The procedures followed in selecting sampling points within spray blocks can be read in Cole's paper.

The example cited is not a biological evaluation, but it illustrates the method. Plans have been developed for biological evaluations. Knight (1960) developed such a plan for northwestern pine beetle surveys. In this plan predictions are made that the number of trees killed will increase, remain static, or decrease in the next generation by making counts of beetles developing to the adult stage in presently infested trees. The sequential method has its limitations, but it is soundly based mathematically and is proving to be extremely useful in the evaluation of forest-insect abundance.

Life Tables. Life tables are being used as a tool in population ecology. Morris and Miller (1954) summarize the procedure used in develop-

TABLE 6   **Format for a Life Table with Possible Sampling Stages**

x SAMPLING INTERVAL	$1x$ NO. ALIVE AT BEGINNING OF x	dF x FACTOR RESPONSIBLE FOR dx	dx NO. DYING DURING x	$100qx$ PERCENT MORTALITY $dx/1x$
I. Eggs (fall)	——	Parasites	——	——
		Other	——	——
		Total	——	——
II. Larvae (fall)	——	Parasites	——	——
		Tempera-		
		tures		
		Other		
		Total		
III. Larvae (spring)	——	Parasites	——	——
		Predators	——	——
		Other	——	——
		Total	——	——
IV. Pupae (summer)	——	Parasites	——	——
		Predators	——	——
		Other	——	——
		Total	——	——
V. Adults (summer)	——	Sex ratio	——	——
		Predation	——	——
		Weather	——	——
		Other	——	——
		Total	——	——
Generation			——	——

ing the tables and explain their use. Several additional papers have been published since 1954 which also utilize life tables to express population changes in an understandable and systematic form. Such life tables reveal the accumulative effects of all mortality factors throughout the insect's life cycle. In insect studies the survival of a large group (born at about the same time) is measured at fairly close intervals throughout its existence. Ideally the same individuals should be observed at each sampling, but in field studies of forest insects this is generally impossible. Thus, survival is estimated not by observing the same individuals, but by sampling the population. It should be pointed out that life tables are not an end point. They are merely a format on which survival data can be systematically presented.

This format can be best illustrated by setting up a table with hypothetical sampling intervals and mortality factors. The table headings of Table 6 have been utilized by numerous authors.

The two chapters on surveys have served only to introduce this broad subject. We have not attempted to do more than present some of the ideas that are currently being used in this field. The forester will find these methods useful in entomology and in other phases of forestry. New methods are being developed and will be adopted in place of many that are in use at present. One of the newer methods already in use is an index method utilizing regression procedures. Survey procedures utilizing the method have been developed for the European pine shoot moth and other plantation insects in the Lake States. The regression method will be useful in other entomological applications as will many other innovations. The forester should adopt new methods as they are developed and are proved effective.

BIBLIOGRAPHY CHAPTER 7

Bliss, C. I., and R. A. Fisher, 1953. Fitting the negative binomial distribution to biological data and note on the efficient fitting of the negative binomial, *Biometrics,* **9**: 175–200.

Cole, W. E., 1960. Sequential sampling in spruce budworm control projects, *Forest Sci.,* **6**: 51–59.

Knight, F. B., 1960. Sequential sampling of Black Hills beetle populations, *U.S. Dept. Agr. Forest Serv. Rocky Mt. Forest Range Expt. Sta. Res. Note* 48.

Morris, R. F., 1955. The development of sampling techniques for forest insect defoliators, with particular reference to the spruce budworm, *Can. J. Zool.,* **33**: 225–294.

———, and C. A. Miller, 1954. The development of life tables for the spruce budworm, *Can. J. Zool.,* **32**: 283–301.

Steel, R. G. D., and J. H. Torrie, 1960. "Principles and Procedures of Statistics," McGraw-Hill Book Company, New York.

Stevens, R. E., and R. W. Stark, 1962. Sequential sampling for the lodgepole needle miner, *Evagora milleri, J. Econ. Entomol.*, **55**: 491–494.

Terrell, T. T., 1950. Training manual bark beetle surveys northern Rocky Mountain region, *U.S. Dept. Agr. Bur. Entomol. P. Q. Div. Forest Ins. Invest., Coeur d'Alene Lab.*

Trägårdh, Ivar, 1934. A new method of obtaining an accurate estimate of the number of insects infesting storm-ravaged forests, *Proc. Fifth Pacific Sci. Congr.*, Victoria and Vancouver, B. C., Canada, 1933, 3397–3404.

————, and V. Butovitch, 1938. Methods and concepts, *Bull. Entomol. Res.* 29, pp. 191–210.

Waters, W. E., 1955. Sequential sampling in forest insect surveys, *Forest Sci.*, **1**: 68–79.

————, and W. R. Henson, 1959. Some sampling attributes of the negative binomial distribution with special reference to forest insects, *Forest Sci.*, **5**: 397–412.

Wilford, B. H., 1960. Forest insect surveys in the central Rocky Mountains, *J. Econ. Entomol.*, **53**: 458–462.

CHAPTER **8**

DIRECT
CONTROL
OF TREE
INSECTS

Insect control may be defined as the regulation of insect activities in the interest of man. It includes practices of all sorts that are directed toward that end. Some of these activities will be corrective and some preventive, but all will aim at the same objective.

CERTAIN ASPECTS OF CONTROL

Purpose of Control. The purpose of control is to avoid economically important injury, and the success of any control operation must be measured in terms of the value of the products protected. Usually the aim is not the eradication of the insect but rather the reduction of its numbers below the level of injuriousness. Eradication can best be attempted when the pest is newly introduced and dangerous. One conspicuous reason for this attitude toward eradication is the cost. To eradicate completely a native insect would usually be prohibitively expensive. However, recent developments using sterilizing methods show promise as eradication procedures for a few insects.

Eradication of a native insect should not be attempted for another less obvious reason. There is a fundamental biotic principle that any niche left vacant will soon be occupied by some other organism and that organism is likely to be a species similar to the original occupant. Therefore, if we eliminate one insect pest, another similar one, previously present in small numbers and now relieved of competition, may become a pest in place of its former associate. Thus by eradication we might solve one problem only to create another.

If we can hold the pests within reasonable bounds but still permit them to be present in such numbers that they can continue to compete successfully with their subordinate associates, the biotic balance will be maintained at an innocuous level. By so doing, we should accomplish control in an ideal manner.

Outbreaks of forest insects result from fluctuations of the biotic balance. Conversely, as long as the balance can be maintained at low levels without major fluctuations, outbreaks are impossible. In its simplest terms, therefore, the purpose of control is to maintain the balance between the pests and the trees at a level below the threshold of serious injury.

Although natural disturbances may upset the balance, causing a species to attain injurious levels, the activities of man are the most far-reaching and important. The cutting of trees, the building of trails and roads, the construction of buildings, the drainage of land, the damming up of water, all these and, in fact, practically all man's activities tend to modify or change environmental conditions, thereby increasing or decreasing the probability of outbreaks.

The value of the forest to man depends upon the use he can make of it. Obviously, he cannot use it without causing some disturbance. Nevertheless, every possible effort should be made to carry on his activities so that the balance will be disturbed as little as possible. Through understanding and care it is possible to make all the necessary changes in conditions and yet to a very large extent maintain the biotic balance. We have seen that that balance is maintained only when the two opposing forces of reproductive potential and environmental resistance are equal. Therefore whenever one or more factors of resistance are either removed or reduced in intensity, other factors of equal force must replace them if the equilibrium is to be maintained. This is what is done when we carry on control measures. We merely substitute one set of resistance factors for another set that has been removed. The change in environmental resistance may be either due to man's activities or the result of natural forces.

Good illustrations of this point are common in agriculture. For instance, the Colorado potato beetle, *Leptinotarsa decemlineata*, under natural conditions was kept in check by food and other limitations. The individual plants of the native species of solanum upon which it fed were scattered, and consequently the difficulties and dangers attendant upon finding food were great. As a result, enough beetles were lost so that the number per unit area remained low and approximately stationary from year to year, thereby producing a balanced condition between the beetle and its host. When potatoes came to be cultivated as a field crop, food became so abundant that it ceased to be a limiting factor. Under the new conditions, the beetles that drifted into potato fields found that almost any plant upon which they chanced to alight provided suitable food, and risks connected with hunting for food were much reduced. In cultivated fields, therefore, this formerly innocuous species became an important pest. Obviously it was impossible to grow potatoes in a mixed stand and restore the forces of resistance that originally existed. Therefore it became necessary to introduce some other limiting factor. To accomplish this, potato plants are now sprayed or dusted with poisons toxic to the beetle but not to the plants. As a result a new balance, even more favorable to the potato than the natural conditions, has been established.

Cost of Control. Like every other forest operation, the application of forest-insect control must be looked upon from the business point of view. The material saved by the application of control measures must justify the expense involved. The cost of control must be less than the loss that would have occurred had no protective measures been applied. The lower the value of the trees or wood products to be protected or the smaller the margin of profit, the smaller will be the amount that can justifiably be expended for protection.

The forest entomologist must keep these economic requirements in mind when he is called upon to decide whether or not control is justified in a specific instance. As a rule, the nearer the ultimate product, the more valuable the materials become. In the early years of a forest rotation, the value of the trees is comparatively small. At that time even small injudicious expenditures may easily wipe out the entire expected profit. The value of mature timber justifies greater expenditure for its protection than does the value of younger trees, the value of partially manufactured products warrants a greater expenditure than does standing timber, and in the protection of manufactured wood products a still greater expenditure is justified.

The strictly economic values, however, are not the only considerations. Trees may have very real values in checking soil erosion or for aesthetic purposes. These indirect values must be taken into consideration along with commercial values in planning for their protection. Where trees are used to prevent the erosion of soil on steep slopes and watersheds, their destruction means not only the loss of a certain amount of wood but also damage through erosion of hillsides and silting of reservoirs. Such damage may be so great that, by comparison, the loss in wood may appear infinitesimal. Under such conditions, larger expenditures for protection than in the timber forests are justifiable. Similarly, parks, recreation areas, roadside forests, and ornamental trees have an aesthetic value far in excess of the value of the wood produced. This value is estimated by some of our best landscape architects and tree surgeons to be $5 per circumferential inch for well-placed perfect ornamental trees of the best species. A better way to estimate the value of ornamental trees would be to determine the price that the owner would be willing to pay for their replacement.

The forest entomologist will frequently be faced with some difficulty in making evaluations for control purposes. He can easily calculate the approximate cost of a certain control operation, but when he attempts to decide whether or not the expenditure is justifiable in terms of the values involved, his problem is not always simple. On watersheds and where the aesthetic considerations are paramount, the values are so great that almost any practicable control expenditures are justified. The only question then is whether he can raise the required funds. In commercial forests, on the other hand, he must be able to determine the actual monetary worth of the products saved before he can decide with confidence to apply a certain control procedure. The difference between the total operational expenditure and the monetary value of the loss expected without control represents the amount saved. Naturally, control should not be recommended if this difference is a negative value. In such a case, some less expensive control method must be used, or the insect loss must be accepted as unavoidable.

Estimating the expected loss is not always easy and must be based largely on experience. Not infrequently the needed experience is lacking. Then one can only judge from what is known about closely related species. But a well-trained forest entomologist should, in most cases, be able to judge approximately the amount of injury that a certain infestation is likely to cause. In many instances he should be able to estimate this with a high degree of accuracy. The amount of injury will depend upon the kind of insect, the forest type, and the site conditions. This subject is discussed further in the various chapters dealing with special insect groups.

Another important matter bearing on control is the length of time that treatment will protect trees from the particular pest in question. How many times during a rotation must treatment be repeated? Usually this question cannot be answered with certainty, but there are some principles that will serve as guidance in securing a reasonably correct answer. For instance, if the control operation changes the forest composition so that it is no longer favorable for the pest, the control measure will not need to be repeated. Conversely, if the treatment leaves the forest in the same susceptible condition as before, another outbreak can be expected within a few years, the number depending mostly upon the insect's reproductive potential and the weather conditions. For example, spraying a plantation to control sawfly does not change the character of the stand, and another treatment may be necessary within a few years. Repeated treatments in the same tree rotation are likely to be prohibitively expensive.

From this discussion we see that the forest entomologist must know not only how a forest insect can be controlled but also when it is profitable to apply a certain measure. Decisions on the latter require knowledge of the expected severity of injury, the values involved, whether or not control will be permanent, and the cost of control operations.

On the basis of justifiable cost of control, forest insects are divided into three major divisions: (1) forest pests, (2) ornamental-tree pests, (3) forest-products pests. Many of the same insects may be active in each division, but the methods of control will be quite different. The problem of the forest entomologist is to develop not only ways by which insect ravages may be checked but also methods that can be applied economically under specific conditions. He must continuously bear in mind that the control measure he recommends must show a profit in the long run, if it is to be justifiable.

Classification of Control Measures.   Methods that can be used for the control of tree insects may be classified into more or less arbitrary groups as follows:

A. **Direct Control.**   Operations aimed directly at the insect for the purpose of immediate suppression.
  1. **Mechanical methods:**
     Collecting, trapping, destroying infested materials, barking to destroy broods, heating.
  2. **Biotic methods:**
     Predators and parasites used for immediate suppression.
  3. **Chemical methods:**
     Dusting, spraying, fumigating, injecting, sterilizing, using poisonous bait.

B. **Indirect Control.**   Operations designed to modify environmental factors to secure ultimate limitation of insect numbers.
  1. **Chemical and mechanical methods:**
     Modifications of food supply, moisture conditions, and temperature conditions.
  2. **Biotic methods:**
     Competition, introduction or encouragement of parasites and predators.
  3. **Silvicultural practices:**
     Regulation of composition and density, selection of site, regulation of drainage, selection of resistant varieties and species.

4. **Statutory regulations:**
   Quarantines, embargoes, inspection, and certification.

Naturally the early attempts at insect control were prompted by emergencies. As a result they were direct or suppressive. Later, the possibilities of using preventive practices were realized and various means of creating conditions unfavorable for insect pests have been devised. Direct methods curb outbreaks but do not change the conditions that made the outbreak possible; therefore, their effect is temporary. Indirect or preventive methods create conditions unfavorable for outbreaks and, therefore, are more permanent in character. This lasting quality is a matter that deserves serious consideration in planning forest practices.

The remainder of this chapter and the two following chapters will deal with the various methods of direct control, leaving a discussion of indirect control to Chaps. 11 through 14.

DIRECT CONTROL BY MECHANICAL METHODS

Many of the mechanical methods of direct control had their origin in Europe and are still largely in use there. In the United States, where labor costs are much higher, these methods have often been prohibitive. There are, however, times when mechanical methods can and should be used to control insect pests in this country.

Collecting Insects. One of the most obvious methods of insect control is the direct attack upon the pest by collecting and destroying it during some one of its stages. For example, one of the methods frequently recommended for controlling the white-pine weevil is the collection of the adult weevils in the early spring during the feeding period that precedes the period of oviposition. The beetles are knocked off the pines into a net by jarring the terminal shoots. Such a method may be practicable on ornamental trees, but it is too expensive to use in forest plantations.

Trapping Insects. Many ingenious devices for trapping insects have been developed by entomologists, such as pits or furrows, light traps, bait traps, trap logs, and trap bands. The use of trap pits or furrows is commonly recommended in European literature for the capture of insects that spend at least part of their active life on the ground. Owing to the excessive labor cost, this method has seldom, if ever, been used in American forests. Trapping by means of lights has been used to some extent in this country, but it has not proved very successful because the insects attracted to lights are largely males. The few females that are caught by this device have in many cases already deposited their eggs. Gravid females are seldom attracted in large numbers to ordinary lights. Experimental work indicates that control by such trapping may, in some instances, be improved by using colored lights. Some insects are attracted by one color and some by another. Traps baited with some attractive food material or chemical have been somewhat more successful in capturing females. Such traps have been used, especially in experimental work, with such insects as the oriental fruit moth, the gypsy moth, calosoma beetles, and the Japanese beetle.

Fermented sugar or molasses baits are generally attractive to many insects, but rapid advances are being made in developing baits that are more or less specific for certain insects. For instance, geraniol is especially attractive to the Japanese beetle; traps baited with this chemical are used to indicate the presence or absence of the beetle in a locality. The principle of almost all insect traps is similar. The insects, attracted to the trap by light or chemical, are guided into the trap through a narrow slot. Once inside they cannot find their way out. In the trap they are usually poisoned and fall into a container from which they can easily be removed. Further developments in methods of trapping adult insects before they have laid their eggs may provide foresters with an effective means of insect control.

In European forests, trap logs and trap trees intended to protect standing timber from the attack of bark beetles are sometimes used. The principle involved is that certain species of these beetles prefer freshly cut or girdled trees to healthy uninjured trees; as a result, they will deposit their eggs in freshly cut logs or girdled trees provided by the forester for this purpose. Later the broods of beetles in these traps can be destroyed by barking the logs or by utilizing them. This method has been of great value in the United States in control of the northern spruce beetle, *Dendroctonus obesus* (Nagel et al., 1957). Unlike the European experience the beetles are not particularly attracted to girdled trees but populations in felled trees become extremely high. Trees are felled in small groups at intervals of $\frac{1}{4}$ to $\frac{1}{2}$ mile so that they lie in partial shade. After the logs are infested, the beetles are killed. If enough trees are felled to absorb a large proportion of the beetles in the area, control can be achieved with this method alone. However, the method may also be used advantageously as a supplement to chemical control.

In the control of certain of our ornamental-tree pests that tend to congregate in secluded places during some portion of the day, loose bands of burlap or other material placed around the tree trunks are sometimes used. The insects will gather under the protection of the band, where they can easily be destroyed in large numbers. This method is, of course, applicable only to ornamental and shade trees.

Destroying Infested Materials. In forest entomological literature one of the most frequent recommendations for the control of bark beetles and wood borers is to cut and burn the infested portion of the tree. Doubtless this is an effective means of control provided that practically all the infested trees in a community are so treated. Consequently, cutting and destroying the infested portion of trees should become a community control method. One insect that might be controlled by this method is the smaller European elm beetle, the chief victor of the Dutch elm disease. If by community cooperation all dying trees were cut before the beetles emerged, an outbreak of this elm disease could be checked.

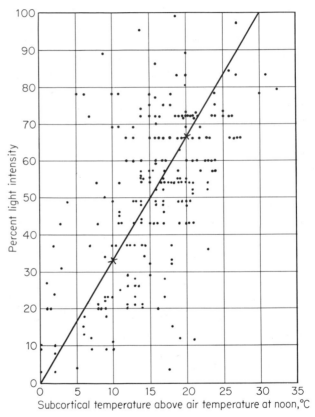

FIGURE 25. The influence of shade on the subcortical temperature of similar logs.

The destruction of infested material is an extremely important part of the planned control of this disease. The "sanitation" procedure of removing and destroying all dead and dying elm trees or branches of trees is a necessity if control is to be successful.

The method is not only used in protecting ornamental trees and forest products. In the West the northern spruce beetle infests logging slash and as a result often becomes a serious problem in the adjacent standing timber. It is common practice to wait until the slash has been attacked by beetles and then pile and burn all the infested material, destroying the developing broods in the process.

Barking to Destroy Broods. In certain cases, notably in the control of dendroctonus and other bark beetles, the barking of cut or standing trees has been employed to destroy the broods of these injurious insects. Removal of the bark is sufficient to kill those species that spend their entire developmental period between the outer bark and the wood. For those bark beetles which pupate in the outer bark, it is necessary to follow removal of the bark with further treatment, such as burning it or exposing it to the direct rays of the sun. Operations of this sort are designed to reduce the number of beetles to a point where the few that remain cease to be a menace to the surviving trees.

Application of Heat. The use of heat to kill wood-boring insects is occasionally applied in the forest, but it is more frequently employed to kill forest-product insects in furniture factories and other wood manufacturing plants. In the woods solar energy provides the source of heat.

Temperatures beneath the bark on the top side of logs lying in full sunlight frequently exceed the fatal temperature for log-inhabiting insects. These temperatures exceed the temperature of the surrounding air in direct proportion to light intensity. If logs lying in bright sunlight are turned every week or two during warm bright weather, all insect life in the surface layers may be destroyed (Craighead, 1920). For this solar treatment to be successful, the logs must be exposed on all sides to the full force of the sun's rays.

In manufacturing plants, kiln treatment is the simplest and most convenient method for destroying insects in wood. In standard practices the kiln temperatures practically always exceed the fatal point for wood-boring insects. Even the lowest kiln-seasoning schedule, with temperatures ranging from 105 to 115°F, has proved effective in killing certain species (Craighead, 1921). The higher schedules appear to be effective against all wood-inhabiting insects.

DIRECT CONTROL BY BIOTIC METHODS

Although biotic factors in insect control are generally used indirectly, there are some instances where their use is aimed directly at immediate suppression of a pest. When biotic factors are employed in this way, they are classed as direct means of control. Numerous attempts to apply biotic methods directly have been made, but most of them have never passed beyond the experimental stage. In a few instances, however, these efforts have been successful. Some of the successful cases have been so striking in their results that probably we shall see a much wider application of this kind of control in the future.

Illustrations. A striking example of the successful direct application of biotic methods to the control of an insect pest is to be found in California. In the citrus orchards of that state, the mealybug, *Pseudococcus gahani,* has been a most serious pest. From 1918 to 1929 it was effectively controlled by the direct use of a predatory beetle, a coccinellid called *Cryptolaemus montrouzieri.* According to Smith (1925, 1926) and Compere and Smith (1932), the use of this method passed beyond the experimental stage and proved itself to be not only effective but also much cheaper than chemical or mechanical methods.

The procedure followed in California has been to rear these predaceous beetles in large numbers and liberate them in the infested orchards in sufficient quantities to destroy the mealybugs before they have caused much damage. Special insectaries for the rearing of the beetles are operated in strategic locations from the proceeds of the sale of the beetles reared. During the season of 1929, over 14 million beetles were produced by these laboratories, and as a result, the mealybugs were effectively controlled over an orchard area of about 75,000 acres. The total cost of this work was approximately $125,000. The beetles were not liberated in every orchard in the infested region but were concentrated in those that were in danger of serious injury. If it is assumed, as Smith does, that one-third of the orchards were actually treated, the cost per treated acre was about $5. If, however, the cost was spread over the entire area affected, the cost per acre was only $1.66. These costs have, of course, increased with rising labor and other expenses, but no later figures are available. When compared with spraying, which cost, in 1929, from $25 to $30 per acre for one application, the expense of the biotic method was very low indeed.

At present, *Cryptolaemus* is not being used so extensively as formerly because the citrophilus mealybug has been brought under excellent indirect control by the introduction of two very effective internal parasites, *Coccophagus gurneyi* and *Tetracnemus pretiosus,* introduced from Australia in 1928. The use of *Cryptolaemus* is now mostly limited to the control of another somewhat less injurious mealybug. Nevertheless, it still remains one of the most striking illustrations of how a predatory species may be used directly for the control of a noxious species.

Several other predatory insects have been liberated for the direct suppression of forest pests. For example, 300 lady beetles were collected in Minnesota and released in a red pine plantation in Michigan to control an outbreak of the pine tortoise scale. The results were highly satisfactory, the scale being eliminated from the treated plantation in a single season. Insects of the genus *Chrysopa* are another highly predatory group. They have been reared in quantity and liberated for purposes of suppressing aphid outbreaks (Finney, 1950).

Attempts have been made to rear and utilize parasitic insects in the same way. *Trichogramma minutum,* a tiny egg parasite, has been the subject of much successful experimentation. The Canadian Parasite Laboratory is having some success in rearing and distributing parasites of certain pests for the direct control of insects in greenhouses. Also the same laboratory reared and released *Microplectron,* a parasite of the European spruce sawfly, for the purpose of direct as well as indirect control. The effect of the release was obscured by the spectacular effect of an introduced virus that brought the pest under almost complete control.

The direct control of insects by use of disease-producing fungi has usually failed. Hewitt, in Canada, tried to use an entomogenous fungus in forests that were being injured by the larch sawfly, but unfortunately the attempt failed. One instance where a fungous disease was used with apparently successful results against an agricultural pest might be mentioned. In the Central states a fungus was distributed for the purpose of checking a chinch-bug outbreak and was followed by the destruction of the bugs. It is, however, the consensus of opinion that this may easily have been a coincidence. The spread of the disease was apparently made possible by favorable weather conditions. Inasmuch as the disease organism was already present in the region, the favorable weather that occurred might have been sufficient in itself to have made possible the fungous epidemic that destroyed most of the chinch bugs.

The use of viruses has increased greatly in the past several years. Pine sawflies are often affected by these diseases, and at least four species can now be effectively controlled by ground or aerial application of virus polyhedra in water suspension. This is only the beginning, as many other viruses have been found affecting forest insects and direct controls using these are being developed. Control by means of viruses is ideal because it is specific, effective, and inexpensive.

Bacterial diseases likewise provide the forest entomologist with materials for the direct control of forest insects. The so-called milky disease of the Japanese beetle illustrates the possibilities of using bacteria for insect control. The larvae in the ground are infected when they ingest the spores with their food. The rate at which the disease spreads, therefore, is directly related to the number of larvae in the soil. Thus, under outbreak conditions, the disease spreads most rapidly.

Obstacles. The success of fungous diseases in reducing insect abundance depends so much upon favorable weather conditions that the use of these organisms offers comparatively little promise. Similarly airborne bacterial infections are influenced by weather conditions. Other organisms not so dependent upon the weather may ultimately be used. Soil-inhabiting bacteria and viruses seem to offer the greatest promise.

The successful use of insect parasites and insect predators depends upon the possibility of rearing them on a large scale at a reasonable cost. If it were not for difficulties in the technique of rearing these organisms, we should now be able to use them extensively in direct control. Another obstacle to be overcome is the difficulty of providing a sufficient quantity of suitable food to make wholesale rearing possible. This is no easy task. Artificial or partly artificial food has been used for rearing various insects. Therefore, the development of artificial food formulas for parasitic or predatory insects seems entirely possible.

In the rearing of the predaceous beetle *Cryptolaemus* in California, the food problem was solved in a very ingenious way. Mealybugs can be produced in large numbers by feeding them upon potato sprouts. By the use of this cheap and easily handled food for producing adequate quantities of the beetle's prey, *Cryptolaemus* was reared very inexpensively.

If it had been necessary to rear the mealybugs on citrus trees in order to provide food for the predators, the rearing expense would have been prohibitive. Struble in an unpublished report in 1938 described the successful use of fly larvae as a food for certain predatory beetles that attack bark beetles. Various artificial media that are both cheap and easily obtained are being used to feed parasites and predators experimentally.

Although no obstacle presents so great a difficulty as the provision of suitable food, other difficulties stand in the way of large quantity production of parasites or predators. For instance, it may be difficult to provide conditions suitable for mating (Jones, 1926), or transportation of the insects to the localities where they are needed may present difficulties. The problem of synchronizing laboratory production of parasites with the development of the pest in the forest so that a maximum supply of the beneficial species will be on hand at the proper time must be solved. But most of these difficulties can be overcome by the use of modern cold-storage equipment.

The use of biotic agencies for the direct control of forest insects, therefore, has real possibilities, even though at present they have not been fully explored. The future is almost certain to witness an increased use of biotic methods for direct control.

BIBLIOGRAPHY CHAPTER 8

Balch, R. E., 1937. Fall cankerworm and banding, *Rept. Entomol. Soc. Ontario,* **1937:** 1–5.

Bird, F. T., 1961. Transmission of some insect viruses with particular reference to ovarial transmission and its importance in the development of epizootics, *J. Insect Pathol.* **3:** 353–380.

Burgess, E. D., 1950. Gypsy moth sex-attractant traps, *J. Econ. Entomol.,* **43:** 325–328.

Cameron, J. W. M., 1963. Factors affecting the use of microbial pathogens in insect control, *Ann. Rev. Entomol.,* **8:** 265–286.

Compere, H., and H. S. Smith, 1932. The control of the citrophilus mealybug by Australian parasites, *Hilgardia*, **6:** 585–618.

Craighead, F. C., 1920. Direct sunlight in forest insect control, *Proc. Entomol. Soc., Wash.*, **22:** 106–108.

———, 1921. Temperatures fatal to larvae of the red-headed ash-borer, *J. Forestry*, **19:** 250–254.

DeBach, Paul, et al., 1949. Periodic colonization of aphitis for red scale control, *J. Econ. Entomol.*, **43:** 784–802.

Finney, G. L., 1950. Mass culturing of *Chrysopa californica, J. Econ. Entomol.*, **43:** 97–100.

Haller, H. L., et al., 1944. Nature of female gypsy moth sex attractant, *J. Am. Chem. Soc.*, **66:** 1659–1662.

Jones, D. W., 1926. Technic of handling parasites, *J. Econ. Entomol.*, **19:** 311–316.

Metzger, F. W., 1935. Japanese beetle traps, *U.S. Dept. Agr. Misc. Publ.* 201.

Nagel, R. H., David McComb, and F. B. Knight, 1957. Trap tree method for controlling the Engelmann spruce beetle in Colorado, *J. Forestry*, **55:** 894–898.

Patterson, J. E., 1930. Control of mountain pine beetle with solar heat, *U.S. Dept. Agr. Tech. Bull.* 195.

Smirnoff, W. A., J. J. Fettes, and W. Haliburton, 1962. A virus disease of Swaine's jack pine sawfly sprayed from an aircraft, *Can. Entomologist,* **94:** 477–486.

Smith, H. S., 1925. The commercial biological control in California, *J. Econ. Entomol.*, **18:** 147–152.

———, 1926. Biological control work in California, *J. Econ. Entomol.*, **19:** 294–302.

Tanada, Y., 1959. Microbial control of insect pests, *Ann. Rev. Entomol.*, **4:** 277–302.

Turner, W. B., 1918. Female Lepidoptera at light traps, *J. Agr. Res.*, **14:** 135–149.

———, 1920. Lepidoptera at light traps, *J. Agr. Res.*, **18:** 475–481.

CHAPTER **9**

DIRECT CONTROL BY CHEMICAL METHODS

Although direct control methods involving biotic insecticides, sterilization, mechanical procedures, and the mass liberation of predatory beetles have been developed for a number of insects, we are, nevertheless, dependent on chemical methods for the control of most infestations. The usefulness of any insecticide is governed greatly by its application, the properties of the insecticide itself, the site on which it is used, and the nature of the pest involved. The first two of these items will be discussed in this and the following chapter.

APPLICATION OF CHEMICALS

The use of chemicals for the control of insects has had a phenomenal development since 1868, when paris green was first used against the Colorado potato beetle, *Leptinotarsa decemlineata*. Since that time insecticides have been improved and perfected to such an extent that chemical warfare against insects has come to be almost universal. For many years its use in the control of tree insects was limited to ornamental

and orchard trees. Because of the high costs involved in applying insecticides and because of the inaccessibility of forest lands, chemical control
was little used in forests. Today, however, the development of new machines for applying concentrated spray materials has reduced costs
greatly. Nevertheless these new machines have by no means replaced the
older types that spray the insecticides in greatly diluted solutions or
suspensions.

The three general methods of applying insecticides are as sprays, as
dusts, and as fumigants. These are discussed in terms of tree application
in the following sections. The different types of equipment are numerous,
and many new modifications of each type are continually appearing; therefore this discussion will be limited to a consideration of general methods
without describing specific models or designs of machinery.

To Ornamental Trees. Although the cost of treating forest trees with
old-type sprayers is prohibitively high, it has always been practicable to
spray ornamental trees with these machines. The chief advantage of the
old-type sprayer is the high degree of accuracy in control of the spray.
It is also cheaper in original cost and much safer when used by inexperi-
enced workmen.

The spraying of tall trees with the old-type sprayers, however, requires
the use of heavy and expensive equipment: large-capacity tanks, special
nozzles and spray guns, and sufficient length of high-pressure hose to
extend from a road to the infested trees. The spray liquid is discharged
from the nozzle at pressures as high as 400 to 800 pounds per square inch
and at rates up to 80 gallons per minute. Specially designed nozzles discharge a solid stream that breaks into a fine mist in the air. For tall-tree
spraying the conventional sprayers are mounted on a trailer or truck and
are equipped with a tank holding at least 150 gallons of spray material.
Some tanks hold as much as 500 gallons if the machine is designed to be
used on good roads. Since the long hose required to reach the trees causes
a great reduction of pressure between the pump and the nozzle, the pump
pressure must be at least 500 and sometimes as much as 1,500 pounds.
For small trees less elaborate equipment is adequate. Trees up to 30 feet
in height can be treated with any of the power machines used in orchards.

Current literature contains much detailed information on the numerous
types of spraying equipment. References in "Entoma," published biennially by the Entomological Society of America, serve as an excellent guide
to this subject. Low vegetation and small trees can be treated with a
poisonous dust instead of a liquid spray. The various dusting machines
range in size from the small hand dusters that hold a pound or less of the
insecticide to the elaborate power dusters used in field and orchard
work. Even with the most powerful machinery it is impractical to throw
a column of dry dust to the tops of tall trees. Furthermore, dusting is
wasteful of materials and cannot be accurately controlled. Therefore,

dusting from the ground is not often used for the control of tree insects.

To Forest Trees from the Ground. Spraying equipment suitable for use in forests has been developed to a high point of efficiency. Small accessible trees are treated from the ground with either dusts or liquid sprays. For this purpose, dilute sprays are most often used.

The knapsack sprayer or back pump is one of the most common types suitable for the hand treatment. In treating scattered infestations in forest plantations, hand treatment from the ground is sometimes the least expensive procedure. The back pumps, used for fire fighting, can be adapted for this work by equipping them with nozzles that deliver a spray instead of a stream of liquid. Another type of sprayer used frequently for hand spraying is the compressed-air sprayer. This type is more difficult to carry than the knapsack sprayer, but it is just as efficient.

The chief objection to both the knapsack and the compressed-air sprayers for use in forest plantations is the large quantity of water needed for dilution of the insecticide. The time involved in frequent trips to a dispensing point for a load is a major item of cost in a back-pack operation. Even in using power sprayers it is difficult to supply adequate water for dilution of spray materials. In order to reduce the amount of water needed for spraying, special atomizers have been designed to handle concentrated sprays. To atomize concentrated suspensions, higher pressure than is produced in a knapsack sprayer is required. Special atomizers have been designed and used effectively for applying these sprays to small trees, but this method has never become popular because overdosage with the insecticide is difficult to avoid.

The stirrup pump is commonly used in treating bark-beetle-infested trees. These pumps have been used in many large projects in remote areas inaccessible to power equipment. This type of pump is inserted into a jeep can of insecticide and pumped to the tree at pressures up to 150 pounds per square inch through a neoprene hose and a long 6-foot wand. Surfaces up to 30 to 35 feet above ground can be thoroughly soaked with the insecticide, a height necessary in bark-beetle control.

Power machines for applying concentrated sprays have, however, proved both practical and effective in places where the trees are accessible by truck or tractor. The mist blower is one of these modern developments. The insecticide is injected into a large-volume air stream moving at a rate of 150 to 250 miles per hour. If the amount of material injected and the forward speed of the machine are regulated, the insecticide is blown onto the trees in any quantity desired. The smaller mist blowers are light enough to be moved on a pickup truck or even in a wheelbarrow. These lightweight blowers can spray up to a height of 30 feet. The larger and more powerful ones must be moved by truck or trailer. Some of them can be used to spray tall trees, since they are capable of blowing the insecticide to heights of over 100 feet. When forest plantations are sprayed, the mist is discharged almost horizontally. In this manner a swath about 300 feet wide can be treated as the machine moves along.

Another modern development is the fog machine. A jet of concentrated insecticidal solution is directed against a heated surface, and thus an insecticidal fog is generated. The fog is then carried away from the machine by air currents. If advantage is taken of the temperature inversion that often occurs in the air at night, the fog can be held close to the ground. The particle size of the fog is important and can be controlled within certain limits by regulating the temperature or the generator.

Even the most effective fog has a killing range for many forest pests of only about 200 feet from the machine, although it apparently spreads much farther. The failure of the fog to kill beyond a limited distance is due to the small size of most of the particles. The particles of effective size are deposited mostly within 200 feet of the generator, while the finer ones drift farther away. Potts (1946) found that particles less than 30 microns in diameter are repelled by the "field of resistance" surrounding all objects and that much larger droplets, 100 to 300 microns in diameter, are required for effective spraying.

Yeomans (1950) reports that "airblast machines" (mist blowers) can provide a more uniform deposit across a swath with larger spray particles than can be obtained with the wind-borne "aerosols" (fog machines). Only 25 to 50 per cent of the particles less than 50 microns in diameter will be deposited within 2,000 feet. The mist blower is, therefore, much better than the fog machine for treating trees with chemicals.

To Forest Trees from the Air.   Shortly after World War I the airplane came into use for applying insecticides to fields, orchards, and forests. This method proved very popular. Its use made possible rapid and effective treatment of areas that could not have been reached otherwise.

Although the cost was relatively low, it was still too high for any but high-value forests. The low-carrying capacity of most planes and the large quantity of insecticide required per acre were the chief factors that contributed to the expense. On the average, using arsenicals, it was necessary to apply about 20 pounds of dust per acre in order to obtain satisfactory control of defoliating insects. Thus with a "pay load" of 300 pounds, a plane could treat only 15 acres before returning to the landing field for reloading. Sometimes difficulty was experienced in obtaining sufficiently rapid discharge of the insecticide to give adequate coverage. In such cases a second flight had to be made over the same area.

In the early treatment of forests from the air, the limited carrying capacity of the planes precluded the possibility of using the common aqueous arsenical suspensions. Usually, therefore, the insecticide was a powder, most often calcium arsenate.

These limitations of carrying capacity have been largely removed with the development of potent synthetic organic insecticides, especially DDT.

FIGURE 26. Douglas-fir tussock moth control project in northern Idaho in 1947. A Ford trimotor plane distributing 1 gallon of spray oil containing 1 pound of DDT per acre. Swath width 300 feet. Note swirling motion of the spray. (U.S. Dept. Agr. Forest Service.)

Instead of 20 pounds or more per acre, DDT is effective against many forest pests at 1 pound per acre or less. Thus, with DDT in an oil solution a plane can spray at least $2\frac{1}{2}$ times the area that the same plane could dust with a single load of calcium arsenate dust.

Helicopters, also used in spraying forests, have some advantages over other aircraft. The insecticide can be better controlled because these machines can operate at low speeds and can take off from a road or a small cleared space; the conventional plane, on the other hand, requires a landing field. As a result, an operation using conventional planes often must load the insecticide at a point 20 miles or more from the area to be sprayed, whereas the helicopter can be loaded nearby. Experiments comparing the cost of spraying forests with regular-type planes and with helicopters indicate that the advantages of loading close to the spraying area may be offset by the high operating cost of the helicopter (Yuill and Eaton, 1949).

ADMINISTRATION OF AERIAL SPRAYING

Since aerial spraying has become a standard practice for the control of many defoliating and some sucking insects, the operations have become the important concern of foresters. Operations are usually directed and controlled by administrative officers in charge of the infested area, but these men are usually aided and advised by professional forest entomologists. Sometimes, however, this professional advice is unavailable, especially on small projects. Therefore, every forester should understand aerial-spraying practices and how to plan, supervise, and execute a spraying job.

Laying Out the Project. The spraying project is laid out on the basis of the survey that determined the extent and severity of the infestation. The area to be sprayed is calculated from previously prepared maps, and the infested portions of the forest divided into spraying units that can be recognized from the air. The boundaries of these units may be roads, ridges, edges of plantations, margins of cuttings, or other features that are easily identifiable. The size of the units will, of course, vary with topography and the distribution of the infestation. They should be so shaped or arranged that they can be flown with a minimum number of turns. This is especially important if conventional planes are used. If the spraying is done with helicopters, this is less important.

Selecting the Loading Base. The next consideration is the loading field. This should be located as close to the area to be sprayed as possible and must be accessible by road. Frequently, a local airport is favorably situated, and arrangements can, as a rule, be made to use these established landing fields. On the other hand, the location of the spraying operation may be so far removed from an airport that the time consumed in flying back and forth will preclude its use. Then a temporary field must be provided.

In the selection of a temporary base, the advice of a competent aviator is essential. The loading area must be level and large enough to permit safe take-off by a heavily loaded plane. The required length of runway will, of course, depend upon the type of aircraft used. If no suitable landing field is available for fixed-wing airplanes, there is still the possibility of spraying with helicopters.

In selecting a loading base, the forester should not forget that he must provide proper accommodations for the workers involved in the project. Since spraying must be done when the air is still, the hours of work will be in the early morning shortly after dawn or in the evening. Dissatisfaction among the crew over the disagreeable hours may often be prevented by providing good food and comfortable sleeping quarters. On large operations that require a week or more, it is impractical for the crew to live at great distances from the landing field.

Another important consideration in selecting a loading base is the matter of servicing the planes. Satisfactory facilities are available at most established airports, but if a temporary field is used, competent mechanics, equipped with necessary tools, must be on hand to make emergency repairs. Gasoline and oil can be provided by tank trailers at temporary loading fields.

Handling the Insecticide. For large spraying operations ready-prepared spraying mixtures can often be obtained and are convenient and usually less expensive than materials prepared on the job. In smaller operations, however, it is usually necessary to mix the materials. This mixing must be done in advance of spraying so that the plane tanks can be loaded quickly. The economy of any spraying operation will be greatly influenced by the speed of loading the planes between flights. On small jobs, the insecticide may be mixed and carried in oil drums. By mixing in the tank of a power sprayer with a mechanical agitator, the process can be done more easily, and the materials for a small job can be pumped directly into the plane from the tank. A conventional-type sprayer with a 500-gallon tank is well suited for this operation. In most aerial operations, the insecticide is usually an oil solution of DDT or other organic insecticide. Such a solution can be mixed several days before its application. Suspensions or emulsions must be mixed immediately prior to application, and therefore, the mixing cannot be completed much in advance of spraying. The not uncommon practice of purchasing prepared concentrates the season before they are to be used and storing them over the winter is unwise.

The amount of insecticide applied and the area covered must be recorded for each flight or group of flights so that dosage may be controlled. On small jobs, the amount of insecticide used on any run is estimated from the capacity of the tank in the plane or by gauging the amount taken from the oil drums or storage tanks. On larger operations, the prepared spray is usually hauled to the loading field in tank trailers or trucks and pumped from these directly into the planes by power pumps. The quantity of spray pumped into each plane is measured by a meter as it flows from the storage tank.

After the plane is loaded and ready to take off, the job is in the hands of the flier and the forester can do nothing to expedite the work. Careful planning prior to the take-off will reduce delays, facilitate the operation, and reduce the cost.

Controlling the Spray. Controlling the application of the spray as to both particle size and amount is essential. This is accomplished by nozzle adjustment and by regulating the rate at which the insecticide is discharged from the plane, the speed of the plane while spraying, and the width of swath covered in each run. In spraying, care must be exercised by the pilot to lay down the swaths so that they do not overlap more than is necessary and that no gaps are left unsprayed. The suitability of the equipment to do a satisfactory job should be checked in ample time to permit adjustment. Even distribution of the proper amount of spray per acre is essential to good control. The amount of the insecticide applied per acre can be regulated not only by adjustment of the rate of discharge but also by modifying the swath width. During the operation, a constant check should be kept on the amount of insecticide applied and the area covered by each run or series of runs so that any errors that occur may be promptly corrected. Such checking will reduce careless tendencies to the minimum.

Prior to application of the spray, each pilot must be briefed concerning the area to be sprayed so that he can recognize it easily from the air. This is accomplished first by examination of a map showing direction, distance from the landing field, and general landmarks. Examination of the map will be followed by actual observation from the air. An aerial photograph mosaic is an important aid in briefing the pilots. A flier should never be permitted to spray a piece of forest without first flying over it in order to familiarize himself with the area.

In localities where topographic relief is evident from the air, a flier can lay down parallel swaths with accuracy by following natural landmarks. On level land, however, control of the strips by landmarks may be impossible. Then it is necessary to use some ground control for each swath. One of the most effective means of accomplishing this is by using hydrogen- or helium-filled balloons. As the spraying progresses, men at each end of the spraying area move the captive balloons across the area, one swath at a time.

Commercial Spraying Services.　With the increase of aerial spraying operations, the business of providing spraying services has grown correspondingly. Prior to 1940, such services were difficult to obtain and not always reliable. Much of the work was done by poorly equipped individuals owning a single plane.

Since World War II this situation has changed, and many well-equipped and reliable concerns are prepared to apply aerial sprays to any crop. These concerns are prepared to contract for spraying forests at a set charge per acre. The price varies, of course, with the conditions, but the efficiency of the commercial operators combined with improved equipment has resulted in marked economy. In spraying large forests, contractors usually provide only the flying service, but sometimes they also furnish the insecticide. The detailed planning and administering of the operation fall upon the forest officers. On smaller operations, it may be more efficient for the contractor to provide flying service and the insecticide and to assume much of the administrative responsibility. He cannot, however, be expected to make the preliminary plans for even the smallest operations.

Securing Weather Information.　Another responsibility which rests with the forester is the securing of weather information. Aerial spraying can be done effectively only when atmospheric conditions are favorable. The air must be clear, calm, and without appreciable convection currents. Such conditions commonly prevail for several hours in the early morning and for a shorter period in the evening just prior to the fall of darkness.

Most spraying operations are conducted immediately following dawn. The first flights are started as soon as there is sufficient light for the take-off and continued as long as conditions remain favorable. As soon as the air becomes turbulent or the wind rises above 5 or possibly 8 miles per hour, spraying must cease.

Wind, fog, and rain are all serious handicaps to aerial spraying. They cause cessation of operations, and if they prevail any length of time, they may prevent timely treatment. The full importance of timing in the control of various insects will be discussed at length in later chapters. Suffice it to say here that timing is of great importance in control work and that the atmospheric handicaps of aerial spraying are sometimes detrimental to proper timing.

Unless flying conditions become actually hazardous, the pilots have a tendency to continue applying the spray after meteorological conditions cease to be suitable. Furthermore, conditions at the loading field are frequently quite different from those over the spraying area. Therefore, weather observers on or near the spraying area should report frequently by telephone or radio to the loading field. When very large areas are being treated, several observers located in different parts of the area will be required. When the wind rises to a point where the spray drifts away before it can settle on the swath for which it is intended, spraying should be discontinued.

Checking Distribution. In addition to his other duties, the forester must provide checkers so that he can be sure that a satisfactory job is being done. Even distribution, as has been previously noted, is essential to satisfactory control. Therefore every practicable effort should be made to secure it. This checking for even distribution should be done while the operation is in progress. Pilots, like most other people, are more careful when they know the quality of their work is being evaluated.

A method utilizing chemically treated cards is perhaps the simplest way to determine spray distribution. Treated cards that are oil sensitive are laid out at regular intervals over all or part of the area to be sprayed. After being sprayed, the cards are picked up and examined. If approximately the same number of insecticidal droplets are found on all the cards, the distribution is satisfactory. If on some more than the usual number are present or if there are no spots on some, uneven distribution is indicated. Serious misses should be corrected by another run over the skipped area, and any overdosage should be called to the attention of the pilot. Checking a large area in this manner is prohibitively time-consuming, but spot checks should be made on every unit. Although these treated cards are very useful in indicating distribution of the spray, they do not indicate the amount of mortality of the insects that may be expected. This is because the amount of spray on the cards is not necessarily correlated with the amount of insecticide on the trees (Maksymiuk, 1963).

Determining the Effects. The general effect of the spraying treatment may easily be determined by the number of poisoned larvae that drop from the trees. But an accurate estimate of the number of insects surviving will require a more careful evaluation. An adequate number of sample counts should be made to determine the number of insects on a series of twigs or branches before spraying and again after. The difference, of course, represents the number of larvae in the sample that were killed. This can then be expressed in either percent of the population killed or the number surviving. A sample count of this sort should be made with care so that the samples examined before the spraying will be correctly comparable to the postspraying count. If the insects cannot be counted directly, the number of twigs infested before and after spraying or the amount of frass dropped before and after will indicate the effects of the spray.

Estimating Costs. The cost of control varies with every operation. The cost per acre of flying small areas or units of moderate size is usually far greater than for large operations. Similarly when materials can be purchased ready-mixed in tank cars or tank trucks, they are often much cheaper than in small lots mixed by hand on the job.

Comparing the per-acre cost of large projects and moderate-sized projects, we find that one spruce-budworm project covering about 200,000 acres cost $1.50 per acre. Another covering only 20,000 acres cost about $3.50 per acre (Balch, 1956). In two small operations, one spraying pine plantations for spittlebug control cost $2; another, also on pine plantations for red-headed pine sawfly, cost $2.50 per acre. These figures are comparative and indicate the range that may be expected under various conditions. The variations may even be much greater, so that the actual costs as stated here are not particularly significant. However, most very large projects, 100,000 acres or more, have been sprayed at a cost of about $1 per acre.

The three chief items that must be included in an estimate of spraying costs are (1) application, (2) materials, and (3) overhead. The first two will depend largely on the level of wages, the quantity of materials used, and market conditions. The last will depend chiefly upon the size of the project.

Almost as much overhead personnel is required on a project of moderate size consisting of a few hundred or a thousand acres as would be needed for 100,000 acres. Thus overhead on a very large project might be only a few cents per acre, whereas on a small project it could easily rise to $1 per acre if accidents or bad weather caused delays.

The following list [1] includes the typical personnel associated with a large-scale aerial spray project. On smaller projects many of these posi-

[1] "U.S. Forest Service Handbook," 1958.

tions would be combined, and on very large projects some positions would require numerous individuals.

1. Project leader
2. Unit supervisor
3. Contracting officer
4. Formulation checker
5. Safety officer
6. Project air officer
7. Aerial observers
8. Weather observers
9. Air contractor
10. Chief pilot
11. Ground supervisor
12. Aircraft mechanics
13. Pesticide loaders
14. Aircraft fuel loaders
15. Spray pilots
16. Observation pilots
17. Pesticide transportation, storage, and pumping contractors
18. Administrative officer
19. Clerks
20. Load checkers
21. Flight checkers
22. Communication chief
23. Unit biologist
24. Insect or disease development checkers
25. Spray deposit checkers
26. Postspray mortality checkers

The list merely illustrates the complexity of an aerial spray operation. Many of these jobs are overhead jobs, and the operational costs continue throughout a project despite delays due to unfavorable weather, mechanical failures, or poor planning.

The conclusion is unavoidable that overhead costs can raise the price of a small spraying project to a level that is entirely out of line with the benefit derived therefrom. From the realistic viewpoint, therefore, the forester is often compelled to cut the service and supervisory personnel to the minimum number required to handle the insecticide, load the plane, and establish any ground control in the field that may be needed. Weather observations are left to the pilot, while the checking of spray distribution and the making of mortality estimates are often done visually and almost casually. Inadequate supervision inevitably leads to carelessness and will account for some unsatisfactory results.

OTHER TECHNIQUES OF CHEMICAL CONTROL

Chemical warfare against insects is not confined to the dusting and spraying of trees in the forest. Other techniques for applying chemicals are in common use, especially where the insect pests are not operating in the forest but are in nurseries or in forest products. The remainder of this chapter will be devoted to a discussion of various techniques of chemical control in these areas.

Dipping. Nursery stock that has been dug for shipment and forest products of various kinds may be treated by dips and washes to control insect infestations. The insecticides are often the same as those used in the treatment of standing trees. In dipping nursery stock, the chemicals must be used in diluted form to avoid injury to the trees. Suspensions, aqueous solutions, or oil emulsions, diluted as for conventional spraying, are the common dipping materials.

On wood products, more concentrated materials are suitable. Chemicals in various solutions that are too toxic for treating plants may be applied without injury to processed wood. For example, such chemicals as 10 percent DDT solution in oil, 2 percent chlordane solution, 12 percent orthodichlorobenzene solution in oil, or 5 percent pentachlorophenol, are excellent insecticidal dips and washes for wood infested by insects. These and other chemicals will be discussed in the following chapter.

Insecticidal dips and washes must be selected carefully to suit conditions. For example, wood that is to be painted or varnished should never be treated with creosote or carbolineum, even though these substances are both excellent insecticides. Neither should these same materials be used where their color is objectionable. In contrast, oil solutions of such substances as pentachlorophenol will not affect either the paintability or the color of the wood. Dips for the treatment of living plants must be selected with equal care and used in dilutions that will kill the insects without harming the plants.

Poisoning the Soil. Some soil-inhabiting pests in nurseries, such as white grubs, wireworms, and other root eaters, may be killed by poisons mixed with the soil. The substances used for this purpose are usually inert powders and are intended to make the soil uninhabitable for the pests for several years.

Usually the poisons are applied to nursery soils in the course of preparation for seed or transplant beds, but occasionally they may be drilled between the seedling rows in established beds. The concentrated types of soil poisons should be diluted before application by thoroughly mixing the required quantity with a bulky fertilizer. This will increase the total volume of material to be applied and will make easier the even spreading of the insecticide. After the poison has been spread evenly or drilled into the prepared soil, a light cultivation will mix it into the top few inches of soil.

Fumigating with Gas. Fumigation is usually a technique that is applied in enclosed spaces; occasionally it may be used to kill insects in wood. Since a fumigant must vaporize readily at room temperatures, the number of useful insecticides of this type are limited. Generally, compounds which boil at or below room temperature are most useful. Examples are hydrogen cyanide, methyl bromide, and ethylene dioxide. In soil fumigation some of the other compounds which boil at higher temperatures have also proved effective. Examples are ethylene dibromide, dichloroethyl ether, and para-dichlorobenzene. Many of the contact insecticides exhibit a limited amount of fumigant activity.

Fumigation is used for many purposes, but perhaps the greatest use in forestry is in nursery practice. In Michigan, a fumigation chamber has been developed for the treatment of nursery stock infested by the Europeon pine shoot moth. Seedlings and transplants are placed in the chamber before shipment and are treated with methyl bromide to kill the insects. The method is effective, simple, and inexpensive.

Fumigation is also being used in nursery practice in the Pacific Northwest, where the European pine shoot moth is also a problem (Carolin and Coulter, 1963).

Fumigation of the soil with methyl bromide under a polyethylene covering is standard practice in many forest-tree nurseries as a preliminary to sowing seedbeds. This treatment controls both insects and fungi infesting the soil.

FIGURE 27. Nursery beds may be fumigated by construction of inexpensive chambers such as the one illustrated here or before planting by a plastic covering laid on the ground. (U.S. Dept. Agr. Forest Service.)

Poisoning by Baits. Some insects, such as cutworms and grasshoppers, are at times injurious to small trees in nurseries or newly established plantations. These insects and various others are attracted to and feed upon various baits. If a poison is added to these attractive mixtures, the pests can be killed. The baits are scattered thinly over the ground where the pests feed. Bait formulations will be discussed in the next chapter.

Tree Injection. Poisonous solutions, when injected into the sap stream of trees, may serve a double purpose. They may kill insects infesting the tree trunks and, at the same time, protect the wood against subsequent infestation by wood-boring insects and infection by wood-rotting fungi.

Experimental work by Craighead and his associates demonstrated that broods of the southern pine beetle could be destroyed during the growing season by the injection method (Craighead and St. George, 1938). Later Bedard (1938) tested the method on western white pine infested by the northwestern pine beetle,[1] *Dendroctonus ponderosae,* and found that satisfactory destruction of the brood was accomplished if the trees were treated within 90 days after attack.

The method of injection used by Craighead was to remove a band of bark from around the tree, cut a saw kerf girdling the tree midway of the band, and introduce an aqueous solution of a poison into the kerf. The solution was held in contact with the kerf by a rubber dam placed over the kerf and securely tacked along each edge to the wood. The poison was placed in a container fastened to the tree above the dam, and the liquid was conducted to the dam by a rubber hose. Bedard simplified the saw-kerf procedure by fastening a trough of rubber or plastic sheeting immediately below the kerf. Into this trough the poisonous solution was poured. Grease was used to make the tacked edge of the trough watertight.

The injection methods are not generally used as a means of destroying bark-beetle broods because they are expensive in comparison with other chemical treatments. They are, however, of value in treating rustic materials to protect them from insects. When this treatment is used on rustic materials, the trees are cut and immediately, without lopping the branches, a preservative solution is brought into contact with the cut surface of the bole. Small trees may be set in containers holding the preservative, and larger trees may be treated by use of a waterproof dam fastened over the butt of the tree and connected by a tube with a vessel holding the solution. Trees from 4 to 10 inches in diameter can be treated by stretching a section of a tire inner tube over the barked butt of the tree. The open end of the tube can then be supported to form a reservoir, which can be filled with the liquid. Complete injections should be attained within 24 hours or less. Various aqueous solutions are suitable for injection treatments, but copper sulfate seems to be one of the best. Conifers can be injected at any

[1] Formerly the mountain pine beetle, *Dendroctonus monticolae.*

season when temperatures are above freezing, but broad-leaved trees must be treated during the summer.

Basal treatment of standing trees with debarking agents is becoming a common practice. Some of the debarking agents, such as sodium arsenite, also protect the wood from attack by insects until the trees can be utilized.

Treating Seasoned Wood. Wood preservative treatments are generally designed to prevent fungous attack and the resultant decay. The same substances will also protect the wood against insects by killing any that are present and by making the wood free from subsequent attack. Until recently, most wood preservation was intended to prevent rot in wood contacting the ground, but the development of synthetic organic compounds has introduced new possibilities of wood protection.

FIGURE 28. The layout of an experiment testing the control of termites. (U.S. Dept. Agr. Forest Service.)

Wood in buildings can be made permanently immune to insects by treating with oil solutions of DDT, pentachlorophenol, and other chemicals. Furthermore, the wood thus treated can be painted or varnished without danger of peeling or discoloration of the finish.

Treatment of wood with chemicals is accomplished by methods that vary from simple surface application by brushing or spraying to a complex system of impregnation by application of vacuum and pressure. The latter are available only in wood-preservation plants. Insect control is usually accomplished either by surface treatment or by dipping. To ensure success, all surfaces must be treated, and if only the surface layers of the wood are penetrated, any cuts made through the treated surface in shaping and fitting must be treated before the piece is placed in position.

BIBLIOGRAPHY CHAPTER 9

Balch, R. E., F. E. Webb, and J. J. Fettes, 1956. The use of aircraft in forest insect control, *Forestry Abstr.* Leading Article Series 23, *Forestry Abstr.* **16** (4), 1955; **17** (1) and (2), 1956.

Bedard, W. D., 1938. Control of mountain pine beetle by tree injection, *J. Forestry*, **36**: 35–38.

Carolin, V. M., and W. K. Coulter, 1963. Eradicating European pine shoot moth in commercial nurseries with methyl bromide, *U.S. Dept. Agr. Forest Serv. Res. Paper* PNW1.

Cook, W. C., 1949. Soil fumigants for wireworms, *U.S. Dept. Agr. Tech. Bull.* 980.

Craighead, F. C., and R. A. St. George, 1938. Introduction of chemicals into trees, *J. Forestry*, **36**: 26–34.

Davis, J. M., and K. R. Elliot, 1953. A rapid method of estimating aerial spray deposits, *J. Econ. Entomol.*, **45**: 696–698.

"Entoma," A directory of insect pest control, published biennially by the Eastern branch, Entomological Society of America.

Fettes, James J., 1956. Problems of forest aerial spray dispersal and assessment, *Proc. 10th Intern. Congr. Entomol.* 4 (1958): 281–289.

Fleming, W. E., 1947. Chlordane for Japanese beetle in turf, *J. Econ. Entomol.*, **40**: 932–933.

Kowal, R. J., and R. A. St. George, 1948. Soil-poisoning tests, *J. Econ. Entomol.*, **41**: 112–113.

Maksymiuk, Bohdan, 1963. Spray deposit on oil-sensitive cards and spruce budworm mortality, *J. Econ. Entomol.*, **56**: 465–467.

Potts, S. F., 1946. Particle size of insecticides, *J. Econ. Entomol.*, **39**: 716–720.

Worthley, L. H., 1917. Solid-stream spraying, *U.S. Dept. Agr. Bull.* 480.

Yeomans, A. H., 1950. Wind-borne aerosols, *U.S. Dept. Agr. Bur. Entomol. P. Q.*, ET-282.

Yuill, J. S., and C. B. Eaton, 1949. The airplane in forest-pest control, *U.S. Dept. Agr. Yearbook*, pp. 471–476.

CHAPTER 10

INSECTICIDES
AND
THEIR
EFFECTS

The number of chemicals available for insect control runs into the hundreds, and each year many new materials are placed on the market. Only a few, however, have been adequately tested in the forest. Some others used on farms have desirable characteristics but are either too expensive or too dangerous for forest spraying. In this chapter we shall limit our consideration to a restricted number of chemicals that have been proved suitable for the control of insects in trees and in forest products.

Chemicals are extremely important as a means of controlling emergency situations. These materials should not be used unless needed; when they are needed, they should be utilized wisely. Thus, the continuing great need is for knowledge about the chemicals available and the techniques for efficiently using them. The use of chemicals is vital to forest management.

DESIRABLE CHARACTERISTICS

The general characteristics desirable for satisfactory insecticides may well be considered before we discuss their classification and their specific qualities.

General. The ideal forest insecticide has never been produced. In fact we can never expect to have a single ideal product, since special cases require different characteristics and some of these requirements are conflicting. Although we may never obtain the ideal material, we can set up ideal standards that will be useful in evaluating the insecticides with which we must work.

Table 7 lists some of the requirements and some of the desirable char-

TABLE 7   Desirable Qualities for Insecticides

QUALITY	FOR LIVING TREES	FOR DEAD TREES OR FOREST PRODUCTS	FOR NURSERY SOILS
High degree of toxicity for pest	*Yes*	*Yes*	*Yes*
Nontoxic to living plants	*Yes*	No	No
Nontoxic to man or in safe form	*Yes*	*Yes*	*Yes*
Nontoxic, in dosages used, to beneficial organisms	*Yes*	No	*Yes*
Low cost	*Yes*	*Yes*	*Yes*
Simplicity of application	*Yes*	*Yes*	*Yes*
Short residual effect but not permanently stable	*Yes*	No	No
Long-time or permanent stability	No	*Yes*	*Yes*
Good storage qualities	*Yes*	*Yes*	*Yes*

acteristics. The same qualities that are desired in an insecticide for spraying living forest trees may be of no value or even actually undesirable in treating forest products or nursery soils. Therefore, in the table the suitability of each quality is indicated for each of the three classes. The required characteristics are shown by italics; those that are desirable but not absolutely essential are in roman type.

Toxicity. Insecticides must, of course, be highly toxic to the pests against which they are directed. At the same time, if they are used for spraying trees, they must be relatively nontoxic to the foliage. These two conflicting requirements limit the number of substances that are suitable for treating living plants.

Safety of application is accomplished in several ways. A substance that is toxic to insects may be safely applied to plants if it is a stable solid and is insoluble in water. Such a substance cannot be absorbed by the plant tissues and, therefore, cannot cause injury.

Water-soluble material must be sufficiently toxic to kill the pest when it is diluted to a concentration point safe for the plants. Unless a substance meets these requirements, it should not be used as a spray. Oil solutions are capable of penetrating plant tissues, and most oils are toxic to plants. Therefore, all oil insecticides must be very thinly dispersed if injury to the plants is to be avoided. A thin dispersion can be accomplished for conventional spraying by emulsifying the oil and diluting the emulsion with water. In aerial spraying or in the use of the mist blower or the fog machine, the oil is separated into fine particles as it leaves the machine and dispersed so widely that little or no plant injury will result.

Workmen who handle insecticides day after day are inclined to become careless and, therefore, cannot be trusted to protect themselves from highly toxic materials. Almost all chemicals used for insecticides are toxic to man if absorbed in sufficient quantities. Therefore, it is essential that all insecticide materials be so prepared that they can be handled safely. In order to meet this requirement, extremely toxic substances are usually placed on the market in partly diluted form. In spite of care on the part of the manufacturer, serious illness or even death may result from carelessness. *Insecticides are deadly poisons, and every possible precaution should be used to avoid inhaling them, ingesting them, or absorbing them through the skin.*

Nevertheless direct deaths due to the use of insecticides are few in number and have almost always been directly related to carelessness and misuse.

In aerial spraying especially, both pilots and ground crews find it almost impossible to keep the spray materials off their faces and clothing. For this reason, some of the more toxic chemicals should not be applied from the air.

Stability.   The quality of stability deserves special consideration. Some insecticides decompose slowly or not at all after application; others decompose or volatilize in a few minutes or hours. If the insecticide is placed in a location where the insects will eat or contact it later, enough stability to permit this contact is essential. If, on the other hand, the insecticide is applied directly upon the insect, stability after treatment may not be of any consequence.

After an insecticide has done its work in the forest, the quicker it disappears from the environment the better. If it remains, it may cause injury to benficial organisms. Unfortunately many otherwise excellent insecticides have a higher degree of stability than is ideal. Insoluble arsenical salts of lead, copper, and calcium decompose slowly or not at all after they are applied. DDT and some other organic insecticides may remain active in the soil for indefinite periods. Repeated heavy application of these substances can result in undesirable accumulations. Therefore, they should never be used more often than is absolutely necessary or in heavier dosages than the minimum required to accomplish control.

CLASSIFICATION OF INSECTICIDES

Before the advent of the various types of synthetic organic insecticides, the classification of insecticides was a simple matter. The relatively few materials in use could be separated with a minimum of confusion, according to either their action on the insect or their physical characteristics. Today it is difficult to devise a clear-cut and simple classification. This is because so many chemicals fall into more than one insecticidal subdivision, no matter how carefully these subdivisions are defined. The same insecticide may, in some cases, enter the insect's body through either the mouth or the sensory pores. It may be applied in the form of a dust, a suspension in water, an oil emulsion, or an oil solution. A logical classification could be based upon the chemical characteristics of the various substances, but that method does not seem appropriate here. There will, therefore, inevitably be considerable overlapping in the following discussion.

Three classes of insecticides are generally recognized. These are (1) stomach poisons, (2) contact poisons, and (3) fumigants. The last is the most effective but is limited in application because it must be used in confined locations. But when insects in the open must be killed, a spray or a dust is needed. For this purpose we must use either a contact or a stomach poison.

The stomach poisons are sprayed or dusted on the materials to be protected or may be impregnated into the wood. The insects ingest the poison with their food. These insecticides are especially effective against insects with chewing mouth parts. Insecticides of this type may be used in four principal ways (Metcalf and Flint, 1962).

1. The natural food of the insect is covered with the poison, the insect consuming the poison when it eats.

2. The poison is mixed with a material that is attractive to the insect as a bait and is placed where the insect will find it.

3. Some poisons may be placed where insects travel so that the insects get the poison on their feet and antennae. They then consume the poison while cleaning their appendages.

4. In recent years much attention has been given to systemic materials. These are toxic substances that are absorbed and distributed harmlessly throughout the tissues of living organisms, either plant or animal, so that insects feeding upon them are killed.

Contact poisons are of much greater significance than the other types. They enter the blood stream directly through the chitin, the intersegmental membranes, or into the respiratory system through the spiracles. Application may be directly to the body by spraying or dusting the insects or indirectly through a residue left on plant surfaces or other places visited by the insects. These insecticides are effective against either chewing or sucking insects.

Contact insecticides vary greatly in their stability. Some, such as DDT, have a long residual life and are effective controls for long periods after application. Others are highly volatile and dissipate soon after application. These must be applied so that the spray or vapor from the spray will contact and penetrate the insect's body before dissipation. Free nicotine sprays, nicotine sulfate sprayed in an alkaline solution, and pyrethrum sprays—all illustrate these volatile materials. Such poisons are characterized by their ability to stupefy and kill quickly but often are not so toxic as the more stable materials.

SOME COMMON INSECTICIDES

In this discussion of insecticides attention must be concentrated on those materials that have been tested and proved useful in forests and on forest products. Many others now on the market but not ordinarily used for the control of forest insects are omitted or merely mentioned.

To facilitate this discussion the chemicals will be arranged into groups that have been commonly recognized.

Botanicals. Among the commonly used materials which act as contact insecticides are many of botanical origin. These are not much used in forestry but should nevertheless be mentioned. The nicotine alkaloids are insecticides that are derived from tobacco combined chemically or mechanically with various substances. They constitute an important group. As early as 1763 tobacco extract was recommended as a control for plant lice (Metcalf and Flint, 1962). It has continued as an important control for piercing-sucking insects. Nicotine is extremely poisonous to warm-blooded animals.

The so-called fixed nicotine compounds act as stomach poisons. The commonest of these are nicotine tannate and nicotine bentonite. Nicotine sulfate also is stable where used in nonalkaline solutions; when mixed in a soap solution or with any other alkaline detergent, free nicotine is released and volatilizes promptly.

Nicotine is used not only as a plant spray but also as a dust. Nicotine dusts are prepared by mixing free nicotine with carriers of various kinds. When dusted on infested plants, the nicotine volatilizes and forms a gas that penetrates the bodies of the insects dusted. Nicotine may be combined with various other insecticides for special purposes. In nurseries and small forest plantations, nicotine sprays or combinations of nicotine and other substances are used to control aphids, tip moths, and other insects. Nicotine sprays are expensive and therefore are used only where cost is not a serious consideration.

Generally, modern synthetic insecticides are used for this purpose today. These are less expensive and often less dangerous to use. Insecticides containing the plant products rotenone and pyrethrins are excellent contact insecticides, but because of their cost they, as well as nicotine, have only limited possibilities for use on forests or forest products. Rotenone and the associated compounds (deguelin, tephrosin, toxicarol, sumatrol, and elliptone) are present in the roots of certain leguminous plants of the genera *Derris* and *Lonchocarpus* in tropical America and also in the roots of *Tephrosia* and *Mundulea* in the tropic of the Eastern Hemisphere. The roots are dried, ground, and used to make insecticidal dusts. The pyrethrins are present in the flowers of certain plants belonging to the genus *Pyrethrum*. The flowers are ground into insecticidal dust, or the active pyrethrins are extracted and concentrated for use in insecticide formulation. All these plant products vary greatly in the amount of toxic materials that they contain. Therefore, in buying either the ground materials or the extracts, one should always know the proportion of active materials.

Inorganic Compounds. Most of the important insecticides in this group are stomach poisons. Their use today is limited in forestry because they have been replaced by the cheaper and often more effective synthetic compounds.

Arsenical insecticides were formerly the most important materials for the treatment of forests and ornamental trees.

Arsenicals that are applied to living plants are always insoluble salts. Copper arsenate, commonly called paris green, was developed earliest but was found to burn the foliage of many trees. Later lead arsenate and calcium arsenate came into general use. In treating forests, calcium arsenate is the form usually preferred, chiefly because it is somewhat cheaper and yet equally as effective as lead arsenate. Calcium arsenate slowly decomposes in the presence of carbon dioxide and water vapor, releasing water-soluble forms of arsenic. This water-soluble arsenic will injure foliage, but in forest treatment the amount of injury has never been of any great consequence.

Calcium arsenate has usually been applied from the air as a dust, but it can be applied with equal effectiveness either by the older methods in dilute suspension or in newer concentrated suspensions by means of the mist blower. For conventional spraying, the usual dilution is 3 pounds per 100 gallons; in concentrated suspensions, from 3 to 6 pounds per gallon may be used. Calcium arsenate may be diluted with equal parts of hydrated lime for ground dusting or used undiluted when applied from the air. The amount needed per acre will vary somewhat with the size and density of the trees but is usually about 20 pounds per acre. The price of calcium arsenate has varied greatly, depending on market conditions and the quantity purchased in a single order.

The water-soluble arsenicals commonly used in baits and for termite control are arsenic trioxide and sodium arsenite. Since all these arsenicals are stomach poisons, the materials must be ingested in order to kill the insects. Most nonarsenical insecticides commonly applied to forests and forest products kill by contact. Some, however, may also act as stomach insecticides.

Fluorine compounds were developed as insecticides to provide substitutes which would not leave highly poisonous residues on edible crops. The two most commonly recognized are sodium fluoride, NaF, and cryolite. Cryolite has low toxicity to mammals and is effective against many chewing insects. These compounds have never been used intensively in forestry.

There are many other inorganic compounds which are toxic to insects and other organisms. Many have been used against agricultural pests but few are of importance today.

Chlorinated Hydrocarbons. DDT, or *dichloro diphenyl trichloroethane,* is the most publicized and the most commonly used insecticide. This synthetic compound was first synthesized in 1874, but its insecticidal properties were not discovered until 1939. This is a remarkable chemical, but actually it has no greater potentialities for insecticidal purposes than several other similar, though lesser known, compounds.

For forest spraying, however, DDT is the most important of all the newer insecticidal materials, chiefly because it has been investigated and experimented with to such an extent that the forest entomologist knows how to use it with confidence. It has been tested against numerous pest species, and its toxicity to many beneficial forms of life has been determined. Therefore, even though other similar materials may be equally good or perhaps better, DDT will remain foremost for forest spraying until some better material has been thoroughly tested.

DDT is a nonvolatile, white, crystalline material that is very soluble in xylene and a number of commercial solvents. It is prepared for spraying as an oil solution, as an oil emulsion, or as a wettable powder.

DDT is almost insoluble in water and is resistant to destruction by light and oxidation. It may, however, be detoxified in its contact effects by ultraviolet radiation. Thus, the material is extremely stable. This characteristic has resulted in many benefits in terms of effective control but also in difficulties due to residue.

Methoxychlor, or *dianisyl trichloroethane,* is an important compound which is closely related to DDT. Methoxychlor gives a more rapid knockdown than does DDT and has a lower toxicity to warm-blooded animals. An important difference is that methoxychlor does not accumulate in animal fats and thus is favored for use on animals and animal forage. It has become an important substitute for DDT in control of the bark-beetle vector of Dutch elm disease chiefly because it is less toxic to birds than DDT.

Benzene hexachloride is commonly used in controlling infestations of wood-infesting insects. The gamma isomer is the form most toxic to insects, and a highly purified product of this isomer, lindane, is on the market. Benzene hexachloride is somewhat more toxic to warm-blooded animals than DDT. It has been highly successful as a control of cryptic forest insects because it has characteristics of a fumigant as well as a contact insecticide. The residual characteristic of this insecticide, according to recent work in California, makes it possible to use it in winter bark-beetle control projects.

There are several other chlorinated hydrocarbons which may be used for special purposes and more will be developed as time goes by. Some of current importance are toxaphene, chlordane, heptachlor, aldrin, dieldrin, endrin, and kepone.

Organophosphorous Insecticides.   The development of the organophosphates has had an important effect on chemical control. There are many insecticides in this group and their applicability is varied. Some have a short residual action as in TEPP and Phosdrin; others, such as Diazinon and Guthion, have a prolonged activity. Parathion has a broad spectrum of activity, whereas schradan is highly selective.

Malathion is one of the organophosphate chemicals that has been used effectively against forest insects. It is one of the safest of all insecticides for human handling and in addition is a persistent, general-purpose insecticide. Diazinon is somewhat more toxic to warm-blooded animals but is also an effective general-purpose insecticide with some characteristics which make it safer to use than DDT.

Many of the organophosphates are systemic in their action; i.e., they can be introduced into the bodies of animals or the sap streams of plants and will kill insects which feed upon the treated organisms. Systox, schradan, and Thimet have been used in this manner to protect plants from sucking insects, tip moths, and mites. Ronnel can be fed to cattle to kill cattle grubs living in their bodies. Dimefox is a phosphoryl fluoride. It has been used effectively against mealybugs. Others are dimethoate, phosdrin, and phosphamidon.

Organophosphorous insecticides have the decided advantage of being detoxified rapidly both when exposed to air and in animal tissues. They are not stored in fatty tissues, as are the chlorinated hydrocarbons. Many of them, such as parathion, are extremely toxic to man and should be used only by highly trained applicators. Some phosphorous materials are used as systemics, and plants so treated may poison browsing animals that eat them.

Carbamate Insecticides.   The carbamate insecticides are a fairly recent development. Some have been tested with success against forest insects and are being used as substitutes for DDT. They do not accumulate in the fats of animals and are rapidly detoxified. Sevin is a good example of a general-purpose insecticide from this group.

Fumigants.   Among the fumigants, several are effective against forest insects. Methyl bromide is often used against termites, powderpost beetles, and other structural pests and for sterilizing soils and treating dormant nursery stock. Such fumigation is widely practiced using either tents of plastic films or fumigation chambers. Ethylene dibromide and orthodichlorobenzene have both been used successfully in bark-beetle controls but may also be used as soil fumigants.

The student is referred to the current volume of "Entoma" and to the most recent volumes of the *Journal of Economic Entomology* for further information on these and the newer materials that are continually appearing on the market.

FIGURE 29. A field mixing site for emulsions used in control of bark beetles. Not far from the edge of a stream in the infested area water is added to an ethylene dibromide concentrate. Such operations must be conducted with care in order to avoid pollution of the stream. (U.S. Dept. Agr. Forest Service.)

New materials are continually being developed. Therefore the student must keep up with the literature in order to be sure he uses the safest and most effective materials. Table 8 illustrates the comparative safety of some of the common insecticides. The Food and Drug Administration registers the insecticides and sets allowable tolerances for various usages.

FORMULATION OF INSECTICIDES

Insecticides other than dusts are usually received from the manufacturer in concentrated form and hence must be diluted or otherwise formulated before being applied. The method used varies with the material and type of equipment.

Dilution for Conventional Spraying.   Since old-type spraying machines can handle only liquid sprays of low viscosity, insecticides applied by them must be diluted with large quantities of water. Some insecticides, like the nicotine compounds, are soluble in water and can be easily diluted to any desired concentration. Other substances which are oils or dissolved

TABLE 8   Comparative Lethal Dosage Values for Common Insecticides

INSECTICIDE	LD50 (RATS), MG PER KG*	METHOD OF ADMINISTRATION
Lead arsenate	825	Oral
Nicotine	30	Oral
Pyrethrin	Nontoxic to mammals	——
Rotenone	25–75	Oral
DDT	200	Oral
DDT	3,000	Contact
Methoxychlor	6,000	Oral
BHC (gamma isomer)	200	Oral
BHC (gamma isomer)	500	Contact
Chlordane	450	Oral
Chlordane	750†	Contact
Heptachlor	90	Oral
Heptachlor	2,000	Contact
Aldrin	67	Oral
Aldrin	150†	Contact
Endrin	10	Oral
TEPP	2	Oral
TEPP	40	Contact
Parathion	6–15	Oral
Parathion	40–50†	Contact
Diazinon	100–150	Oral
Diazinon	1,000	Contact
Malathion	1,400–5,800	Oral
Sevin	5,000†	Contact
Sevin	540	Oral

* Several examples using rabbits are indicated with a dagger.

in oils can be dispersed in water only after being mixed with an emulsifying agent.

Some insecticides are insoluble powders, for example, arsenicals and wettable forms of DDT, benzene hexachloride, and chlordane. These must be mixed with water, a few pounds of the powder with 50 to 100 gallons of water. The suspensions thus formed have a tendency to separate. To avoid this, the larger conventional sprayers have tanks equipped with agitators, which keep the solid particles of powder from settling to the bottom. In small sprayers, frequent shaking during spraying is necessary to avoid separation of the suspension.

Most insecticides must be diluted to make them easier to apply. They seldom are used full strength. Some of the common formulations are:[1]

1. *Dusts* — These are used dry. The toxic material is mixed with or impregnated on organic materials, such as walnut shell flour or fine mineral particles, such as talc or bentonite.

2. *Granular Materials* — These formulations are similar to dusts but have a larger particle size. They are commonly used in dressings on or in soil and may be directly mixed with fertilizers before application. Under some circumstances they are applied from the air.

3. *Wettable Powders* — This material looks like a dust but is generally more concentrated. Wettable powders are meant to be diluted with water and used as sprays. To achieve suspension in water a dispersing and wetting agent is added to the formulation.

4. *Solutions* — Most of the synthetic organic compounds are insoluble in water but can be dissolved in certain organic solvents. Some of these solutions, especially oil solutions, are used directly for insect control but seldom directly on plants by using ground equipment, because of phytotoxic reactions. Oil solutions are, however, applied from the air. In such treatments the phytotoxic action is prevented by the dispersion of the oil particles.

5. *Emulsifiable Concentrates* — This is a common and versatile formulation consisting of the insecticide, a solvent for the insecticide, and an emulsifying agent. This concentrate mixed with water forms an emulsion of the oil-in-water type. Since the quantity of solvent is small, these sprays may be used directly on plants from ground equipment. Emulsions are not stable and will eventually "break" into their component parts. Thoroughly shaking the container will return the formulation to its proper form.

6. *Insecticidal Aerosols*[2] — Aerosols are minute particles suspended in air as a fog or mist. This may be accomplished by burning, vaporizing with heat, atomizing mechanically, or, as in the case of the aerosol bomb, releasing with a liquefied gas.

7. *Fumigants* — Insecticides that are effective in their gaseous form are often formulated as liquids under pressure. Methyl bromide is one of these. When released into air the material rapidly volatilizes. Some fumigant gases are released chemically. Hydrogen cyanide, for example, is released by dropping a cyanide salt into dilute acid.

[1] Adapted from R. E. Pfadt (ed.): "Fundamentals of Applied Entomology," 1962, with permission of The Macmillan Company.
[2] Users of either aerosols or compressed liquefied gases should be warned against transporting these materials by air at high elevations unless they are in very strong containers. Lowered atmospheric pressure may cause containers to leak or explode with disastrous results. For example, the small cans of methylbromide now being sold should never be transported by air.

Addition of Spreaders and Adhesives.   Since water is characterized by high surface tension, aqueous sprays tend to form droplets and run off the foliage. To avoid this, various kinds of spreading or wetting agents are added to aqueous solutions and suspensions. These substances reduce the surface tension of the water and cause the liquid to spread over the surface, thus preventing excessive runoff. A few of the materials thus used also act as adhesives, causing the insecticides to stick to the foliage.

All water-soluble emulsifying agents also act as spreaders. Soap is readily available as an effective spreading agent. It has the objectionable characteristic of combining with calcium or magnesium salts to form insoluble solids. Therefore, the amount of soap needed will depend upon the "hardness" of the water. Tests should be made to determine the quantity necessary for the water used. Enough soap to produce a suds will be sufficient. Six pounds per 100 gallons of water is the quantity most often required. Other spreading agents are usually added to the spray solution at the rate of 1 pound per 100 gallons. Some of these spreading agents are calcium caseinate, various sulfonated alcohols, sulfonated castor oil, sodium lauryl sulfate, alkylphenyl benzene sulfonic acid, butylhydroxyphenyl benzene sulfonate, and other organic materials. Many of these spreaders were developed for use as detergents in the textile industry. These organic substances are sold under various trade names too numerous to mention. (See the current issue of "Entoma.")

Raw linseed oil, fish oil, cottonseed oil, soybean oil, and some petroleum oils are often added to sprays to increase adherence of the insecticide. Calcium caseinate, mentioned above, also acts as an adhesive when added to sprays.

Dilutions for Concentrated Sprays.   When sprays are to be distributed by fog machines, mist blowers, or from the air, the materials are diluted as little as possible. Arsenical powders are diluted at the rate of 3 to 6 pounds per gallon. Some of the synthetic organic wettable powders are diluted to similar heavy suspensions when distributed by air blast or as a mist. Wettable DDT and benzene hexachloride, for example, are usually diluted for this purpose at the rate of 1 pound in enough water to make 1 gallon of finished solution.

Strong solutions of chemicals in oils are sprayed on the bark of trees or logs to kill bark beetles. A 12 percent solution of orthodichlorobenzene in diesel oil or fuel oil applied with conventional sprayers is a common mixture for bark-beetle control.

Oil solutions utilizing ethylene dibromide or BHC are also effective against bark beetles. Emulsions are also used against bark beetles. For example, a recommended insecticide to control the northern spruce beetle consists of an emulsifiable concentrate and water. The concentrate consists of ethylene dibromide, emulsifiers, and fuel oil (Massey et al., 1953).

Dilutions for aerial spraying are usually concentrated oil solutions of DDT, but emulsions of this chemical may be applied for special reasons. Emulsions, although very effective as insecticides, are usually not advised for forest spraying because of their adverse effects on valuable animal life. A common DDT formulation is 100 pounds of DDT dissolved in 25 gallons of xylene or other solvent, with enough fuel oil added to make 100 gallons of finished spray. This is approximately a 12 percent solution of the insecticide, or 1 pound per gallon.

FIGURE 30. Helicopter spraying of a hemlock looper infestation in Washington. Spray deposits can be precisely controlled by using this equipment. (Washington State Department of Natural Resources.)

The stock solution of DDT may be emulsified by adding to each 12.5 gallons of solution 1 pint of an emulsifying agent. Water is then added to make 50 gallons of finished emulsion. These concentrated solutions and emulsions should not be applied with conventional sprayers on living trees, or serious injury will result. Furthermore, in spraying forests the quantity of insecticide per unit of area must be kept at the minimum needed to kill the pest. Otherwise unnecessary injury to desirable forms of life may result.

Wettable powders of DDT are commercially prepared insecticides, manufactured by grinding DDT crystals with an inert powder that is easily wet with water. The percentage of DDT in these powders is always indicated on the package and must be taken into consideration in calculating dosages.

The amount of DDT required to control forest pests varies to some extent. Fortunately a very light treatment will kill most insects. One pound per acre is effective against Saratoga spittlebug, *Aphrophora saratogensis;* spruce budworm, *Choristoneura fumiferana;* gypsy moth, *Porthetria dispar;* and many other forest pests. Even lower dosages are effective in controlling mosquitoes and flies. Occasionally as much as 2 pounds per acre are applied to small areas for special purposes, but in widespread operations on forests 1 pound per acre is all that should be permitted.

For Soil Poisoning. Insecticides for poisoning root-eating insects are mixed with the top few inches of the soil, where they kill the insects either by contact or by being eaten. Inert substances not only kill the insects present at the time of application but also prevent reinfestation by poisoning the soil for a year or more. Many chemicals have been employed for such use: DDT, chlordane, benzene hexachloride, and some arsenicals, especially calcium arsenate. Soil poisoning is too expensive to use in forest plantations but has a possible place in the control of insects in forest nurseries.

A specialized application has been developed for control of white grubs in plantations. Aldrin may be applied directly to the roots of the plants from an attachment on the planting machines. This procedure is very inexpensive and has given excellent results.

Most of the tests of soil poisoning have been applied to lawns, golf greens, and similar situations rather than to forest nurseries. Therefore, the recommendations that have been published cannot be accepted without reservations by the forest entomologist. Those tests that have been made in forest nurseries demonstrated that the effects on plants growing on the poisoned soil vary from place to place. Thus in some nurseries a treatment may be safe while in others injury to the young trees results. Calcium arsenate, for example, can be used safely on lawns growing on fertile soils but is unsafe in forest nurseries. The reason for this is clear. On fertile soils, the small quantity of soluble arsenic released by the gradual decomposition of the arsenical is adsorbed on the surface of colloidal particles. Therefore it cannot be absorbed by the sensitive plant roots. On forest nursery soils, because they are usually acidic and low in colloids, the soluble arsenic does not become bound and is absorbed by the tree roots. Treatment with arsenicals may, therefore, ruin a forest nursery. Thus the use of arsenic on nursery soils is not advisable. General recommendations for treatment to prevent white grub damage are presented in Stoeckeler and Jones (1957).

In places where soil insecticides are safe, they provide the nurseryman with a powerful weapon against soil-inhabiting insects. On the other hand, if they injure the seedlings, the characteristics of stability may put a poisoned soil out of production for many years. Therefore, a nurseryman should be advised to test any soil insecticide that he may plan to use on a small plot before applying it extensively. By so doing, he can determine definitely whether or not the substance is suited to conditions in his nursery.

Formulation of Baits.   Some insects, such as cutworms and grasshoppers, can be injurious to small trees in nurseries or newly established plantations. These insects and some other organisms are attracted to and feed upon various baits. By the addition of a poison to these attractive mixtures, the organisms can be killed. Many bait formulations are effective.

Some of the common insecticides used are paris green, sodium arsenite, sodium fluosilicate, benzene hexachloride, chlordane, toxaphene, aldrin, dieldrin, and parathion.

The following are representative formulas suggested by Craighead (1950):

Bait for Cutworms

Coarse wheat bran	100 lb
Sodium fluosilicate	4 lb
Water (enough to moisten)	10–12 gal

The poison is mixed in the water and the resulting suspension used to moisten the bran. The bait should be sprinkled over the nursery at the rate of approximately 30 pounds per acre.

Bait for Grasshoppers

Mill-run bran, mixed feed, or shorts	25 lb
Sawdust	3.5 bu
or	
Standard bran	50 lb
Sawdust	2.5 bu
or	
Bran	100 lb
To one of the above add:	
Chlordane (50 percent wettable powder)	1 lb
or	
Toxaphene	2 lb
Water (enough to dampen)	10–12 gal

Any of these baits can be most conveniently blended in a mechanical mixer; when done by hand, the dry ingredients may be spread on a tight floor and turned over with a shovel until thoroughly blended. Then water should be sprinkled a little at a time over the mixture to moisten it. The bait should be distributed at the rate of 10 to 15 pounds per acre. When finished, baits should be moist but not lumpy.

SIDE EFFECTS OF INSECTICIDES

No insecticide can be applied in the forest so that its effects will be entirely restricted to the pest against which it is directed. Inevitably some associated organisms will be injured. When we use poisons against noxious insects, our objective should be to minimize, as far as possible, injury to desirable forms of life.

Most people were completely unaware of the serious problems associated with the widespread use of pesticides until the publication of Rachel Carson's book "Silent Spring" in 1962. This very readable book on an important subject has been a bestseller in the United States. Its effect generally has been good because it has resulted in an increased awareness of the need for research on chemical effects and for care in the handling and use of pesticides. All Americans can be thankful that the book has not resulted in widespread banning of *essential chemicals*. Fortunately, many of the evils referred to in "Silent Spring" have already been corrected and other safeguards are being considered. This is not the place to discuss the many facets of the insecticidal use problem, but the reader is advised to read "Silent Spring" and other materials on this problem. The National Academy of Sciences, National Research Council (1963) has published a series of three bulletins on pest control and wildlife relationships which present the problem as related to wildlife in considerable detail.

Effects on Parasitic and Predatory Insects. The parasitic and predatory insects are, as a rule, little affected by stomach insecticides. On the other hand, they may be seriously affected when exposed to contact poisons. This undesirable effect of contact insecticides is difficult or impossible to avoid. Only by making the insecticidal application at a time when a minimum of parasite adults are in flight can the adverse effects be ameliorated.

Not infrequently, pests exhibit differential degrees of susceptibility to certain insecticides. For example, aphids and spider mites are less susceptible to DDT than are their parasites and predators. As a result of this fact, aphids and mites sometimes increase enormously following forest spraying with DDT. The explanation is obvious. Most of the insect predators and parasites are killed while only a part of the aphids or mites are destroyed. The surviving pests reproduce rapidly and reach excessive numbers before the surviving or immigrating parasites and predators can increase sufficiently to control them. These outbreaks that result from the application of insecticides are usually sporadic and sub-side before serious damage to the forest results.

Effects on Terrestrial Vertebrates.   Since DDT has proved to be espe-cially valuable for spraying forests, there has been a tendency toward undertaking tremendously large forest-spraying projects. Because areas of 100,000 acres can be treated without difficulty, the trend has been toward larger and larger projects. Although the large spraying operations are efficient and usually far cheaper per acre than smaller projects, they have their disadvantages, as we shall see later.

Fear has frequently been expressed that widespread spraying may have a deleterious effect upon forest vertebrates. As a result, much effort has been directed toward measuring the effects of various insecticides, espe-cially DDT, upon birds and mammals. No direct injury to mammals has thus far been demonstrated, but some adverse effects upon birds have been observed when repeated doses of DDT have been applied (Robbins, 1951). Apparently moderate doses are only slightly injurious (Kendeigh, 1947).

Of all the possible synthetic organic insecticides that might be used, only DDT has been adequately tested in its effects on vertebrates. George (1948) found that considerable injury to birds resulted from the applica-tion of 4 pounds per acre to low-growing, woody, and herbaceous vegeta-tion. Wrens, warblers, chats, grosbeaks, and buntings were almost elim-inated, while cuckoos, tree-inhabiting warblers, and vireos were less affected. In a forest the injury would have been less owing to the inter-ception of much of the spray by the upper tree crowns.

George (1948) also demonstrated that nesting birds may be killed if they are fed exclusively upon DDT-poisoned insects; if poisoned and unpoisoned insects are mixed, the nestlings show no apparent ill effects. Since the usual dosage of 1 pound per acre does not kill all insects in treated forest areas, neither young nor adult birds appeared to suffer serious adverse effects. These findings support those of Hoffmann and Linduska (1949) and the field studies of Kendeigh in Ontario. It is clear, however, that DDT dosages in forests in excess of 2 pounds per acre are likely to produce adverse effects upon birds. Reptiles and amphibians are apparently somewhat more susceptible than are birds, but very little specific information is available on the reactions of cold-blooded terrestrial vertebrates to DDT or other insecticides.

Effects on Aquatic Organisms.   Application of DDT at 1 pound per acre destroys a large proportion of the insect life in streams, but only certain kinds of fish are directly affected. Some bottom-feeding fish in trout streams are killed as are some surface-feeding fish. Trout, however, are usually unaffected, even when their insect food is destroyed. Accord-ing to Adams et al. (1949) these fish are capable of changing their food habits and temporarily feed upon organisms that are not killed by the DDT. Heavier dosages of DDT are directly injurious to trout, $2\frac{1}{2}$ pounds per acre being fatal to some individuals. Dosages as low as ½ pound per acre have killed young of the Atlantic salmon in New Brunswick.

Information on the effects of DDT on aquatic organisms is conflicting. We must conclude, however, that these organisms, as a rule, are far more susceptible to DDT than are terrestrial vertebrates. But damage done to lakes and streams is usually but not always corrected within a season by immigration of new organisms and reproduction of survivors.

Tests of various DDT formulations have clearly demonstrated that emulsions are far more toxic to aquatic animals than are oil solutions. This effect is probably due to the capacity of the emulsion to mix with water and thus carry the poison into direct contact with free-swimming animals. Much of the oil solution, on the other hand, because it floats on the water surface, is carried away and accumulates on emergent vegetation or along the shores, where it can contact comparatively few organisms.

Some other chlorinated hydrocarbons are far more toxic than DDT, as we have already seen. The use of these in widespread forest spraying should be avoided. Sometimes chlorinated hydrocarbons applied at dosages that cause no direct injury to animals may be concentrated by earthworms in the soil or plankton organisms in water so that animals higher in the food chain may receive a lethal dose. Much research is needed before final conclusions can be drawn concerning the seriousness of these side effects from certain toxicants, but experiences illustrate that caution is needed in the widespread use of pesticides. Other insecticides may become more important in forest spraying especially along streams, where DDT has caused severe losses to fish and fish foods. For example, Sevin, a carbamate, has been tested intensively (Burdick et al., 1960). It caused no fish mortality but caused drastic reductions in fish food. Sevin is practically harmless to terrestrial wildlife and is not stored in fat (Connor, 1960).

Effects on the Soil. Accumulations of DDT in the soil kill not only injurious soil-inhabiting insects but also many beneficial species. No serious effects from ordinary dosages, however, have been observed on nitrifying organisms. Nevertheless, we must suspect that serious injury is likely to result from heavy accumulations of DDT or other stable compounds.

Hoffmann and Linduska (1949) emphasize this point when they say,

There are still many unknowns regarding the biological effects of the many new economic poisons. With reference to DDT and its remarkable stability under some conditions, one of the most critical needs is for a better understanding of the hazards implied by possible cumulative action. Studies now under way should bring enlightenment regarding this possibility, not only as it could affect humans and wildlife populations, but fundamentally the soil and plant life.

We know that the chlorinated hydrocarbons remain active for long periods of time, that they do accumulate in the soil, and, that they may be responsible for important ecological changes.

NEW DEVELOPMENTS IN CONTROL

Integrated Pest Control. Many ecologists believe that the use of the integrated pest-control approach is a necessity in both agriculture and forestry. We all recognize the dangers associated with the use of chemicals, but the solution is not through the elimination of chemicals in pest control. Our hope lies in more knowledge and greater discrimination in the use of pesticides to forestall undesirable side effects. Integrated pest control has already proved to be of value in several instances.

This is not a new procedure, for economic entomologists have been practicing it for many years. However, in recent years it has received more emphasis. Integrated control is simply applied pest control which integrates biological and chemical measures into a single unified program (Smith, 1963; Smith et al., 1962). Such a procedure requires a thorough knowledge of the ecological relationships in the areas in which a pest population lives.

Smith (1963) describes three basic principles of integrated pest control.

1. *Consider the Ecosystem* — The total complex of organisms, both plant and animal, the ecosystem, must be considered as a unit.

2. *Utilize Economic Levels* — The population levels at which a pest species causes damage or creates a nuisance must be precisely determined. Control is applied only when needed to keep the population below these injurious economic levels. This procedure contrasts markedly to treatments by the calendar, which are so common in agriculture and horticulture.

3. *Avoid Disruptive Actions* — This principle requires that control be designed to be adequate in a manner which does not upset other portions of the ecosystem and thus create additional problems. Sometimes this may mean that the cheapest procedure cannot be utilized. Involved here is the selective use of insecticides, augmentation of natural enemies, and close supervision by highly trained individuals.

Integrated control has been very effective where carefully applied. This procedure has a great deal of promise for the control of forest insects.

Other Approaches to Direct Control. In recent years a number of new procedures, many of them chemical in nature, have been proposed for use in insect control. These are discussed by Knipling (1959, 1960, 1964) and Hall et al. 1963).

Probably the greatest success story concerns the use of the sterile male technique in eradication of the screw-wormfly, *Callitroga hominivorax*, from the island of Curaçao and from portions of the southeastern United

States. The method, in brief, involves the release of large numbers of sterile males into the native population. In the successful projects against the screw-wormfly the males were sterilized by radiation. However, for some purposes such sterilization is not practical, and for some of these the use of chemical sterilants shows promise. Chemosterilization also offers promise of inducing sterility in natural populations. This would be important for those populations where the rearing of large numbers of sterile males for release is impractical or perhaps impossible. Only a beginning has been made in developing sterilization techniques. They will require a great amount of research before their potential value can be fully appraised.

Another development of outstanding promise is in the use of sex attractants. Many insects, especially the Lepidoptera, have sex-attractant glands, the secretions from which enable the male to find the female for mating. These attractants have been isolated from several species and have been used for survey purposes for many years. The sex attractants of the gypsy moth, *Porthetria dispar,* has been useful in making surveys of this species. Recently, a similar attractant called Gyplure has been synthesized. It is commercially available at very low cost and seems to be as attractive as the natural material.

Coppel et al. (1960) reported on a sex attractant for the introduced pine sawfly, *Diprion similis* (Hartig). They reported one caged female attracting well over 11,000 males.

Sex attractants have been used in survey work, but it is expected that control procedures utilizing them will soon be developed. For example, males could be trapped in great numbers, be treated with a sterilant, and then be released. Another suggestion for utilizing sex attractants may have possibilities (Babson, 1963). If a dilute solution of an attractant were sprayed over an area, the males might become so confused as to be unable to locate the females except by chance.

LIMITATIONS OF CHEMICAL CONTROL

Control of forest insects by means of chemicals has a strong popular appeal, partly because some of its fundamental limitations are not immediately apparent. Nevertheless, these limitations must be recognized by the forester if he is to approach insect problems intelligently.

Temporary Character of Treatment. One of the more conspicuous limitations of chemical control is the temporary character of its effects. The treatment does not improve forest conditions in respect to insect susceptibility. A few weeks after treatment, the trees are as subject to new infestations as they were before. Therefore, we have no guarantee that the application of chemicals will not be required again within a few years, since the same causal conditions that gave rise to the original outbreak are apt to be still present. If we are to rely on chemical control, we must recognize the probability that frequent treatments will be required during a tree rotation.

The exception will be a situation where a certain age-class of trees is attacked by a pest immediately prior to the time when such trees will grow out of a susceptible condition. For instance, serious injury by the Saratoga spittlebug is limited to that period after the pines have reached

FIGURE 31. The mist blower may be used in seed orchards for control of cone-infesting insects. (U.S. Dept. Agr. Forest Service.)

a height of 3 to 4 feet but before the crowns close in and kill the ground cover. Spraying immediately prior to closure, therefore, would be likely to carry the trees through the few remaining years of high susceptibility.

Resistance of Certain Insect Races. Repeated treatment of an insect population with an insecticidal material is likely to result in developing resistant strains that cannot be controlled by the poison. For example, the San Jose scale, *Aspidiotus perniciosus,* a serious pest of fruit trees, developed a marked resistance to lime-sulfur sprays that formerly had produced good control. Similarly the codling moth, *Carpocapsa pomonella,* has developed great resistance to arsenical sprays, so that new insecticides for this species have been required in some localities. This phenomenon has produced in some strains of the housefly a great resistance to DDT, a characteristic which has continued through many generations. The same is true of mosquitoes and other insect pests that receive repeated treatments.

Presumably this building up of resistance is the result of selection by the insecticide, susceptible individuals being killed and nonsusceptible individuals surviving. The progeny of the survivors are also likely to be nonsusceptible, so that after several repeated applications of the same insecticide resistant races appear. This phenomenon has been observed repeatedly, and entomologists recommend that different insecticides be used in successive treatments in order to avoid developing resistant strains. Unfortunately the development of resistance to one of a group of chemicals may result in resistance to other related chemicals.

Effects on the Biotic Balance. Since we cannot treat one insect species with insecticides without, at the same time, injuring others, we must conclude that spraying has a marked influence upon the normal condition of biotic balance. We have referred to a temporary situation of this sort when outbreaks of aphids or spider mites have followed treatments with DDT.

Disturbances of this kind are likely to be temporary if only a few square miles of forest are treated and those only occasionally. On the other hand, repeated treatments of extensive forest areas could so change the biotic conditions that more and more frequent spraying would become necessary. A similar situation in orchard practice may be cited. During the decade following 1910, three applications of spray were sufficient to control most orchard pests. Today from eight to twelve treatments are necessary to control the same group of pests. Unless we recognize the limitations and hazards of forest spraying, we may find ourselves in a position comparable to that of the orchardist.

A Realistic Viewpoint. Insecticides provide the forester with a powerful weapon against forest insects. If intelligently and conservatively used, it can save, for man's purposes, millions of trees that otherwise might be destroyed by insects. On the other hand, when carelessly or unwisely used, insecticides have the potentialities of great injury to valuable organisms and the serious disruption of the biotic balance.

For these reasons *insecticides must be used with caution and only when and where they are required to save losses that otherwise could not be avoided.* The promiscuous application of insecticides to forests cannot be justified.

BIBLIOGRAPHY CHAPTER 10

Adams, L., G. H. Mitchell, and N. W. Hosley, 1949. Effect on fish, birds, and mammals of DDT, *J. Wildlife Management,* 13: 245–254.

Babers, F. H., and J. J. Pratt, Jr., 1951. Development of insect resistance to insecticides (review of literature), *U.S. Dept. Agr., Bur. Entomol. P. Q.,* E-818.

Babson, A. L., 1963. Eradicating the gypsy moth, *Science,* 142: 447.

Barber, George W., and J. B. Schmitt, 1949. Resistance to DDT in housefly, *J. Econ. Entomol.,* 42: 287–292.

Burdick, G. E., H. F. Dean, and E. F. Harris, 1960. Effect of Sevin upon the aquatic environment, *N.Y. Fish Game J.,* 7: 14–25.

Carson, Rachel, 1962. "Silent Spring," Houghton Mifflin Company, Boston.

Chisholm, R. D., and L. Koblinsky, 1947. Light and DDT residues, *Agr. Chem.,* 2: 35–37.

———, et al., 1950. DDT accumulation in soil, *J. Econ. Entomol.,* 43: 941–942.

Connor, P. F., 1960. A study of small mammals, birds and other wildlife in an area sprayed with Sevin, *N.Y. Fish Game J.,* 7: 26–32.

Coppel, H. C., J. E. Casida, and W. C. Dauterman, 1960. Evidence for a potent sex attractant in the introduced pine sawfly, *Diprion similis, Ann. Entomol. Soc. Am.,* 53: 510.

Craighead, F. C., 1950. Insect enemies of Eastern forests, *U.S. Dept. Agr. Misc. Publ.* 657.

"Entoma." A directory of pesticide materials, equipment, and services, published by the Entomological Society of America. Source for this text, 14th ed. 1961–1962.

Gambrell, F. L., 1950. Control of grubs in nurseries, *J. Econ. Entomol.,* 43: 550–551.

George, J. G., 1948. The effect of DDT-treated insects on nesting birds *J. Econ. Entomol.,* 40: 782–789.

Hall, S. A., et al., 1963. New approaches to pest control and eradication, Symposium, American Chemical Society, *Advan. Chem. Ser.* 41.

Hoffmann, C. H., and E. P. Merkel, 1948. Fluctuations in insect populations following aerial applications of DDT, *J. Econ. Entomol.,* 41: 464–473.

———, and J. P. Linduska, 1949. The biological effects of DDT, *Sci. Monthly,* 69: 104–114.

Kendeigh, S. C., 1947. DDT on birds, *Ontario (Canada) Dept. Lands Forests, Div. Res., Biol. Bull.* 1.

Knipling, E. F., 1959. Sterile-male method of population control, *Science,* 130: 902–904.

———, 1960. Use of insects for their own destruction. *J. Econ. Entomol.,* 53: 415–420.

———, 1964. The potential role of the sterility method for insect-population control with special reference to combining this method with conventional methods, *U.S. Dept. Agr., Agr. Res. Serv.,* ARS-33-98.

Larrimer, W. H., et al., 1962–1963. Pest control and wildlife relationships, Part I, Evaluation of pesticide-wildlife problems; Part II, Policy and procedures for pest control; Part III, Research needs, *Nat. Acad. Sci., Nat. Res. Council Publ.* 920 A, 920 B, 920 C.

Massey, C. L., R. D. Chisholm, and N. D. Wygant, 1953. Chemical control of the Engelmann spruce beetle in Colorado, *J. Econ. Entomol.,* **46:** 952–955.

Metcalf, C. L., W. P. Flint, and R. L. Metcalf, 1962. "Destructive and Useful Insects," 4th ed., McGraw-Hill Book Company, New York.

Pfadt, R. E., 1962. "Fundamentals of Applied Entomology," The Macmillan Company, New York.

Robbins, C. S., et al., 1951. Effect on birds of DDT application for five seasons, *J. Wildlife Management,* **15:** 213–216.

Sheals, R. A., 1947. Airplane spraying for gypsy moth control, *J. Forestry,* **45:** 712–714.

Shread, J. C., 1948. Comparative toxicity tests with DDT, benzene hexachloride, chlorinated camphene, etc., useful against soil inhabiting insects, *J. Econ. Entomol.,* **41:** 318–324.

Simkover, H. G., and R. D. Schenefelt, 1951. Effect of benzene hexachloride and chlordane upon soil organisms, *J. Econ. Entomol.,* **44:** 426–427.

Smith, Ray F., 1963. Principles of integrated pest control, *Proc. North Central Branch Entomol. Soc. Am.,* **18:** 71–77.

———, B. P. Beirne, R. L. Rabb, F. B. Knight, and H. F. Schoof, 1962. Integration of biological and chemical control, *Symp., Bull. Entomol. Soc. Am.,* **8:** 188–201.

St. George, R. A., H. R. Johnston, and R. J. Kowal, 1960. Subterranean termites, their prevention and control in buildings, *U.S. Dept Agr. Home Garden Bull.* 64.

Sternburg, James, and C. W. Kearns, 1950. Degradation of DDT by resistant flies, *Ann. Entomol. Soc. Am.,* **43:** 444–458.

Stoeckeler, J. H., and G. W. Jones, 1957. Forest nursery practice in the Lake States, *U.S. Dept. Agr., Forest Serv., Agr. Handbook* 110.

Wilson, J. K., 1946. Effects of DDT on soil microbes, *J. Econ. Entomol.,* **39:** 537–538.

CHAPTER **11**

METHODS
OF
INDIRECT
CONTROL

The control of forest insects by direct methods described in preceding chapters is, in its very nature, expensive. Furthermore, these methods are curative and are emergency in character, designed to save materials that are immediately threatened. They neither produce permanent improvement in forest conditions nor reduce the probability of future outbreaks. In contrast, the indirect type of control, which will now be discussed, is preventive rather than curative. The effects are relatively permanent, in that they create long-lasting conditions that restrict the increase and spread of potentially injurious insects. Indirect control will cover all those procedures that are designed to prevent damage to forests by insects.

Indirect control must usually be applied before the pest becomes epidemic. Therefore, it may not be so spectacular as spraying from an airplane flying 50 feet above the treetops, but it is quite as effective and far more economical. The application of indirect control calls for a thorough understanding of the habits of the pests, their relation to other associated organisms, and their reactions to the physical elements of their environment. Needless to say, our knowledge is not always sufficiently complete to make possible the application of indirect methods to all problems, but much progress in this direction has been made—far more, in fact, than is sometimes realized.

For many years indirect-control measures have had a place in the protection of freshly cut wood. More recently, these measures have been applied to the control of insects attacking living trees. In the following chapters are discussed some of the important indirect methods that have actually been applied to the control of insects of forests and forest products and some that show promise. The discussion of indirect control will be divided into four parts: (1) prevention of spread; (2) modification of nutritional and physical conditions: food supply, moisture, temperature; (3) use of parasites and predators; (4) application of silvicultural practices.

PREVENTION OF SPREAD

A list of the forest pests of the United States and Canada includes numerous enemies that have been introduced from foreign lands. Outstanding among them are the gypsy moth, *Porthetria dispar;* the poplar and willow borer, *Cryptorhynchus lapathi;* the European spruce sawfly, *Diprion (Gilpina) hercyniae;* the elm leaf beetle, *Galerucella xanthomelaena;* the larch casebearer, *Coleophora laricella;* and possibly the larch sawfly, *Pristiphora erichsonii.* The great majority of these unwelcome immigrants reached America prior to 1912.

In addition to these immigrants, some of our native species have expanded their range to include localities from which they were originally absent. In an effort to check this invasion and spread of pests, regulations have been adopted by both Federal and state governments providing for quarantines and embargoes to prevent invasion of new pests and inspection and certification to ensure that products in commerce are not infested with dangerous insects.

Legislative Approach. The first quarantine act was passed by the Congress of the United States in 1912. Since that time other acts, complemented by similar legislation in Canada and Mexico, have implemented national inspection and quarantine systems until a high degree of efficiency has been attained (Strong, 1938). In line with Federal legislation, the various states have enacted laws to control the movement of plants or plant products that might harbor dangerous pests.

Prior to 1912, plant products of all kinds could be moved freely both into and within the United States. As a result of low costs in Europe, nursery stock of all sorts was propagated overseas later to be shipped to American nurseries as lining-out stock. Some conifers, such as Colorado blue spruce, were grown in Europe to the height of a foot or more before being shipped with the roots balled in earth. Without inspection or any restrictions on movement of stock from infested to uninfested areas, the number of introduced pests grew at an alarming rate and action became imperative.

Laws regulating the movement of plants may be grouped into two general categories: (1) quarantines and embargoes and (2) inspection and certification (Wardle, 1929). No attempt will be made here to discuss the specific legislative acts. This has been effectively covered by Popham (1958). In the following two sections we shall present only the objectives and the results that may be expected.

Quarantines and Embargoes. Quarantines are designed to regulate the movement of products from one locality to another in such a manner that the introduction of pests into uninfested localities will be either prevented or retarded. Embargoes prohibit the entry of products from localities where a certain pest is known to occur. Quarantines prohibit movements except under specific restrictions that are deemed adequate to prevent spread of undesirable pests. For example, a shipment may be placed in quarantine at port of entry until it has received treatment, such as fumigation or dipping, in order to destroy any pests contained therein. Or a shipment may be planted temporarily in a quarantined area until close inspection demonstrates the presence or absence of pests. If free from infestation, the plants may then be distributed into uninfested territory. If infested, they are destroyed or treated to eliminate the pests.

Embargoes prohibit entirely the movement of products from one locality to another. They are applied to products that cannot be effectively inspected and that grow in localities known to be infested. For example, there is a strict embargo against importing any plants with roots balled in earth. Embargoes on localities are usually temporary and are lifted when it is considered safe to do so. Quarantines and embargoes are used both between the United States and other countries and among the various states. Occasionally they may be applied to areas within a state.

Inspection and Certification. Plant products entering the United States and Canada are all subject to governmental inspection at port of entry. If found free of dangerous pests, they are then permitted to enter. If infested, they are destroyed or, if practicable, treated to eliminate the infestation. Similarly, importations into states are subject to state inspection. The task of inspecting all forest products moving in commerce would be stupendous and would require a force of men entirely out of reason. In order to reduce the task of inspection of individual shipments, therefore, certification may be made at the point from which a shipment originates. After nurseries have taken all prescribed precautions and made all required treatments, they are given an examination and, if free from dangerous pests, a certificate for one season is issued covering their stock. A copy of this certificate must be attached to each individual shipment. In order to implement this law, common carriers are forbidden to accept any living plant materials that do not bear a certificate of inspection unless such shipment is routed through an inspection office.

Pros and Cons of Regulations.   The combined enforcement of all these regulations has resulted in tremendous benefits. One of the most important results has been the elimination of infestations at source, both within the United States and abroad. The probability that an infested shipment will be detected, confiscated, and destroyed has greatly discouraged carelessness on the part of nurserymen and importers. Undoubtedly the regulations have prevented the introduction of many pests and have retarded the spread of those already here.

The enforcement of regulations has been efficient and for the most part effective in both national and local services. Nevertheless, we cannot expect that any pest can be permanently excluded from any locality where suitable conditions prevail. No matter how careful an inspector may be,

FIGURE 32. Fumigation chamber attached to a greenhouse. Plants may be fumigated in such chambers before shipment to field planting sites. An inexpensive means for preventing spread of pest organisms. (Courtesy Institute of Paper Chemistry, Wisconsin.)

there is the ever-present danger that some pest may escape his eye. Also, an insect that is relatively innocuous in its native habitat may become injurious when introduced into a new locality. The inspector may not be warned against one of these and, therefore, may fail to observe its presence. When human frailty is considered, the quality of the inspection services deserves the highest commendation; nevertheless, we must recognize the weaknesses inherent in the system. We must expect every potential pest ultimately to reach every suitable point on the earth, regardless of our efforts. However, if through the enforcement of intelligent regulations the spread of pests into new areas can be retarded, the enforcement services will have justified themselves.

Since we cannot expect inspection to be perfect, there are certain precautions that foresters should observe: (1) The movement of planting stock outside the natural range of a species should be discouraged. (2) Within their natural range, living trees should never be moved from an area infested with a dangerous pest into an uninfested area. (3) Whenever a species is to be introduced into a new locality, it should be grown there from seed. (4) Local nurseries should be established to serve each general locality. (5) Insofar as practicable, nursery windbreaks should be of species not grown in the nursery. These precautions, supplementing the enforcement of statutory regulations discussed above, will help prevent the movement of pests from an infested locality to another that is uninfested.

MODIFICATION OF FOOD SUPPLY

For control purposes, the food supply of an insect may be modified in three different ways: It (1) may be made inaccessible by erecting either chemical or mechanical barriers, (2) may be made less available by reducing its actual quantity, (3) may be made unavailable by changing its composition. Various methods of obtaining these modifications will now be discussed.

Inaccessibility through Barriers. Although the use of chemical barriers in the control of wood and tree insects has not been developed to a high degree of efficiency, it has been demonstrated that many of the common spray materials may be used in this way. A number of them have a decided repellent effect upon insects, for example, Bordeaux mixture, lime sulfur, iron sulfate, various organic compounds, and to a certain extent, even whitewash. All these repel insects for a time after they are applied. In addition to these materials, there are a number of tree paints on the market that are intended to give protection from insect attack. Caution should be exercised in selecting proprietary repellents, as some of them are valueless and some are actually injurious. In general, the use of paints should be avoided, although a few acceptable washes have been developed. Generally, washes are tedious to apply, and usually several treatments during a single season are required.

In the protection of trees from insect attack, mechanical barriers are often used. In Europe such barriers have found a place in timber forests; in America, because of high cost, their use is confined to ornamental trees. Sticky bands encircling the trunk are used to prevent defoliating insects from climbing to the foliage from the ground. This method is widely used on ornamental trees to control cankerworms, tussock moths, the gypsy moth, and other insects that spend a part of their lives on the ground and move to the treetops by creeping up the trunks. The commercial material called "tree tanglefoot" is convenient to use for this purpose, as it can be purchased ready for use in any desired quantity. Workers in the U.S. Department of Agriculture have developed an excellent formula that is somewhat less expensive than tanglefoot (Collins, 1920). To be effective, all bands should be watched closely to ensure renewal whenever they lose their sticky quality.

In the protection of forest products, particularly seasoned materials, the use of mechanical barriers is important. For instance, one of the most efficacious barriers against insect infestation is an unbroken coat of paint or varnish covering the surface of susceptible wood. This is particularly effective against dry-wood insects, for example, the lyctus powderpost beetles (Snyder, 1926). Because these beetles deposit their eggs in the open pores of seasoned hardwood lumber, a coat of paint or varnish that closes these pores prevents infestation.

Reducing Quantity of Food.   Reduction in the quantity of food available for insect pests offers an effective means of insect control, especially in the protection of forest products. This may be accomplished in several different ways. Three of the most usual are by prompt utilization, by barking freshly cut logs, and by the disposal of waste materials. These methods are discussed in the following paragraphs.

Prompt utilization of logs and other forest products is one of the most obvious methods of preventing insect injury to this class of materials, but it is surprising how often the importance of this simple means of protection is overlooked. A tree is most susceptible to insect attack shortly after it has been cut or killed. As the phloem region and sapwood dry, the wood becomes less and less attractive to a large proportion of wood-inhabiting insects. The greatest amount of insect damage usually is done during the first season after the tree has been cut or has died. After that, the organisms causing decay hold the center of the stage.

For this reason, one of the most effective ways of preventing insect injury and likewise the succeeding fungous injury is to utilize the logs as soon as possible after they are cut or to salvage without delay trees killed by fire, insects, or other causes before they have deteriorated. This calls for prompt action. When trees have been killed by a spring fire, the problem of prompt utilization is almost hopeless because the trees will be infested with borers within a few weeks after the fire. Unless it is possible to begin salvage immediately, heavy losses cannot be avoided. On the other hand, when the trees are killed in the summer or fall, the wood will not be seriously injured until the following spring. There is, therefore, more time to plan and execute salvage operations. The mere cutting of the trees, however, does not mean that there will be no loss. Logging is only the first step in the process of salvage. If losses are to be avoided, the logs should either be sawed immediately or treated by one of the methods discussed in other sections. Wind-thrown trees are also subject to attack by borers and should be salvaged and utilized promptly.

The utilization of recently killed trees is important not only for controlling the insects that attack the products themselves but also for preventing the increase of harmful species that might attack standing timber. Disastrous outbreaks of bark beetles have resulted from their excessive multiplication in windfalls. The tremendous outbreak of the northern spruce beetle, *Dendroctonus obesus,* that reached a peak about 1950 after destroying vast quantities of spruce in Colorado illustrates well the danger of neglecting wind-thrown material. The Douglas-fir beetle, *Dendroctonus pseudotsugae,* frequently builds up to outbreak proportions in fire-killed or wind-thrown materials.

Prompt utilization will also protect green logs cut in regular logging operations. The shorter the time between felling and manufacture, the smaller will be the amount of food available for the insects and the less will be the chance of loss from insect attack. The necessity for salvage is especially important in the case of firs and hardwoods but is less urgent with large virgin-growth Douglas fir, redwood, and sequoia.

Food for some wood-boring insects can be eliminated by removing the bark from freshly cut wood. For example, many cerambycids and buprestids require phloem during their early larval stages. The removal of the bark destroys this succulent tissue on which the young larvae are dependent. Barking has one objectionable feature that is sometimes difficult to overcome. As the barked log or stick of pulpwood dries, the outer portions shrink more rapidly than the inner parts, with the result that checks develop, which may reach almost to the center of the logs.

Ordinarily, checking in pulpwood is of little consequence, although occasionally soot, smoke, or dust, of a character not easily washed from the pulp, may settle in the open checks and cause trouble. Peeled pulpwood should, therefore, be stored so that this will not happen. Badly checked logs will be seriously reduced in value unless the checking is controlled. This can be done to a considerable degree in straight-grained logs of moderate size. Checks always develop radially and follow lines of weakness. By hacking with an axe as deeply as possible into a peeled log along a longitudinal line, the wood will be weakened along this line and, instead of many small checks, a single large one will develop at that point. If the log is sawed intelligently, the loss from this check will be very slight.

The proper disposal of waste materials in which injurious insects may breed can prevent many of our insect troubles. For instance, in manufacturing plants that use hardwoods, the danger of powderpost-beetle infestation will be greatly reduced if all waste wood is promptly disposed of. The accumulation of such waste is very likely to lead to insect troubles sooner or later.

Likewise, in the forest, the proper handling of logging waste or slash is sometimes important from the standpoint of insect control. The ordinary methods of slash disposal are directed primarily toward fire prevention; as a result, only the smaller and more inflammable portions of the slash are taken care of. This type of disposal has little or no deterrent influence upon dangerous forest pests, because the potentially injurious species are found only in the larger parts such as the big branches, broken logs, and stumps (Graham, 1922). In order to check the multiplication of potentially injurious insects effectively, disposal of the larger parts by utilization, barking, burning, or some other suitable method is necessary.

The general consensus of opinion is that hardwood slash is almost never a breeding place for insects that attack living trees. Even coniferous slash is not so serious a menace as has been sometimes stated. There are instances, however, when it presents important problems (Keen, 1927). As long as logging is going on and fresh slash is continually being supplied by successive operations, the insects breeding in this material will find adequate feeding places for each generation. When logging operations end in a locality, then the slash insects, because of a scarcity of food, may attack standing trees, injuring advance growth and even killing some trees. Such outbreaks are usually sporadic and seldom occasion great losses.

One important insect that is associated with pine slash is the pales weevil (Speers, 1958). This insect breeds in green pine stumps, and the adult beetles, emerging therefrom, injure small seedlings by chewing the bark.

Changing Food Composition. Since each species or group of species has its own special food requirements, another means of insect control is made available. If we can change the character of the insect's food so that it is no longer suitable for consumption, we can reduce the growth and development of the insect correspondingly. Fortunately this modification is often possible, and consequently some of the most effective control methods are based on this plan. These methods are especially applicable to the control of phloem and phloem-wood insects working in freshly cut wood. The phloem region, even at best, is suitable for the development of these insects for only a comparatively short time. If this period can be still further shortened so that there is not time for development, or if a change in composition can be brought about before the wood is exposed to insect attack, injury by phloem-wood insects can be reduced or eliminated.

One of the ways by which wood may be protected from the attack of phloem insects is to give an opportunity for changes to take place in the inner bark before time for the insects to begin work. This can be accomplished by cutting at the proper time of year. Unpublished results by Craighead, Hall, and others show that logs cut at different seasons of the year exhibit decided differences in susceptibility to insect attack. Observations in the field indicate that, in northern California and Virginia, logs cut in autumn and early winter are less subject to attack than are those cut at other times. Experiments in northern Minnesota by the senior author show that logs cut during late summer and early autumn are less subject to borer injury than are logs cut at other seasons of the year. Timber cut at that time is not immediately attacked, because no phloem insects are flying at that season. Not until the following spring, 8 or 9 months later, will these insects be on the wing. By that time, changes in the inner bark will have taken place that reduce its attractiveness and desirability for use as a breeding place. Exactly what changes occur during the fall and winter is not known, although they are evidently both physical and chemical in nature. When the phloem darkens, it no longer furnishes suitable food for the borers; even when no apparent change has occurred, timber cut in the autumn is not so susceptible to attack as the same tree species cut in late winter or early spring.

Cutting at a specified time is one method of insect control that has been little used, but from the results of experiments, it appears that, in some instances, a bonus might profitably be paid by buyers for material cut in late summer and autumn. This would tend to encourage small operators to increase cutting at that season of the year, thereby reducing the quantity of wood susceptible to insect attack.

When it is impracticable to cut wood during a certain period of year, it may still be possible to change food conditions in other ways. The period of susceptibility can be shortened by rapid drying. This can be secured in thick-barked pieces by removal of the bark. Barking accomplishes a double effect. It reduces the total quantity of food available for the phloem eaters, and it makes possible the rapid drying of the sapwood, with the consequent food changes. Thus the wood soon becomes unsusceptible to the attack of those insects that feed in green sapwood. Rapid seasoning of thin-barked pieces may be accomplished by stacking the wood in well-ventilated piles. In the cooler northern latitudes, however, the rate of drying may be so slow that even thin-barked pieces will be infested while still green. In such localities, both barking and piling in well-ventilated piles are necessary to prevent infestation.

In the South, on the other hand, rapid sun-curing for the purpose of modifying the character of the food has been used successfully. Under this method, the pieces of wood are either piled in open piles or, in the case of logs, placed side by side on skids. In the latter case, it is necessary to rotate the logs every few days to ensure even curing on all sides. The rotation of the logs results not only in hastening the seasoning rate but also in killing directly by heat any insects that may attack the logs during treatment.

Seasoning wood for the purpose of producing unfavorable food conditions for insects is applicable not only to logs and bolts, but has its place in the protection of sawed lumber as well. During the drying process, food modifications occur that prevent all future attacks of some insects, even though moisture conditions may later become favorable. Ambrosia beetles are representatives of this group. The more rapid the seasoning, the shorter will be the period during which attack by these pests will be possible. Careful piling of green lumber in such manner that there is free circulation of air through and around the piles hastens drying, but where the equipment is available, kiln drying is an even better procedure.

Still another means of protecting freshly cut wood from insect attack is by water treatment. The chief effect of this treatment is to change the moisture conditions unfavorably. This effect will be discussed in the following section. But water treatment also changes food conditions. It is a matter of general knowledge that, after logs have been in water for some time, they cease to provide suitable food for many wood-boring species. Logs driven to the mill in water are only slightly susceptible to insect infestation when removed from the water. Deadheads when taken out of the water are practically safe from insect attack. Craighead (1950) has shown that a submergence of 12 months so changes the physical and chemical nature of logs that they are no longer susceptible to infestation. Short periods of floating in water have comparatively little effect upon food composition within the wood. For this reason, short periods of driving followed by removal from the water have little or no effect either upon the insects present in the logs or upon the susceptibility of the wood to later infestation. To be effective in changing food conditions, water treatment must be continued over a period of several months to a year.

MODIFICATION OF MOISTURE

It was shown in Chap. 4 that one of the most important factors determining the rate of insect development is moisture. Insect development is limited by the moisture requirements of each species to a definite moisture zone. Outside this zone of moisture toleration, development is impossible; consequently, control of insects in logs may be accomplished either by lowering the moisture content of the logs below the limits of the insect's toleration or by raising the moisture content above that zone.

Reduction of Moisture. We have seen in the preceding section that piling, barking, and sun-curing are methods that may be used to change unfavorably the composition of insects' food. The same methods may sometimes be used for the purpose of reducing the moisture content to a point below the zone of moisture toleration. The common recommendation to stack freshly cut wood in well-ventilated piles is of little value for thick-barked logs. Only logs with very thin bark will season quickly, and even these, unless exposed to high temperatures in a dry atmosphere, will retain a high moisture content for several months. In most cases, therefore, comparatively rapid seasoning of freshly cut wood cannot be obtained except by removing the bark previous to piling.

If really rapid drying can be secured, it is an excellent means of control, for it operates in two directions at the same time. Indirectly, it prevents future attack by wood-boring species, and at the same time, it directly checks the activities of insects that have already become established in the wood, slowing up their rate of development and sometimes even stopping it entirely. An example of this is found in the ease by which the larvae of the balsam-fir sawyer, *Monochamus marmorator*, are killed by thorough drying of the wood in which they are working. This effect has been observed by the senior author in attempts to rear this insect. Unless the logs are kept moist, few, if any, of the beetles will emerge.

Increasing Moisture.   In many instances it is much easier to raise the water content of freshly cut wood above the point of insect toleration than to lower it below the favorable zone. We have already seen how water treatment, like seasoning, may control insects by changing the composition of their food. Now we shall see that the same treatment, with certain limitations, may be used to change the moisture content to such an unfavorable condition that insect development will be checked and sometimes entirely stopped.

There are two different ways of applying the water treatment: (1) by sprinkling the wood or (2) by floating it in a pond. The method selected for any particular case will depend upon existing conditions. Each has its advantages and disadvantages.

The sprinkler system has been used only upon pulpwood, although it could be used with equal effect upon saw logs. Under this system, during the season of insect activity, the wood throughout a pile is kept continuously dripping wet by throwing water on it. This may be accomplished by an overhead system of pipes, or the water can be thrown from the ground by either stationary water guns or a hose. The overhead system is expensive to construct and may interfere with the handling of wood in the yard, but since it requires a minimum of attention, it is very cheap to operate. The method of throwing water onto the wood from the ground requires little or no additional equipment, inasmuch as most woodyards are equipped with water mains for fire-protection purposes, but it does require a certain amount of labor in directing the stream of water. In both methods of sprinkler system it is, of course, necessary to provide drainage to carry off the surplus water.

In treating wood by the sprinkler system, it should always be borne in mind that the effectiveness of the operation depends primarily upon the thoroughness of the wetting. Unless all the wood in the pile is kept wet, the treatment will have little or no beneficial effect. This system is likely to give the best results when applied to irregularly piled wood of short length. On evenly stacked piles, the water is likely to run off rather than to drip through the pile.

The second method of raising the water content of freshly cut wood above the point of insect toleration is, as stated above, by floating it in water. This method can be used to protect not only wood stored at the mill but also freshly cut material in the woods. There is no more economical way of preventing injury to wood that must be held in the forest during a season or more than to get it into water.

If the wood is free from infestation when it is floated, infestation will usually not occur, especially if the logs are being worked. If it has been infested by wood borers prior to floating, the borers will develop no further, and if the wood remains in the water long enough, the insect inhabitants will die. Like most generalizations, this one has certain exceptions; for instance, large logs floating in water may be attacked on the upper side by ambrosia beetles.

The chief objections to the floating method of protection are: (1) Adequate water space may not be available. (2) A considerable proportion of the floated wood will become waterlogged and sink, thus resulting in a total loss or a heavy expense for salvage.

In connection with this discussion of water treatment, other benefits than the protection against insect injury should not be ignored. Wood treated by either sprinkling or floating is protected not only against insects but also against the growth of fungi. Both stain and decay are checked or prevented by water treatment. Another benefit is the reduced fire hazard. It is practically impossible to burn wood stored under either of the methods discussed. The danger of fire in and around mills using one of these systems is, therefore, reduced, with the result that insurance rates are lower. All these benefits combine to make water treatment an especially desirable means of protecting wood.

MODIFICATION OF TEMPERATURE

Wood-boring insects have, as stated in Chap. 5, a definite zone of temperature in which they are active. Within this zone, the rate of development varies with the temperature. The higher the temperature, the more rapid their development. Conversely, the lower the temperature, the slower the rate of development. This reaction to temperature provides us with another useful weapon in insect control. Theoretically, we can either lower or raise the temperature of wood to a point where insect activities are checked. Actually, however, there is little opportunity for controlled use of high temperature in an indirect way. Usually the indirect control of insects by temperature regulation is through lowering of temperature.

Reduction of Temperature. In cool climates where, even at best, there is barely enough heat for the successful development of insects, their control can often be secured by lowering the temperature. The simplest way to do this is to protect the wood from the effects of the sun by shading. In warm, humid climates, of course, the control of insects by reduction of temperature is not ordinarily feasible.

Experiments in Minnesota have shown that the temperature of logs can be greatly reduced by heavy shading and that the rate of development of certain wood borers is correspondingly retarded or even entirely stopped. The pine sawyer, which under favorable conditions completes its development in 1 year, requires from 2 to 4 years in heavily shaded logs. Chrysobothris is even more seriously affected and is unable to exist under heavy shade. Heavy shading not only reduces the development rate but also appears to reduce the amount of infestation of logs by wood borers. To obtain satisfactory results, however, very heavy shading is necessary. Slight shade has a tendency to make conditions for wood-boring insects even more favorable than full sunlight and frequently results in an increased rate of infestation. Therefore, when shade is used to reduce the damage to logs caused by wood borers, it is essential that it be very heavy.

In the Lake States, experiments have shown that the practice of heavy shading may be used effectively in preventing the multiplication of those slash insects that are potential pests of living trees. If the smaller slash is piled over the larger parts, physical conditions in these larger parts become unfavorable for the development of the potentially injurious insects.

BIBLIOGRAPHY CHAPTER 11

Burk, B. D., H. H. Ross, and T. H. Frison, 1938. A portable light (Argon-mercury) for collecting insects, *J. Econ. Entomol.*, **31:** 316–318.

Collins, C. W., 1920. Tree-banding material, *U.S. Dept. Agr. Bull.* 899.

Craighead, F. C., 1950. Insect enemies of eastern forests, *U.S. Dept. Agr. Misc. Publ.* 657.

Graham, S. A., 1922. Slash and insects, *J. Forestry*, **20:** 437–447.

Keen, F. P., F. C. Craighead, et al., 1927. Insects and slash disposal, *U.S. Dept. Agr. Circ.* 411.

Popham, W. L., and D. G. Hall, 1958. Insect eradication programs, *Ann. Rev. Entomol.*, **3:** 335–354.

Smith, H. S., et al., 1933. Plant quarantines in California, *Univ. Calif., Coll. Agr., Agr. Expt. Sta. Bull.* 533.

———, 1941. Quarantines justifiable trade barriers, *Univ. Calif., Coll. Agr.* Unnumbered.

Snyder, T. E., 1921. Termite-proof wood, *J. Econ. Entomol.*, **14:** 496–501.

————, 1926. Preventing damage by lyctus powder-post beetles, *U.S. Dept. Agr. Farmers' Bull.* 1477, pp. 1–13.

Speers, C. F., 1958. Pales weevil becoming a serious pest of pine reproduction in the South, *J. Forestry,* **56:** 723–726.

Strong, Lee A., 1938. Control legislation in the United States, *U.S. Dept. Agr., Bur. Entom. P. Q.,* E-455.

Wardle, R. A., 1929. "The Problems of Applied Entomology," p. 504.

CHAPTER 12

INDIRECT
CONTROL
BY PARASITES
AND PREDATORS

Throughout the ages, whenever harmful insects have been observed, the attention of biologists has been attracted by activities of parasites and predators. The possibility was early recognized that these organisms might be used for control purposes. For use against forest insects they were especially attractive, since the direct control of forest pests seemed, in early times, to present almost insurmountable difficulties.

The use of parasites and predators presents tremendously promising possibilities for indirect control. Unfortunately, however, we do not yet fully understand how to manipulate and encourage the beneficial activities of these organisms so that they will always work for man's best interest. Nevertheless, much progress is being made in this direction.

TWO APPROACHES TO BIOTIC CONTROL

There are two distinct approaches to the use of biotic factors for indirect control: (1) the introduction of these organisms into areas where they do not occur and (2) the encouragement of those already present.

The introduction of parasites and predators into new environments has usually been directed against introduced pests, because these pests are, as a rule, without natural enemies in their new environment. Environmental manipulation, designed to improve conditions for native parasites and predators, applies equally well to both foreign and native pests.

Introduction of Biotic Control Organisms. The attempts to control forest insects by biologic means have most often been directed toward introducing beneficial organisms to check the ravages of foreign pests. For over thirty years the Gypsy Moth Laboratory devoted much effort to introducing natural enemies of the gypsy moth and other associated insects. During that time, more than 60 species were successfully introduced, 16 or more became permanently established, and 7 or 8 have become definitely useful in preventing outbreaks.

In Canada similar work has been done in introducing parasites of injurious species of forest insects from abroad. One of the earliest attempts along this line was the introduction of parasites of the larch sawfly. Fungous and insect parasites of this insect were brought into Canada, chiefly from England. More recently, Canadian forest entomologists have greatly expanded work with parasites and have introduced, among others, a number of parasites of the European spruce sawfly, *Diprion* (*Gilpinia*) *hercyniae*. Of these parasites at least three were widely established in both Canada and the United States and have proved to be valuable additions to our fauna. One of these is the tiny hymenopteron, *Microplectron fuscipennis*.

Another parasite introduced to control a pest from abroad is worthy of special mention. This is *Agathis pumilis*, a tiny wasplike parasite of the larch casebearer, *Coleophora laricella*. After it was released in 1937 in southern Michigan it spread across the Straits of Mackinac by 1950, reducing the casebearer population as it spread (Webb, 1953). The rate of spread, a little less than 25 miles per year, seems remarkable when the minute size of the parasite is considered. Prior to the establishment of agathis, the casebearer had for many years caused severe defoliation annually. Since agathis became established, defoliation has been inconspicuous.

Both in the United States and in Canada the use of biotic control has received increasingly more attention. Since most of the work has been done by entomologists, it is natural that parasitic insects and a few predatory insects have held the center of attention. These animals are, however, not the only organisms that are useful for biotic control. Fungi, bacteria, protozoans, and viruses all attack insects, thereby bringing about reduction of their rates of reproduction. Occasionally microorganisms have been introduced, often accidentally, and have proved to be most valuable control agencies. Some of these will be discussed in the following sections. Evidence that interest in these organisms is increasing is indicated by the establishment of laboratories of insect pathology, one at the University of California in 1945 and another in association with the Canadian Forest Insect Laboratory at Sault Sainte Marie, Ontario, in 1946.

The introduction of biotic control agencies is not always restricted to species imported from other parts of the world. Sometimes parasites are transferred from one locality to another within the United States or Canada. For example, *Campoplex frustranae* was transported from Virginia to the Nebraska National Forest to control the Nantucket pine moth, *Rhyacionia frustrana*. Also, parasites of the spruce budworm, not native to Eastern Canada, have been transported from British Columbia.

Encouragement of Native Organisms.   Although the introduction of new agencies of control has received most attention, forest entomologists have by no means neglected the possibilities of encouraging the good work of resident organisms. These organisms, as do the pests themselves, respond to their physical, nutritional, and biotic environments. By manipulating the environmental factors, we can greatly increase the effectiveness of biotic control. With this in mind, studies have been made of the ecological relations existing between the various beneficial organisms and their environment. Some of this work will be discussed in connection with silvicultural practices (Chap. 14), for the encouragement of the biotic factors must be closely tied in with woods operations.

In the light of present knowledge, specific practices cannot always be suggested. Nevertheless, the forester who understands the requirements of some of these useful organisms may, himself, see opportunities to encourage them. Therefore, this chapter will present characteristics of the various organisms that may be useful in this connection.

KINDS OF ENTOMOPHAGOUS[1] PARASITES

Insects become parasitized by various kinds of plants and animals. Of these bacteria, fungi, viruses, and insects are probably the most outstanding. Discussion will be limited to these groups, although we should remember that other groups are also parasitic upon insects. For example, protozoans, nematodes, and mites are sufficiently important as parasites that perhaps they also should be included in a consideration of this subject.

Bacteria.   References to bacterial diseases of insects are very common in entomological literature. In view of the difficulties attendant upon the

---

[1] The term *entomophagous* is used here in its broad sense meaning insect eater. Some authorities prefer to restrict this term to those organisms that actually devour the insect, as does a predator or certain parasites, using the term *entomogenous* when speaking of microorganisms that cause insect diseases. Actually, there is no point where a definite line can be drawn that meets the ecological requirements of the situation. Therefore, rather than coin a new term, entomophagous is used to include any organism that uses insects for nourishment.

positive identification of the causative organisms, it is likely that some of these reports refer to effects of other organisms. But we do know positively of specific bacteria that are pathogenic to insects. One of these, a bacterial disease of the gypsy moth, was studied by Glaser (1918). This organism, *Streptococcus disparis*, like many other bacteria, is spread from larva to larva by contamination of the food with the feces of infected individuals; therefore, it can be a disease only of dense populations. This probably explains the fact that, although it is a very virulent disease under experimental conditions, it has been of little practical value in the field.

Recently, the highly pathogenic bacterium *Bacillus thuringiensis* has received considerable attention by insect pathologists. In some respects, it appears to hold more promise as an agent of biological control than most bacteria, but its use is still in the experimental stage (Franz, 1961).

Uncertainty of action under forest conditions seems to be characteristic of many bacteria, especially those that infect defoliators and other insects that live on the exposed surfaces of plants. In certain seasons, they may destroy almost every individual of a host species, whereas in others none of the host will be killed. Steinhaus (1949) contrasts the durability of nonspore-producing bacteria to those that produce spores, pointing out that the spores are very resistant to drying and high temperature. Bacteria that do not produce spores are relatively sensitive to physical extremes. From this we may logically assume that the spore-producing bacteria offer greater possibilities for the effective control of forest insects than do the others.

This conclusion is supported by the fact that some of the most promising bacterial diseases belong to the spore-producing group. Prominent among these is the milky disease of the Japanese beetle, *Bacillus papilliae*. The spores of this and similar organisms remain viable for several years in the soil, where they are in a position to infect any larva that may ingest them with its food. The spores produce active forms that reproduce within the body of the host. These active forms produce resting spores in the blood of the host. When the host dies, its infected body remains in the soil. Spores from the bodies of infected larvae are in turn eaten by other larvae. The spores are spread locally through the soil by the movements of larvae from place to place and more widely by birds and mammals that have eaten the infected grubs and beetles. Not only the larvae but also the adult beetles may become infected. These infected beetles may also spread the inoculum from place to place.

The spores of the milky disease are now being produced commercially for distribution into areas infested by the beetles. Larvae are inoculated with the spores and incubated until they develop the disease. The infected larvae are dried, ground, and their spore content determined. The ground material is then diluted with talc, so that each gram contains a million spores. The standardized spore dust is then distributed in spots 10 feet apart with 2 grams to the spot. Within a few seasons after inoculation, the soil becomes completely infectious and hence uninhabitable for the beetle larvae (Beard, 1945).

The symptoms of bacterial diseases are variable but are commonly characterized by color changes and motor disturbances. Often after death, the larvae remain hanging head downward from a twig or leaf. If undisturbed, they usually dry and shrivel but still retain their typical form.

Fungi. Infections of insects by fungi are so common that they have come to the attention of everyone. The dead housefly on the window glass surrounded by a halolike circle of white spores and the mummified body of a dead aphid still attached to a leaf are both common examples of this sort of infection. At times, severe outbreaks of insects may suddenly be brought to an end by a fungal epizootic.

Although they are exceedingly numerous, fungous parasites of insects have never been used successfully by man as a means of controlling a forest insect. The reason for this is evident when we consider that the parasitic fungi are able to check insect outbreaks only under relatively warm-moist conditions whereas insect outbreaks occur most frequently during periods of dry weather. Consequently, at the time when we need them the most, there is little or nothing that can be done to encourage fungous infections of insect pests. Nevertheless, we must recognize that during moist periods the presence of fungous inoculum may aid materially in preventing the rapid multiplication of forest-insect pests.

Many fungi that attack insects may live as saprophytes for long periods. Thus when conditions are favorable, the inoculum is present and ready to attack the living insects. At times larch sawfly prepupae within the cocoons are attacked and destroyed by one fungus of this sort, *Isaria farinosa*. Its effectiveness depends upon the amount of saprophytic growth in the moss, and that in turn depends chiefly upon moisture.

Viruses. Insect diseases that are caused by viruses are often responsible for checking outbreaks of both lepidopterous and hymenopterous defoliators. These viruses usually appear after 2 or 3 years of heavy defoliation and destroy so many larvae that the defoliator outbreak subsides. The wilt disease of the gypsy moth, the virus disease of the European spruce sawfly, and several viruses of other sawflies and Lepidoptera have been isolated. Some have been successfully disseminated.

Our knowledge of virus diseases had its beginning in Europe, where the *Wipfelkrankheit* of the nun moth, *Lymantria monocha*, has been intensively studied since its discovery in 1889. About 1907, a similar disease was observed in populations of the gypsy moth in New England. It is commonly known as the wilt disease, suggested by the wilted appearance of the dead caterpillars. A similar disease of the gypsy moth has been observed in Europe and is assumed to be identical with the wilt disease in America. How the virus reached New England is not known, but according to Glaser (1927), it was not present in 1900. Presumably it was introduced into America long after the gypsy moth had become firmly established, possibly with the wholesale introduction of parasitic insects in 1905.

The wilt disease is infectious, gaining entrance into the body of the insect through the mouth with ingested food. After becoming established in the insect, it attacks and kills the blood cells and certain tissues, with the result that the caterpillar usually dies. However, if infection occurs late in the larval stage, the insect is often able to survive, complete its development, emerge as a moth, and reproduce itself without showing any symptoms of the presence of the disease. In such instances the infection may be passed through the egg to the progeny. Because of the presence of chronic carriers, one can never be sure that the disease does not exist in a locality, even though the caterpillars appear healthy. Under high-temperature conditions, the chronic cases may become acute, with the result that the host will be killed and an epidemic started among the larvae.

Epidemics of wilt have been especially common where the gypsy moth became so abundant that it stripped most of the foliage from the trees upon which it fed. Under such conditions, the larvae are exposed to much higher temperature than normal because the direct rays of the sun can shine through the crowns of the trees upon them. Under these favorable conditions, the wilt disease becomes epizootic.

The larvae, when infected with the wilt disease, first become sluggish and then stop eating. Before they die, they have a tendency to climb high in the trees; after death, they remain hanging by their prolegs. Their tissues become darkened, decomposed, and liquefied. Finally they become completely disintegrated and dry upon the tree. These dried smears, that once were insects, remain infectious for a long time, and it has been suggested that possibly the wilt disease may have been brought into America upon plants on which the diseased larvae had died.

Another very striking case of a virus disease that has brought about the control of a forest insect is the European spruce-sawfly virus. Between 1930 and 1938, the European spruce sawfly threatened to destroy much of the spruce in eastern Canada and parts of New England. In 1938, a virus disease of the sawfly appeared. Presumably it was brought into America accidentally with the importation of insect parasites of the spruce sawfly. Once established, it spread rapidly until the sawfly was brought under control. According to Balch and Bird (1944), the disease built up in areas of very high population but, after attaining momentum, was able to invade areas where the sawfly was not so numerous. This disease has so reduced the numbers of the host that the European spruce sawfly is no longer a threat to spruce stands.

The first evidence of infection in the larvae is a yellowing of the central segments of the abdomen. This change progresses until the entire larva becomes a yellowish green and later, after death, dark brown or even black. The fluid exuded from the mouth of the larva, when disturbed, is milky instead of the normal clear yellowish-green appearance. The larvae cease to feed, shrivel somewhat, and die. The dead larvae are sometimes glued by sticky excrement to the twig on which they have been feeding, but more often they drop from the tree when dead. In this respect the effect of the sawfly virus differs from that of the wilt disease, where the larvae usually hang from twigs of the tree by their prolegs after death.

Since 1938 this virus of the European spruce sawfly has continued to hold in check this potentially dangerous defoliator. In one instance, it has been artificially disseminated successfully into an area when neither it nor other parasites of the sawfly were present (Bird and Burk, 1961).

Insects. Of all the parasites that attack insects, the parasitic insects have received most attention from entomologists. They do not constitute a phylogenetic unit but are to be found in various orders and in widely divergent families within these orders. The great majority of the most valuable species, however, belong to either the Hymenoptera or the Diptera. The adult parasites vary greatly in appearance, as one would expect, but the larval stages are surprisingly similar. They are practically all legless maggotlike grubs. The mouth parts are usually much reduced or even vestigial, except in the early stages. In short, they are specialized for a mode of life that is provided with an abundance of easily obtainable food and illustrate the condition that is called specialization by reduction of parts.

The adults, on the other hand, are specialized to ensure successful infestation of the host. This is accomplished in different ways by parasites belonging to various groups. The Sarcophagidae and some of the Tachinidae are larviparous. This adaptation, by eliminating the helpless egg stage, increases the probability of successful entrance of the parasite into the host. Many Tachinidae that are not larviparous stick their eggs firmly to the body of the host, whereas others attach them to the substratum on which the host is found. Most of the Ichneumonoidea are provided with an elongate ovipositor which they thrust into either the host or its cocoon and there deposit their eggs. Others of this same group are said to place their eggs in the galleries of wood borers, and the larvae when they hatch creep along the gallery until they find the host. *Megharhyssa* (*Thalessa*) *lunator,* which is one of the largest of the Ichneumonidae and a parasite upon the pigeon tremex, *Tremex columba,* is said to have this habit. But in view of the fact that the borers of the family Siricidae, of which the pigeon tremex is a member, pack their burrows full of frass as they progress, the eggs of the parasite must be placed very near the host, if not actually in its body. The large ichneumonids are remarkable for the fact that they are able to drill through solid wood in order to place their eggs in a favorable position in or near their host. The Chalcidoidea are smaller than most of the ichneumonids and usually deposit their eggs within the body of their host, although some species of this group, as well as some of the other Hymenoptera, are able to feed externally. In the case of external feeders, the host usually dies soon after it is attacked, or, in some instances, it is killed by the adult parasite at the time of oviposition. The Proctotrupoidea are mostly small hymenopterous parasites. Many of these tiny insects parasitize eggs, whereas others are larval parasites. As a rule, if they are larval parasites, they attack only small insects.

Parasitic insects are sometimes limited to a single host. These are called specific or obligate parasites. Others are able to attack a number of closely related species, whereas still others are general parasites, because they are able to attack and parasitize a great many different species.

Insects that are parasitic upon other insects are often regarded as being always beneficial to man's interests, inasmuch as they reduce the number of injurious species. Such a generalization is not entirely safe, however, for there are parasites that attack other parasites, predaceous insects, or insects useful to man. Thus, some insect parasites may be injurious. Those species that parasitize other parasites are called secondary or hyperparasites. Hyperparasitism is known to occur to the fourth or possibly the fifth degree. Hyperparasitism, of course, reduces the effectiveness of parasitic control and adds to the complexity of the role played by parasites in environmental resistance.

Competition between primary parasites within a host is not uncommon. When double parasitism occurs, one of the parasites usually destroys the other. Such competitive interactions complicate the problem of evaluating the effects of parasitism upon pest populations.

EFFECTIVENESS OF PARASITIC INSECTS

The effectiveness of a primary parasite in controlling an insect pest depends, to a considerable extent, upon certain characteristics of the parasite. The relative importance of these characteristics varies in individual cases; moreover, workers disagree among themselves in evaluating the various characteristics. But that certain characteristics are desirable is commonly accepted. Some of the more important of these are (1) to reproduce rapidly, (2) to be synchronized with its host, (3) to be able to attack more than one host species, (4) to be able to find and parasitize a large proportion of the host individuals even at low host density, (5) to compete successfully with other parasites. Seldom, if ever, are all these qualities possessed in an equally high degree by any one parasite. We should always attempt, however, to favor those parasites that most nearly approach this ideal.

High Reproductive Potential.   The possession of a high reproductive potential permits a parasite to reproduce at a rapid rate at times when environmental resistance has been reduced. This situation occurs when the biotic balance has been temporarily disturbed and, as a result, the host has increased tremendously. Concomitantly with increased abundance of its host, the parasite's environmental resistance is lowered so that its reproductive rate may approach its potential. If its reproductive potential is high enough, the parasite can reproduce more rapidly than its host and bring the outbreak to an end. If, however, its reproductive potential is low, it may not be able to overtake the host until serious damage has been done to the forest.[1]

An example of the occurrence of serious damage before parasites could overtake the host was reported by Tothill (1923). He states that in New Brunswick during an outbreak of the spruce budworm the rise in numbers of the insect occurred when fir, the favored food, was abundant in sizes suitable for egg laying. The decline came when the amount of suitable fir diminished. Not until the year following the peak of budworm population did the parasites reach the maximum, and then only 25 percent of the budworm larvae was killed by them. In contrast, he cites another case from British Columbia in which parasites were largely responsible for checking an outbreak of the same insect before serious damage to the trees resulted. In that instance 61 percent of the budworms were destroyed by parasites and 39 percent by predators. A single parasite species of the genus *Phytodietus*, not present in New Brunswick, was responsible for killing 24 percent of the host. Thus in one instance the parasites were incapable of multiplying at a sufficient rate to exercise much control, in spite of ideal food conditions, whereas in the other instance the rate of increase was sufficient to bring about the necessary control.

Synchronization with Host.   The accurate synchronization of its life history with that of its host is essential if a parasite is to exercise effective control. As a rule, a parasite can attack only one stage of its host; in order to exercise control, therefore, it must be ready to oviposit at a time when the proper stage is available. A specific parasite should have either the same length of life cycle as its host or a series of brief generations during the period of host availability. It might otherwise be ready to oviposit at a time when the host was not in a suitable stage. This synchroni-

[1] Some authorities feel that the importance of a high reproductive potential has been exaggerated and point out that the possession of this quality is prima facie evidence that nature has neglected the species in some other way. This may be true under conditions close to the equilibrium point when oscillations of moderate amplitude prevail, since the force of environmental resistance must then equal reproductive potential. Under such conditions, neither the host nor the parasite population is changing, and regardless of its reproductive potential, the parasite would exert an even pressure on its host. Under outbreak conditions, however, reproductive potential becomes important, often deciding whether or not the parasite can overtake its host.

zation between parasite and host may be accomplished either by a well-established seasonal periodicity or by the simultaneous and equal response of both host and parasite to environmental factors.

Polyphagous Habit.   A polyphagous parasite that is synchronized with a certain pest may, in the long run, be more effective in controlling that pest than would be a specific parasite equally well synchronized. The ability to feed on more than one host is especially useful during the period immediately following the decline of an outbreak, when the host numbers are extremely low. At such a time, the polyphagous parasite would not suffer so greatly from food shortage as would the one that is restricted to a single host. It would be able to shift its attention to other hosts and thereby maintain its numbers at a higher level than could the specific parasite. It would, therefore, be in an advantageous position to retard the subsequent multiplication of the original host. The work of Tothill (1922) concerning the natural control of the fall webworm, *Hyphantria cunea*, illustrates this point. In two instances specific parasites of the worm were extirpated locally, following the sudden decline in the population of their host, whereas other species, although much reduced in number, recovered slowly when the population of the webworm again increased.

This voluntary alternation of hosts, described above, is a distinct advantage, whereas obligate alternation limits the effectiveness of a parasite. If one generation of a parasite feeds upon one host and the next generation requires a different host, the abundance of such a parasite is limited by the abundance of the least abundant host. To require alternate hosts is, therefore, a disadvantage, but to be able to use various hosts is a desirable characteristic.

Referring again to the agathis parasite of the larch casebearer, this parasite illustrates an especially interesting interaction with another parasite, *Epilampsis laricinella*, that attacks a number of small Lepidoptera, including the casebearer. This latter parasite passes through three generations in a single season. The second generation oviposits ordinarily in late June and early July after most of the normal casebearer larvae have pupated. Therefore, the female parasites of the second generation must seek other suitable hosts. As a result their potential population numbers are limited. If, however, a large proportion of the casebearer population has been parasitized by agathis, the larval life of the host is so lengthened that they are still available to the second-generation female epilampsis. The resultant double parasitism causes the death of the agathis larvae and a corresponding increase in epilampsis. The third generation of epilampsis oviposits on the overwintering larvae of the casebearer.

Cody, in an unpublished piece of research, suspects strongly that this competitive interaction may result in alternating high and low populations of first one parasite and then the other. A. R. Graham (1948) believes that this combination results in more effective control of the host than would be possible with agathis alone. This conclusion is not supported by our experience in southern Michigan.

Ability to Find and Parasitize Hosts. Undoubtedly, the most important single characteristic that determines the effectiveness of a parasite is its ability to find and parasitize its host, especially at low host density. Relatively little difficulty in this respect is presented by insects that live on the exposed surfaces of plants. Such insects are usually unprotected from the attack of any parasites that may be present. There are differences in the ability of parasites to move swiftly from place to place and differences in their ability to find scattered hosts. These differences have a marked effect upon their power to bring about equilibrium at a low host density.

Insects that bore into the tissues of trees present a much more difficult problem to their parasites, but many parasitic Hymenoptera are well fitted to parasitize these hidden larvae. Some of them have long ovipositors, which they are able to insert through solid wood, depositing their eggs in or on the larvae working therein. The larger species can reach a larva 1 inch or even more beneath the surface. The smaller parasites of this group cannot penetrate so deeply because their ovipositors are not so long. For this reason, they must confine their attention to borers that are near the surface.

In studies of the Nantucket pine moth, it was found that the percentage of parasitism is higher among the larvae mining in the tips of jack pine than among those mining in ponderosa pine in spite of a lower incidence of infestation in jack pine. Apparently this difference is due to the comparative diameters of jack-pine and ponderosa-pine tips, the jack-pine tips being more slender than those of ponderosa. Naturally a larger proportion of the pine-moth larvae working in these slender tips would be reached by the small parasites than would be possible in the thicker tips of ponderosa pine. The introduction of a parasite, *Campoplex frustranae*, with a longer ovipositor than any parasites originally present resulted in an astonishing increase in parasitic control.

Ability to Compete. The ability to compete in case of double parasitism in a single host is a valuable quality for a parasite to possess. When two parasites of different species are brought together in the same host, the stronger will survive; the other will usually die or be destroyed directly by the more active and aggressive competitor (Pemberton and Willard, 1918). The survivor may or may not be the more effective in controlling the pest. It would, therefore, be advisable to know as much as possible about the habits of the various species that may be competitors. Without this information, undesirable introductions may be made.

The difficulty in practice of determining prior to its introduction the probable success or failure of a parasite in a new environment has led to the conclusion by many that the only feasible procedure is to introduce first and evaluate later. Others warn that such a procedure is dangerous.

Another kind of competition among parasites is for food. In this case when several parasites live in the body of the same host, the oldest

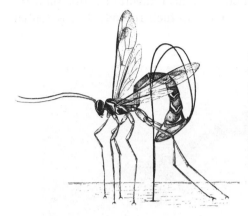

FIGURE 33. One of the largest of the ichneumon flies, *Megharhyssa lunator*. This is a parasite of one of the horntails, the pigeon tremex, and is able to insert its slender ovipositor deep into the wood where the larvae of the host work. (U.S. Dept. Agr. Forest Service.)

usually is the sole survivor. A period of nondestructive feeding by the parasites is followed by a final stage in which the oldest larva consumes not only the host tissues but also any younger parasites that may be present (Tothill, 1922).

Some parasites have the ability to recognize and avoid the sluggish larvae that have previously been parasitized. Double parasitism is also avoided by the arrangement of the different species in more or less of a sequence, so that some parasites will attack the young larvae and others the older ones.

The foregoing discussion has shown the value of the various desirable characteristics of a parasite. The possession of these characteristics may not always be equally valuable in control. For example, a certain general parasite, possessing all the desirable characteristics, might select a small host species, consequently producing only male offspring. If the same parasite were to choose a larger host species, it would produce both sexes, and its effectiveness as a controlling agent would consequently be far greater. Thus we see that the interrelation of parasite and host can be just as important in control work as the mere possession of desirable characteristics. The interrelation of parasites with one another and with their hosts is decidedly complex. Generalizations in this connection are dangerous, and much work in this field still needs to be done.

Ability to Spread. After a parasite has been released, its success in the environment depends to some extent upon its ability to spread out from the point of release. Sometimes the rate at which a parasite will spread from the point of liberation is nothing short of phenomenal, as we have seen in the case of agathis. This astonishing rate of spread is in part the result of especially favorable conditions immediately surrounding the point of release. A place where the host is numerous is naturally selected for the introduction, and as a result, nutritional conditions are usually ideal. If physical conditions are also favorable, the parasites should reproduce for a time at a rate close to their reproductive potential.

FIGURE 34. *Coeloides dendroctoni* ovipositing through the bark of Engelmann spruce log. She attaches her egg to the larva of a bark beetle in the phloem region. (U.S. Dept. Agr. Forest Service.)

The introduction of *Campoplex frustranae* into the pine plantations in the Nebraska National Forest is a case in point. This insect was liberated at one point in 1925. In the following year, the number of larvae parasitized by this species near the point of release was almost 17 percent. In 1927, it had increased to 83.5 percent, and the parasite was collected at a distance of 7/8 mile from the release point. One year later, the percentage of larvae parasitized at the point of liberation was 91.8 and the parasite was recovered 2 1/4 miles distant. In the following year, campoplex had spread throughout the plantations, parasitizing a very high proportion of the host. These data suggest that the rate of spread of a parasite from the point of release may increase geometrically during the first few years after liberation.

Evaluation of Effectiveness. In evaluating the effectiveness of parasites as control agencies a commonly accepted practice has been to rear the parasites from pupae or prepupae of the host species collected in the field. The proportion of the host population from which parasites emerged was assumed to represent the proportion parasitized by each species. That such a procedure is subject to error is illustrated by the above discussion of the interaction between agathis and epilampsis.

Some recent studies by Campbell (1963) illustrate convincingly some erroneous conclusions that can be drawn from such rearing experiments. He shows that certain ichneumonids feed upon the body fluids of gypsy-moth caterpillars, lapping the exudate from punctures they have made by inserting the ovipositor. Such feeding is not necessarily associated with oviposition. However, the injured larvae usually die whether or not an egg is deposited. Many of these punctures provide points of entrance for sarcophagid larvae which otherwise would not be able to enter. These later emerge and have been regarded as parasites. Actually they are scavengers feeding upon the already dead host. Whether or not this saprophagous habit is usual among sarcophagids is still unsettled. The question deserves further study, but the presently available evidence throws doubt upon data based upon rearing experiments alone.

BIBLIOGRAPHY CHAPTER 12

Balch, R. E., 1960. The approach to biological control in forest entomology, *Can. Entomologist,* **92**: 297–310.

————, and F. T. Bird, 1944. Disease of the European spruce sawfly and its place in natural control, *Sci. Agr.,* **25**: 65–80.

Beard, R. L., 1945. Milky disease of Japanese beetle larvae, *Conn. Agr. Expt. Sta. Bull.* 491.

Bergold, G. H., 1950. The insect viruses as organisms, *Can. J. Res.,* E-**28**: 5–11.

Bird, F. T., and J. M. Burk, 1961. Artificially disseminated virus as a factor controlling the European spruce sawfly in the absence of introduced parasites, *Can. Entomologist,* **93**: 228–238.

Cameron, J. W. MacBain, 1963. Factors affecting the use of microbial pathogens in insect control, *Ann. Rev. Entomol.,* **8**: 265–286.

Campbell, R. W., 1963. Some ichneumonid-sarcophagid interactions in the gypsy moth, *Can. Entomologist,* **95**: 337–345.

Franz, J. M., 1961. Biological control of pest insects in Europe, *Ann. Rev. Entomol.,* **6**: 183–200.

Glaser, R. W., 1918. A disease of gypsy-moth caterpillars, *J. Agr. Res.,* **13**: 515–532.

————, 1925. Specificity of bacterial diseases, *J. Econ. Entomol.,* **18**: 769–771.

————, 1927. Polyhedral diseases of insects, *Ann. Entomol. Soc. Am.,* **20**: 319–342.

Graham, A. R., 1948. Developments in the control of the European larch casebearer, *Ann. Rept. Entomol. Soc. Ontario,* **79**: 45–50.

de Gryse, J. J., 1949. Forest Insect Pathology Laboratory, *Can. Pulp Paper Assoc., Woodlands Sec. Index* 1017 (F3), March.

Muesebeck, C. F. W., 1931. *Monodontomerus aereus* Walker, both a primary and secondary parasite, *J. Agr. Res.,* **43:** 445–460.

———, and S. M. Dohanian, 1927. Hyperparasitism, *U.S. Dept. Agr. Bull.* 1487.

Pemberton, C. E., and H. F. Willard, 1918. Interrelations of fruitfly parasites in Hawaii, *J. Agr. Res.,* **12:** 285–296.

Proper, A. B., 1931. *Eupteromalus nitidans,* a parasite of the browntail and satin moths, *J. Agr. Res.,* **43:** 37–56.

———, 1934. Hyperparasitism in the case of some introduced lepidopterous tree defoliators, *J. Agr. Res.,* **48:** 359–376.

Steinhaus, E. A., 1949. "Principles of Insect Pathology," McGraw-Hill Book Company, New York, 1949.

Tothill, J. D., 1919. Natural control of the oyster-shell scale, *Bull. Entomol. Res.,* **9:** 183–196.

———, 1922. Natural control of fall webworm, *Can. Dept. Agr. Bull.* 3 (new ser.).

———, 1923. Outbreaks of spruce budworm, forest tent caterpillar, and larch sawfly in New Brunswick, *Proc. Acadian Entomol. Soc.,* 1922, **8:** 172–182.

Webb, F. E., 1953. "An Ecological Study of the Larch Casebearer, *Coleophora laricella* Hbn.," Doctoral Dissertation, The University of Michigan, microfilmed University Microfilms, Ann Arbor, Michigan.

White, R. T., and P. J. McCabe, 1949. Effect of milky disease on Japanese beetle, *U.S. Dept. Agr., Bur. Entomol. P. Q.,* E-801. Processed.

——— and ———, 1951. Colonization of milky disease spores, *U.S. Dept. Agr., Bur. Entom. P. Q.,* E-816. Processed.

CHAPTER 13

PARASITES
AND
PREDATORS

(Continued)

The introduction of insects for the control of forest pests has been concerned chiefly with parasites. Apparently many workers have felt that parasites are usually more promising agencies of control than are predators. Nevertheless, a number of predaceous insects have been introduced successfully and have proved to be worth-while additions to our fauna. Native predators are often effective control agencies. Examples of parasitic and predatory insects and predatory vertebrates are discussed in this chapter.

EXAMPLES OF PARASITIC INSECTS

The order Hymenoptera contains more examples of insects that are parasitic than any other, most of the species in three large superfamilies being parasitic: the Ichneumonoidea, the Chalcidoidea, and the Proctotrupoidea. The first two contain the species that are most familiar: the ichneumon flies and the braconids in the first and the chalcid flies in the second. Next to the Hymenoptera in number of parasitic species is the

order Diptera, the important parasitic family Tachinidae being by far
the most important.

Ichneumonoids.   Among the ichneumonoid parasites are thousands of
species and hundreds that attack forest insects. They are all armed with
slender ovipositors with which they are able to insert their eggs into their
host. Some are large wasplike insects, whereas others are so minute that
they can scarcely be distinguished with the naked eye. The habits and
the life history of each species differs in detail, but nevertheless, there is
considerable similarity among them.

One of the parasites introduced to control the gypsy moth, a braconid,
Apantales melanoscelus, will serve well for illustrative purposes. This
parasite has proved to be one of the best thus far introduced in connection
with the gypsy-moth work. It is a small black insect, about 3 millimeters
long. Its reproductive potential is tremendous, a single female being
capable of laying 1,000 eggs. It is perfectly synchronized with the
seasonal history of the gypsy moth and, in addition, is able to parasitize
a number of other hairy caterpillars, such as the satin moth, *Stilpnotia
salicis;* the tent caterpillars; and several tussock moths.

Unfortunately, this parasite suffers greatly from the attack of hyperparasites and ants, especially while in the overwintering stage. As a
result, according to Crossman (1922) the parasite is so reduced during
the winter that its first generation in the spring is able to parasitize only
a relatively small proportion of the host whereas the second may parasitize a very high proportion.

The life history of *Apantales melanoscelus* is similar in most respects
to other ichneumonoids (Crossman, 1922). Perhaps the most unusual
feature is the fact that two generations of the parasite occur during a
single generation of the host. Adults emerge from the overwintering
cocoons about the time that the gypsy-moth eggs hatch, and oviposition
for the first generation begins almost at once. The parasite larvae feed
upon the lymph and fat cells of the host until they emerge after the third
instar. The pale-yellowish cocoons are spun near the parasitized larva,
and from them, after about 1 week in the pupal stage, the adults emerge
to start the second generation. The entire first generation of this parasite
is very brief, requiring only a little more than 2 weeks from egg to adult.
The second generation differs from the first only in the length of time required for its completion, almost twice as long being required for the
larval period. On emergence from the host, the parasites spin cocoons as
did those of the first generation, but instead of emerging from them
promptly, the larvae remain in them over the winter, pupating and starting another generation the following spring.

Chalcidoids.   The chalcidoids comprise a group that contains more
species than the ichneumonoids. A very large proportion of them are
parasitic on other insects. Some of them, the ectoparasites, feed exter-

nally upon the host, whereas others, the endoparasites, live within the host. They are all small insects, some of them very minute. As a result of their small size, they are unable to reach and parasitize most borers, although some of them do parasitize certain twig-inhabiting insects. Some of the chalcidoids attack their host while it is within the cocoon. One of these is a common parasite of the larch sawfly. This parasite, *Coelopisthia nematicida*, was studied carefully by Hewitt, who considered it to be one of the most effective of the larch-sawfly parasites. It is distributed throughout the eastern part of the United States and Canada wherever the larch sawfly occurs, and in all probability it is to be found throughout the range of the sawfly in America.

The winter is passed in the larval stage within the cocoon of the sawfly. The adults emerge in May or early June while many of the sawflies are still in the prepupal stage. These adults are small black insects about 2 millimeters in length. They immediately seek out cocoons containing healthy prepupae and deposit their eggs. It is not at all uncommon to find from 50 to 75 of these parasites feeding within a single sawfly cocoon.

The parasitized prepupa appears to be stupefied or dead even before the parasite eggs have hatched. Later on, after the larval parasites have begun to feed on the blood and tissues, the host is obviously dead. Evidently the host is killed by the adult parasite or dies shortly after the eggs are deposited.

Only about 3 weeks are required for completion of a generation of this parasite. Repeated generations are produced during the season, the number depending upon temperature conditions. On first thought it would appear that an insect of this sort with a series of short generations would be limited in its effectiveness as a parasite by the unavailability of suitable host material at certain seasons. Although this is true to a certain degree, it is not such an important limiting factor as might be expected because sawfly prepupae are available at practically any time during the growing season. The period of greatest scarcity is during June, but even at that time, whenever outbreak conditions prevail, many prepupae in diapause are present and easily found. Thus the parasites can obtain suitable host material at almost any season.

Tachinids. Among the parasitic Diptera the various species of the family Tachinidae are the most valuable destroyers of forest pests. The habits of the tachinid parasites vary considerably. Some of them are oviparous, whereas others are larviparous. The oviparous species usually glue their eggs tightly to the body of the host to prevent them from being rubbed off before they hatch. The larvae in the larviparous species are either deposited on the body of the host or inserted into the body of the host by means of the larvipositor.

One of the imported tachinid parasites of the gypsy moth is *Compsilura concinnata*. It attacks not only the gypsy moth but also the brown-tail moth, the fall webworm, the white-marked tussock moth, the forest tent caterpillar, and many other native insects. This parasite has been reared from more than 140 different host species (Craighead, 1950) and has played an important part in reducing the population of the gypsy moth even when that insect has been relatively scarce. At such times as many as 50 percent of the larvae have been parasitized. *Compsilura* has also exercised excellent control of the more recently introduced European pest, the satin moth.

Compsilura is a rather large robust fly about 7 millimeters in length. Its coloring is a combination of black and white, which gives the insect a gray appearance, somewhat resembling a housefly. It is one of those larviparous tachinids that place their larvae within the body of the host.

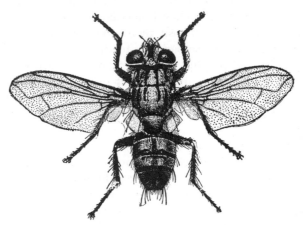

FIGURE 35. The adult *Compsilura concinnata,* an important tachinid parasite of the gypsy moth. (U.S. Dept. Agr. Forest Service.)

In parasitizing the host, the adult female darts quickly at a nearby caterpillar, pierces the body wall with her strongly chitinized piercing organ, inserts her larvipositor, and deposits a larva before the insect can escape. The larvae, according to Culver (1919), are usually inserted into the body cavity; later they attach themselves by means of anal hooks to some part of the tracheal system, often near a spiracle. Thereafter, oxygen is obtained from the tracheal system of the host through the anal spiracles, which are pushed tightly backward against the place of attachment. Thus, the caudal end of the body is attached while the cephalic end lies free within the body cavity of the host.

At the end of the third instar, the larvae, then being full grown, leave the host for pupation. The pupal stage may be passed in bark crevices, in the webs of some host such as the tent caterpillar or brown-tail moth, or in the surface layers of the soil. As is the case with most of the other Diptera, compsilura pupae are enclosed in puparia and not in cocoons. A puparium is the dry, brown, larval skin of the last instar larva.

Compsilura concinnata is active from the beginning of May to the last of October. During this period, they pass through three somewhat overlapping generations. The first adults that emerge in the spring must, as a rule, depend for host material upon caterpillars of species that overwinter in the larval stage. One such species is the brown-tail moth. A little later, in May and June, caterpillars that have hatched from overwintering eggs become available. Among these are the gypsy moths and the tent caterpillars. These insects serve as hosts for the overwintering generation of the parasite. The second-generation adults appear in late June and July. They then find a great variety of hosts available. The third-generation adults of *Compsilura* emerge in August and September, when comparatively few host species are available. Doubtless, this condition limits the numbers of the parasite.

Sarcophagids. The family Sarcophagidae is a group of flies that are chiefly scavengers, as indicated by the common name "flesh flies." Some of these, *Sarcophaga aldrichi,* for instance, appear to be parasitic upon certain caterpillars and their pupae. As mentioned in the previous chapter, however, the recent research of Campbell (1963) throws some doubt upon the parasitic status of some members of this family. Nevertheless, reports by Hodson (1939) maintain that *Sarcophaga aldrichi* is an important parasite of the forest tent caterpillar. Toward the end of a caterpillar outbreak these flies frequently become so numerous that they are a nuisance.

From the foregoing discussion of parasitic insects we see that their use for control is not simple. The number of species alone is confusing. Obviously we have two alternatives: Either we can select relatively few species for control purposes, or we can adopt the more general approach that will use as many species as possible. There has been considerable difference of opinion among the various workers concerning the relative merits of the two alternatives when parasitic insects are to be introduced. One group of workers favors the introduction of all possible primary parasites; the other favors the selection of only the most promising species. The first group feels that the lack of one good quality in a parasite will be offset by the possession of others in higher degree. The second group feels that a weakness in competitive ability might result in the failure of an otherwise ideal parasite and the success of another less desirable species with high competitive qualities when the two are introduced together.

In the introductions for gypsy-moth control, an effort was made to obtain and release as many primary parasites as possible. As a result, dozens of species were liberated that failed to become established. Presumably they were not adapted to the conditions encountered in the new environment. The majority of those that did become established have proved to be complementary, one being ready to attack the moth at one time or in a certain stage, whereas another is ready to exert pressure under some other circumstances. Certainly the introduction of gypsy-moth parasites has contributed much to the biotic control of this pest, although it can be argued that more selective introductions might have produced even better results.

PREDATORY INSECTS

The predatory insects are found in a number of different families in several orders. Some of the most effective as control agencies of forest insects are the lacewing flies, the lady beetles, the checkered beetles or clerids, the ground beetles or carabids, and several families of sucking insects belonging to the order Hemiptera. In addition to the insects there are a number of other arthropods that prey upon insects. Because they are commonly confused with insects and because too little is known specifically about their effectiveness in the control of forest insects to justify separate treatment, they will be included in this section.

Spiders and Mites.   Of the noninsect arthropodous orders, spiders and mites are among the most important predators in the forest. General observation indicates that they are of tremendous importance, but unfortunately, they have never been adequately studied as to their effectiveness in control. Spiders which spin webs not only capture certain innocuous flying insects but also catch small larvae of various kinds, especially those that drop from trees on threads of silk.

Other families of spiders that do not depend upon web traps to capture their prey are also capable of checking the increase of tree insects. These hunting spiders can move about actively in search of food and, therefore, are in a better position to concentrate upon spots where high concentrations of insect pests prevail. The exact part that spiders play in regulating forest-insect populations cannot be known until further study of their actions has been made.

Similarly, very little information can be found in literature concerning the effects of predaceous mites upon forest insects. Nevertheless, general observation indicates clearly that these organisms are among the most active predators of scale insects. Tothill (1919) studied the activities of one of these predators, *Hemisarcoptes malus*. This tiny arthropod exercises an important controlling influence by eating the eggs of the oyster-shell scale, *Lepidosaphes ulmi*. Doubtless many other predaceous mites are equally important, but unfortunately, we know comparatively little about them.

The fact that serological tests can be used to determine that a spider or mite has fed recently upon a certain insect species has been demonstrated by Longhton, Derry, and West in New Brunswick (Morris, 1963). Their work demonstrated that a considerable proportion of the spiders and mites collected had fed upon the spruce budworm. They believe that, through the precipitation test described, an accurate evaluation of spider and mite predation will be possible. Furthermore, a limited number of similar tests indicate that by the same technique assessment of the influence of other predators is feasible. Thus, the forest entomologist has available an effective means of learning by indirect means facts that cannot be observed directly.

Lacewing Flies. Members of the family Chrysopidae, of the order Neuroptera, commonly called lacewing flies, are predaceous upon other small insects in both the larval and the adult stages. They are especially fond of aphids, but they also eat scale insects, small caterpillars, and various other prey. These predators are especially valuable late in the season at which time aphid outbreaks frequently occur. Unfortunately there is apparently considerable mortality of lacewing flies during the winter. As a result, they are not usually abundant in early summer and, therefore, cannot exercise much control at that time of year. The rapid increase in number of the lacewings as the season advances is made possible by their short life cycle, some species passing through three or four generations during a season.

The adult lacewing fly is a slender fragile-appearing insect, about ½ inch in length, with delicate, many-veined, membranous wings. The wings when at rest are folded against the body and meet over the insect's back in a form resembling a tent. The adults present anything but the appearance of predators. The larvae, on the other hand, look quite ferocious. They are elongate, somewhat flattened, and have a pair of long, curved mandibles projecting forward from the mouth. These mandibles are hollow, and it is through them that the insect sucks the blood of its prey.

The habits of the lacewing flies present a number of interesting features, the first of which has to do with oviposition. When a female lacewing is ready to lay an egg, she touches her abdomen to the surface of the leaf or other object on which she is resting, whereupon a drop of viscous fluid exudes from the end of her abdomen. Then she pulls the drop of liquid out into a slender thread by raising her abdomen. This thread quickly hardens in an erect position, and on the top of it an egg is deposited. In this way, the eggs are held almost ½ inch above the surface to which they are attached. This method of placing the eggs on a stalk raises them out of reach of the lacewing larvae, which are cannibalistic, and other predaceous insects.

When the larvae hatch from the eggs, they immediately start out in search of food. Almost any insect that is small enough to be held is attacked, impaled upon the mandibles, and drained of its blood. When food is abundant and temperature conditions are favorable, the larvae grow rapidly, molt twice, and then spin about themselves a light silken cocoon. The cocoons may be located in a bark crevice, on the lower side of a leaf, or in some other more or less secluded location. During the summer months, the pupal stage is completed in several weeks, but when pupation occurs in the autumn, the pupal stage continues over winter. When we learn how to protect these overwintering pupae, we shall be able to increase the effectiveness of lacewing flies as control agencies.

Lady Beetles. The lady beetles are members of the family Coccinellidae and are for the most part predaceous. Like the lacewing flies, they eat small insects in both the adult and the larval stages. Aphids or scale insects are their usual prey, but they will feed upon small caterpillars, mites, or almost any small organism that they may find. In Michigan, the author has observed instances when a comparatively large coccinellid, the 15-spotted lady beetle, *Anatis ocellata,* was partly responsible for checking an outbreak of the jack-pine budworm.

The life cycle of the lady beetles, as might be expected, varies somewhat with the species. Many of them have two or more generations even in northern latitudes, while in the South a still greater number may be completed. The insects pass the winter in the adult stage, hidden away in some protected location. Many of them may creep into buildings for the purpose of hibernating. When spring arrives, the beetles leave their winter quarters and seek suitable places for oviposition. The eggs are laid in a variety of ways, depending upon the species. One of the California lady beetles, *Rhizobius ventralis,* deposits its eggs beneath the scale of the black-scale insect. The larvae that hatch from these eggs feed upon the eggs of the scale.

Some of our common native species deposit their eggs in groups on the surface of the foliage upon which their prey feeds. The eggs are usually yellow and resemble somewhat those of chrysomelids, or leaf beetles. The larvae are campodeiform and active. Immediately after hatching, they begin to search for food. These larvae are strange-looking creatures. Many of them are mottled with contrasting colors and are covered with branched spines. Their mandibles are long and sharp, so that they are well equipped to capture small insects.

After the larvae complete their growth, they transform, usually on the tree, to the pupal stage. The pupae are naked and are often found in conspicuous places. The beetles that emerge from the cocoons during the summer lay eggs immediately for another generation, whereas those that emerge in the autumn seek out a suitable place for hibernation and there spend the winter.

Checkered Beetles. The checkered beetles belong to the family Cleridae and are all predaceous, most of them upon bark beetles and other insects that bore into the bark and tips of trees. One of the most common species in the United States is the American bark-beetle destroyer, *Thanasimus dubius*. This species feeds almost exclusively upon bark beetles. It is a large clerid, measuring nearly ½ inch in length. It is very brightly colored with the bright-red background marked with black and silver transverse bands. This type of marking is characteristic of all checkered beetles. These insects are predaceous in both the larval and the adult stages. The adults feed most often upon adult bark beetles, while the larvae usually eat the immature stages beneath the bark.

The eggs are deposited in the tunnels of bark beetles. The larvae, more or less grublike in form, with poorly developed legs but with powerful mandibles, are usually pinkish in color. When numerous, they materially reduce the number of bark beetles. After completing their development, the larvae cut their way into the outer bark. There they hollow out for

FIGURE 36. Inner side of a piece of ponderosa pine bark showing the winding galleries of the western pine beetle and the broad frass-filled galleries of a cerambycid borer. The irregularly shaped black spot in the center of the picture is a hole cut from the outside by a woodpecker in search of food. (U.S. Dept. Agr. Forest Service.)

themselves cells in which they pass the pupal stage. According to Hopkins (1899), this insect may pass the winter in any stage of development. In the spring they complete their development if they passed the winter in an immature stage. By the time of the spring flight of the bark beetles, they have all transformed to adults and are ready to attack their prey.

There are many other species of clerids that attack bark beetles in various localities. One of the commonest and probably the most important western species is *Enoclerus sphegus*. It feeds actively on various bark beetles and has attracted special attention by its attacks on dendroctonus beetles. Its habits are very similar to those described for *Thanasimus dubius*.

All the clerids exert a decided influence upon bark-beetle populations, and everything possible should be done to encourage them. Since the clerids are more resistant to high temperature than most bark beetles, sun-curing logs to control beetle broods often kills the bark beetles without causing serious injury to the clerids. As a result, the proportion of the predators in relation to the number of remaining bark beetles is increased.

Calosoma Beetles. The ground beetles, or carabids, belonging to the genus *Calosoma,* are among the important predators of lepidopterous larvae. They are the largest and the most conspicuous of all the ground

FIGURE 37. Calasoma beetle, Carabidae, preying upon larvae of the elm spanworm. Note variation in larval color. (U.S. Dept. Agr. Forest Service.)

beetles. Their habits have been studied in great detail by Collins (Burgess and Collins, 1917) in connection with investigations of the gypsy moth and its enemies in New England. The life cycles and habits of all the beetles of this genus are very similar. The eggs are deposited in the ground at a depth of 4 to 6 inches. Upon hatching, the larvae make their way to the surface of the ground, where they run about actively in search of food. At the end of the third instar, having completed their growth, they again penetrate into the soil, where they form for themselves earthern cells in which to pupate. Some species, soon after transformation to the adult, emerge from their pupal cells to feed on the ground, whereas others remain in the ground until spring. A few of these adult beetles even climb into the treetops, in contradiction to their common name.

One of these is the fiery hunter, *Calosoma calidum*, which climbs trees not only while in the adult stage but also as larvae, a very unusual habit for a ground beetle. In the adult stage, the beetles of this genus are all unusually long-lived. Collins reports that in the field, unless they meet with some accident, the beetles will live for 2 or 3 years. One fiery hunter in captivity lived for 4 years. The length of life appears to be related to the rate of reproduction of the individual beetle. Those individuals that lay eggs most freely in early life live for a shorter time than those that reproduce more slowly.

Predaceous Bugs. The Hemiptera, or true bugs, are mostly phytophagous, sucking sap from plants. Several families, however, are almost all predaceous. All the members of the Reduviidae, the assassin bugs, are predaceous. One of the well-known members of this family is the wheel bug, *Arilus cristatus*. This insect is common throughout the eastern and central United States south of the latitude of New York City. The wheel bugs lay their eggs on plants or other objects in groups of 50 or even more. The young nymphs, red in color with long legs and four-jointed antennae, run about over plants in search of insect food. At first they can attack only small insects, such as aphids, but the size of their prey increases with their growth. By the time they have reached their full growth of ¾ inch, no insect seems too large for them.

Another family of the Hemiptera containing many species predaceous upon forest insects is the Pentatomidae. They are called stink bugs, because of their disagreeable odor, and soldier bugs, because of their predaceous habits. Some members of this family are entirely phytophagous, but many feed upon the blood of other insects during at least a part of their lives.

One of the soldier bugs, *Podisus placidus*, is a very effective predator upon tree-inhabiting insects, especially caterpillars. When fully grown, it is nearly ½ inch in length and yellow mottled with brown in color. Its life history is very similar to that of many other soldier bugs and, therefore, will serve to illustrate the group.

The winter is passed in the adult stage, usually buried in litter on the ground. On emergence from hibernation, the adults feed for a short time and then lay their yellow eggs in groups, often on the underside of a leaf. The young nymphs are either red or black in color and for a time feed on the sap of plants. After about 2 weeks, when they adopt the predaceous habit, they promptly pay for the slight injury caused by their feeding on plants. In the North, the soldier bugs complete two generations each season, while in the South they may have as many as four or five.

Several other members of the Hemiptera are also predaceous, but most of them are less important in the forest than those mentioned in this discussion. Still other groups of insects are predatory upon forest insects and might well be considered if space permitted. Altogether, insect predators are important factors that should not be overlooked in planning for the control of forest insects.

INSECTIVOROUS VERTEBRATES

The insectivorous vertebrates, especially birds and mammals, have received much attention as agencies for insect control. Undoubtedly, they do exercise a controlling influence upon forest-insect populations. In Chap. 5 we have already discussed these animals as to their density-dependent influence upon their insect prey. In that discussion some of the limitations of these organisms were brought out and hence need not be repeated. These limitations do, however, influence the use of vertebrates for control and should be kept in mind when these organisms are considered as control agencies.

Mammals.   Almost all carnivorous animals eat insects, and a few live almost entirely on insects and other arthropods. Some of the mammals that are not usually thought of as being insectivorous actually destroy many forest insects. For example, mice and voles, in some years and on certain sites, destroy more larch-sawfly cocoons than all the parasites combined (Graham, 1928).

Skunks, shrews, weasels, foxes, and many other mammals consume great quantities of insects on the ground. Their activities are especially beneficial during the dormant season when many species of harmful forest insects are in hibernation either on or in the ground. Even during the summer, skunks are diligent predators upon soil-inhabiting insects, digging them from beneath the surface. Numerous holes, like small inverted cones, attest to the industry of these animals wherever white grubs are common.

Encouragement and protection of these valuable insect eaters should always be considered in planning the insect control program for any forest. Unfortunately, the opportunities to do this are usually overlooked. In general, desirable conditions for insectivorous mammals may be attained by diversification of both trees and ground cover. Such diversification may sometimes be aided by the use of chemicals. For example, defoliation by the gypsy moth results in abnormal exposure of the ground cover beneath the trees. Thus, the character of the vegetation may be changed by eliminating species sensitive to hot sunlight. Such a change may be expected, in turn, to affect the animal populations normally present. Spraying the forest may, then, by preventing undesirable habitat changes, help to maintain populations of desirable ground-inhabitating predators.

When the use of mammals for the control of forest insects is considered, we naturally think of the introduction of new species. This method has thus far never been used in the forest, and probably attempts along this line should not be encouraged. The danger of introducing predatory mammals is illustrated by experience with the mongoose. This animal was introduced into certain of the West Indian islands to control reptiles. This objective was accomplished reasonably well, but at the same time the animal became a pest. Because of its taste for domestic birds, it has jeopardized poultry raising (Williams, 1918).

Birds. Of all the vertebrates, birds are probably the most important insect eaters. McAtee (1926) mentions numerous instances in which birds have brought insects under control. He cites the elm spanworm, *Ennomos subsignarius*, which once was exceedingly injurious to ornamental trees. With the introduction and establishment of the English sparrow in the cities and towns of this country, it has become a relatively rare insect on city trees. Instances have been observed in which birds have destroyed from 15 to 89 percent of all the fall-webworm larvae in certain localities (Tothill, 1922). In a study of the natural agencies that control the white-marked tussock moth, Dustan (1923) reports that almost every egg mass above the snow line was partially or wholly destroyed by birds. This amounted to 90 percent of the egg masses. The cankerworms, the tent caterpillars, the gypsy moth, in fact practically every kind of leaf-eating insect are fed upon by many species of birds.

Many birds are highly insectivorous throughout their lives. The swallows, martins, and nighthawks are among these. Others are more or less omnivorous: the crows, blackbirds, thrushes, and gallinaceous birds. Almost all the perching birds, including even the seed-eating finches, are highly insectivorous in the nestling stage. Because these seed eaters are nesting during the period of greatest insect abundance, they are valuable aids in holding down insect populations. Therefore the forester should give them every aid that is practicable.

The encouragement of birds, as with mammals, can be accomplished in part by diversification in the forest. The more diversified the environmental conditions, the greater will be the variety of bird species. In this connection we should bear in mind that territorial limitations operate within species and not among species. For this reason, the greatest possible bird population can be obtained only in places where the greatest diversity of environment prevails, because there the largest number of species will find favorable places to live. The forester must remember that in the carefully managed forest favored nesting sites for certain birds are often incidentally eliminated, especially those that nest in the hollows or holes of tree trunks. Without such nesting places, those birds will be eliminated from the forest, at least for the nesting season. In some European forests, the provision of nesting boxes for hole-inhabiting birds is common and is said to pay a high return on the investment.

The introduction of bird predators is often urged as a means of controlling forest insects, but this procedure is attended with more evident risk than is the case with invertebrates. Flexibility of habit and great powers of mobility make these vertebrates effective predators, but these same characteristics may make them undesirable additions to the environment. Several examples illustrate this, although none of the introduced birds happens to be of the forest-inhabiting species. Several introduced birds have become undesirable competitors with native species. For example the English sparrow, mentioned previously, although it accomplished some good, reduced the number of native bird predators in the areas where it became abundant. Similarly the starling, although highly insectivorous, has become a pest in cities, where it roosts in great flocks and has come into direct competition with more desirable native species. These and other instances of introduced predators serve as a warning of the possible risks involved if birds are introduced without careful consideration of their desirability in our forest environment.

CONCLUSIONS ABOUT BIOTIC CONTROL

There is a popular idea that parasitic and predatory species can perform miracles in forest-insect control and that these organisms, properly handled, could eliminate the danger of all insect epidemics. Valuable as these organisms undoubtedly are, they are only a part of environmental resistance. Furthermore, neither parasites nor predators will ordinarily eliminate their host or prey. The fact that all these forms of life have lived together for generations is prima facie evidence that the former do not usually destroy the latter. Therefore, when we introduce one organism to control another, we have no right to expect better results than the beneficial species has been able to produce in its native land. Biotic pressure can exert a powerful influence in holding down pest populations, but working alone, it can neither eliminate pests nor altogether prevent outbreaks.

Precautions. In introducing an organism into a new environment, we should observe certain precautions. First be sure that the organism is provided with satisfactory physical conditions. Introductions should be made only into new areas where the climatic conditions, in their essential characteristics, resemble the native home of the organism. This is an important consideration which has often been neglected and which explains many of the failures that have been experienced in the past.

Introductions should be attempted only in locations where the host or prey is present in abundance. Furthermore, the food species must be in a stage and in a position suitable for attack; otherwise the introduced animals will inevitably starve, and our efforts will be wasted.

Organisms should always be introduced in large numbers. It is far better to release many individuals in one location than to release the same number scattered over a large area. Experience has demonstrated the truth of this over and over again, not only with insects but also with vertebrates.

In the introduction of parasitic insects, care must be exercised to avoid the release of undesirable species. Prominent among these are the hyperparasites. Some species are primary at one time or on one host, whereas at another time or on another host they may be hyperparasitic. Therefore, special care must be exercised, especially with parasites of small size, to avoid introduction of species of this sort. Also, it is unwise to introduce species that promise to be less effective than those already present. Once established in a natural environment, an insect species can seldom, if ever, be removed. Therefore, it behooves us to be sure of our choice of an introductee before it is too late.

Ideally, the complete life history, its reactions to the physical habitat, and its ecological relations with other organisms should be known before an organism is introduced. Practical limitations of time and expense prevent the attainment of this ideal. But no parasite or predator should be introduced until at least the principal facts concerning its life history and habits have been determined.

Interpretation of Results. The results of parasite and predator activities are often difficult to interpret. To do this accurately requires careful population studies, which may be impracticable. However, we are often able, by simple counts of parasitized and unparasitized insects in samples representative of the population, to determine the proportion of a particular stage that has been destroyed. Sometimes these observations are expressed as if they represent the effect upon the population of the insect as a whole when actually it applies to only one stage. For example, a predator may destroy 75 percent of all the pupae of the larch sawfly. This obviously does not mean that the predator is responsible for a 75 percent reduction of the sawfly population, as some authors say, but merely that the pupae alone were destroyed to that extent. Care should always be used when quantitative statements are made relative to the effects of biotic factors that these statements are expressed in accurate terms. The total effects of a resistance factor upon the population of an insect species can be expressed only in terms of the potential population of that species. The effect observed upon a single stage, therefore, is only a segment of the whole and should always be so indicated.

In conclusion, we repeat emphatically that the use of parasites and predators provides invaluable opportunities to control injurious forest-insect populations. These biotic methods should not be overlooked if we are to manage our forests effectively and economically.

BIBLIOGRAPHY CHAPTER 13

Balduff, W. V., 1926. The bionomics of *Dinocampus coccinellae*, *Ann. Entomol. Soc. Am.*, **19**: 465–498.

Burgess, A. F., 1926. Control of the gypsy moth and brown-tail moth by parasites, *J. Econ. Entomol.*, **19**: 289–294.

————, and C. W. Collins, 1915. The calosoma beetle, *U.S. Dept. Agr. Bull.* 251.

————, and ————, 1917. The genus *Calosoma*, *U.S. Dept. Agr. Bull.* 417.

Clausen, C. P., 1956. Biological control of insect pests in the continental United States, *U.S. Dept. Agr. Tech. Bull.* 1139.

Collins, C. W., 1936. Natural enemies' control of the saddled prominent, *J. Agr. Res.*, **32**: 689–699.

Craigheed, F. C., 1950. Insect enemies of eastern forests, *U.S. Dept. Agr. Misc. Pub.* 657.

Crossman, S. S., 1922. *Apanteles melanoscelus*, *U.S. Dept. Agr. Bull.* 1028.

Culver, J. J., 1919. *Compsilura concinnata*, *U.S. Dept. Agr. Bull.* 766.

Dowden, P. B., 1933. Two fly parasites of defoliators, *J. Agr. Res.*, **46**: 963–995.

————, 1962. Parasites and predators of forest insects liberated in the United States through 1960, *U.S. Dept. Agr. Handbook* 226.

————, et al., 1948. Natural control of the spruce budworm, *J. Econ. Entomol.*, **41**: 457–463.

Dustan, A. G., 1923. Natural control of the white-marked tussock-moth, *Proc. Acadian Entomol. Soc.*, **8**: 109–126.

Graham, S. A., 1928. Small mammals and larch sawfly, *J. Econ. Entomol.*, **21**: 301–310.

————, 1930. Ornithology and forest entomology, *Mich. Acad. Sci., Arts, Letters*, **XI**: 389–397.

Hodson, A. C., 1939. Egg parasites of forest tent caterpillar, *Ann. Entomol. Soc. Am.*, **32**: 131–136.

————, 1939. *Sarcophaga aldrichi*, a parasite of forest tent caterpillar, *J. Econ. Entomol.*, **32**: 396–401.

Holling, C. S., 1958. Sensory stimuli involved in the location and selection of sawfly cocoons by small mammals, *Can. J. Zool.*, **36**: 633–653.

————, 1961. Principles of insect predation, *Ann. Rev. Entomol.*, **6**: 163–182.

Hopkins, A. D., 1899. Insect enemies in Northwest, *U.S. Dept. Agr., Div. Entomol., Bull.* 21, pp. 13–15.

Howard, L. O., 1897. Insect parasitism, *U.S. Dept. Agr., Div. Entomol., Bull.* 5.

———, 1926. The parasite element of natural control, *J. Econ. Entomol.,* 19: 271–282.

———, 1931. "The Insect Menace," Appleton-Century-Crofts, Inc., New York.

Knight, F. B., 1958. The effects of woodpeckers on populations of the Engelmann spruce beetle, *J. Econ. Entomol.,* 51: 603–607.

Massey, C. L., 1962. New species of Diplogasteridae (Nematoda) associated with bark beetles in the United States, *Proc. Helminthol. Soc. Wash.,* 29: 67–75.

McAtee, W. L., 1925. Vertebrate control of insect pests, *Smithsonian Inst. Rept.,* pp. 415–437.

———, 1926. The relation of birds to woodlots, *Roosevelt Wild Life Forest Expt. Sta., N.Y. State Coll. Forestry,* 4: 1–154.

———, 1931. Local bird refuges, *U.S. Dept. Agr. Farmers' Bull.* 1644.

McGugan, B. M., 1960. Biological control of forest insects; the role of parasites and predators, *Proc. Fifth World Forestry Congress,* 2: 935–940.

Morris, R. F. (ed.), 1963. The dynamics of epidemic spruce budworm populations, *Mem. Entomol. Soc. Can.* 31.

Person, H. L., 1940. The clerid, *Thanasimus lecontii,* in the control of the western pine beetle, *J. Forestry,* 38: 390–396.

Peterson, Alvah, 1930. A biological study of *Trichogramma minutum, U.S. Dept. Agr. Tech. Bull.* 215.

Ross, W. A., 1918. Ladybird beetles destructive to plant lice, *Agr. Gazette Can.,* 5: 344–347.

St. George, R. A., 1924. A beetle predacious on powder-post beetles, *J. Agr. Res.,* 29: 49–56.

Shelford, V. E., 1926. The relation of parasites to weather conditions, *J. Econ. Entomol.,* 19: 283–289.

Smith, R. C., 1922. The biology of the Chrysopidae, *Cornell Agr. Expt. Sta. Mem.* 58.

Strickland, E. H., 1928. Can birds hold injurious insects in check? *Sci. Monthly,* XXVI: 48–56.

Struble, G. R., and M. E. Martignoni, 1959. Role of parasites and disease in controlling *Recurvaria milleri* Busck., *J. Econ. Entomol.,* 52: 531–532.

Tothill, J. D., 1919. Natural control of the oyster-shell scale, *Bull. Entomol. Res.,* 9: 183–196.

———, 1922. Natural control of fall webworm, *Can. Dept. Agr. Bull.* 3 (new ser.).

Webber, R. T., and J. V. Schaffner, 1926. Host relations of *Compsilura concinnata* Meigen, *U.S. Dept. Agr. Bull.* 1363.

Wilkes, A., 1946. Introduction of spruce budworm parasites into eastern Canada, *Can. Entomologist,* 78: 82–86.

Willard, H. F., and A. C. Mason, 1937. Parasitization of the Mediterranean fruitfly in Hawaii, 1914–1933, *U.S. Dept. Agr. Circ.* 439.

Williams, C. B., 1918. The food of the mongoose in Trinidad, *Trinidad Tobago, Dept. Agr. Bull.* 17, pp. 167–186.

CHAPTER 14

INDIRECT CONTROL BY SILVICULTURAL PRACTICES

Every operation in the forest influences the environment and thereby creates conditions that are either favorable or unfavorable for harmful forest insects. Many of man's practices in the past have unconsciously encouraged insect outbreaks. These errors should be avoided in the future. Fortunately, it is possible not only to avoid creating conditions conducive to outbreaks but actually to produce safer conditions in the course of regular logging operations without any additional cost. In other instances, special operations may be required to correct past errors or to create desirable conditions. Usually the cost of these operations should be less than the expense entailed by direct methods of control. However, we cannot assume blindly that this is true in every case. Without exception, the benefits from any control measure must be weighed against the cost.

BASIS FOR SILVICULTURAL CONTROL

The Biotic Balance. Generally speaking, the control of insects by silvicultural practices is accomplished through the adjustment of the biotic balance and the avoidance of practices that will disturb that balance. In this connection we should bear in mind that, during the development of a forest from youth to maturity, the value of the individual environmental factors is continuously changing. As the force of one factor diminishes, another increases, thus maintaining the equilibrium under changing environmental conditions. This developmental sequence in the life of a forest is accompanied by a sequence of insect species characterizing each stage. As a result, different age-classes of a tree species are not ordinarily subject to injury by the same insects. This, as we shall see, is of importance silviculturally in handling tree species that grow naturally in pure stands.

Following Nature's Plan. Experience has shown that some forest types are highly subject to insect injury whereas others are relatively safe. Obviously our objective should be to decrease the areas occupied by the former and increase those occupied by the latter. Unfortunately, forestry in America is too young to have provided an adequate background of silvicultural experience to serve as a basis for indirect control, but the manner in which our virgin forests developed to maturity without disastrous insect injury, following nature's silvicultural plan, provides a pattern that we can follow. In time, having accumulated a background of silvicultural experience, we may find ways of improving on nature. In the meantime, we shall do well to gain a better understanding of nature's successful practices through the ecological analysis of successful forest types.

REGULATION OF FOREST COMPOSITION

Of all the silvicultural practices, the one that offers the widest opportunity for producing conditions that will discourage insect outbreaks is the regulation of forest composition. When such regulation is handled properly, we have at our command an invaluable means of insect control. On the other hand, if the possibilities for control are ignored, man-made changes in forest composition may actually serve to bring on outbreaks.

Importance of Mixed Stands. Any study of our country's virgin forests will furnish incontestable proof that mixed stands are much safer from insect injury than are pure stands. In fact we may safely say that the greater the diversification of tree species, the less frequent will be insect outbreaks. This is an illustration of the general ecological principle that *other things being equal, the degree of environmental stability is in direct proportion to the number of species living together in an environment.* The truth of this becomes clear when we remember that in a diverse environment important limitations upon dangerous pests prevail. For example, the risk attendant upon the search for food is far greater than in pure stands where every tree provides a food supply. Furthermore, diversity, both of insects living on the trees and of the parasites and predators feeding upon them, results in a multiplicity of interactions that tend to limit the increase of all species in the complex environment. As examples of mixed types in which disastrous outbreaks seldom or never occur, we may mention the so-called mixed mesophytic forests of the

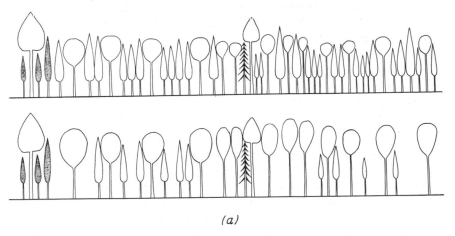

(a)

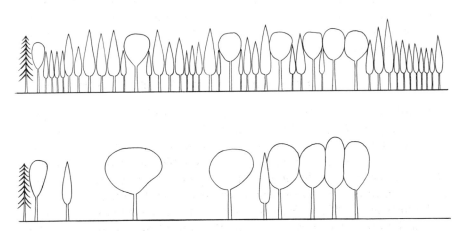

(b)

FIGURE 38. Diagrammatic cross section of two forest areas illustrating the effect of a spruce-budworm outbreak upon forests of different compositions in the same locality. Balsam fir is represented by a narrow unshaded cone, pine by a broad cone, spruce by the figure with drooping branches, other conifers by the shaded cone, and hardwoods by the rounded cone. The upper line of each pair represents conditions existing before the outbreak; the lower, conditions following the outbreak. A is a stand containing a considerable mixture of balsam fir with hardwoods, some pine, and other conifers. B represents a stand that was predominantly balsam fir. B was much more severely injured than A. It is doubtful if an outbreak could have built up in A if it had not been for a preponderance of adjacent stands similar to B.

Ohio Valley, the mixed southern hardwoods, the mixed northern hard-woods, the mixed coniferous forests on the western slopes of the northern Rocky Mountains, and the mixed forests of the Douglas-fir region.

Each of these types is made up of a combination of tolerant and in-tolerant species. In them the natural trend is toward the elimination of the intolerant trees and the perpetuation of the more tolerant, shade-loving kinds. In the northern hardwoods, for instance, only sugar maple, hemlock, and beech can persist indefinitely because they are the only species living in their climatic area that can reproduce and survive in shade. The more intolerant species, such as birch, elm, oak, and ash, find little opportunity to reproduce except in openings of at least $\frac{1}{10}$ acre. Under primeval conditions the reproduction of these intolerant trees has been made possible by disasters—fire, fungi, and insects. Similarly, the trend in the northern Rocky Mountains is toward the tolerant true firs; in the Douglas-fir region, toward hemlock.

Therefore, if we are to maintain the highly diversified "insectproof" condition characteristic of the true mixed forest, now that catastrophic events are largely eliminated, we must seriously consider this objective in planning logging operations. One of the most promising methods that will maintain the mixed condition is to cut in small groups. On the other hand, individual tree selection that does not tend toward groups is prob-ably the worst practice from the standpoint of insect control. Individual tree selection tends to encourage pure stands of tolerant species and will ultimately lead to outbreaks of such insects as the hemlock looper, *Lambdina* sp.; the forest tent caterpillar, *Malacosoma disstria;* the sad-dled prominent, *Heterocampa guttivitta;* and numerous other pests of the tolerant forest types.

In types less diversified than the mixed forests mentioned above, log-ging should be conducted in such a manner that a maximum variety of tree species can develop. Even in the spruce-fir forests, the mixture fol-lowing cutting can be improved by cutting in groups or strips. This system will create openings where spruce, aspen, birch, and balsam fir will grow up together, the hardwoods protecting the conifers from attack of insects until the firs approach maturity.

If cutting areas are so distributed that contiguous units are cut at intervals of not less than 10 to 15 years, it seems almost certain that out-breaks of such insects as the spruce budworm will be prevented. Under this system only from one-tenth to one-fifteenth of an area would be-come subject to attack each year; moreover, these susceptible units would be scattered. In this manner a mixture of species would be main-tained while the trees are young and a mixture by age-classes as the trees approach maturity.[1]

[1] Logging in small scattered units, as suggested above, or planting in such a manner that similar diversification is obtained presupposes that operations are on areas

Under some situations the application of pesticides may be utilized for silvicultural purposes. For example, if defoliation, such as that caused by the gypsy moth, is prevented by a treatment with an insecticide, the normal variety of plants and animals on the forest floor can be maintained. Without such treatment, defoliation and the resultant exposure to intense radiation will eliminate many light- or heat-sensitive plants and animals from the forest (Turner, 1963).

Ensuring Suitable Reproduction. Control of insects by regulation of composition depends for its success upon the establishment, after logging, of an adequate amount of satisfactory reproduction of all the desired species. Many trees cannot reproduce successfully on soil covered with organic debris. Therefore, logging operations that do not scarify the ground, exposing mineral soil for a seedbed, may result in the elimination of certain species from a mixture. This is true of the fir-spruce-aspen-birch mixtures. If the soil is left undisturbed after logging, balsam fir will increase at the expense of the spruce and hardwoods—a most undesirable condition (Crosley, 1949). Scarification can be secured during summer logging by using tractors for skidding. On areas logged in winter, scarification could be accomplished by harrowing, subsequent to logging and prior to the ripening of a seed crop. When reproduction of the desired species does not occur naturally, it may be wise to resort to planting in order to maintain a safe mixture of species.

The dangers which are attendant upon changing mixed stands into pure stands are well illustrated by the history of jack pine in the Lake States. Originally this species grew on comparatively small areas on poor sandy soils, interspersed with other forest types growing on better soils. After the white and red pine were logged off, the jack pine extended its domain over vast areas. The original forest had been notably free from insect injury, but since 1920 the jack pine, now growing over extensive continuous areas, has suffered from at least three serious defoliators and two scale insects.

Diversifying Single-species Forests. A question that may well be asked at this point is when, if ever, can pure forests be grown without danger of major insect attack? Certain species are normally found in natural pure stands, for example, ponderosa, longleaf, and slash pines, as well as red and jack pines. These natural pine stands were not excessively subject to devastation by pests. Therefore, the establishment of single-species stands that are relatively free from attack should be possible. To do this, man must understand the conditions of the natural pure forests that ensured survival and be prepared to duplicate the essential condi-

accessible by road. Logging operations from large temporary camps do not lend themselves to these desirable practices. Fortunately, the trend is away from such operations and toward scattered cuttings. However, monoculture and mechanization in some southern forests seem to be headed in the wrong direction.

tions. The importance of these conditions seems to have been overlooked. Those natural pure stands that proved to be insect-resistant were composed of limited-sized groups of different age-classes. Man has erred in not duplicating these features in his silvicultural practices. A mixture of age-classes creates a safer condition than would prevail in an extensive single-age forest.

Mixed-age-classes in pure forest types can be secured by either scattered cuttings or plantings. In either procedure, the aim will be to mix

FIGURE 39. Overmature jack pine severely defoliated by the jack-pine budworm. Although they had lost more than 80 percent of their normal complement of foliage, these trees recovered.

age-classes groupwise in small units so that no contiguous groups are in the same age-class. In this way, at any one time, only a fraction of a large area can be subject to attack by a certain insect.

Whenever this practice of diversification by age-classes has been ignored in pure stands, man has had to contend with insect outbreaks. An example of this is to be observed in the Lake States where, from 1932 to 1938, thousands of acres of national and state forest lands were planted in solid blocks with red-pine seedlings. Within 10 years, several serious insect pests became so numerous that direct control measures were necessary to save the plantations.

Causes Leading to Hazardous Conditions. Pure stands have been created by destructive logging and fire as well as by planting; regardless of their origin, they are equally subject to insect attack. Examples of pure stands created by logging are common: for instance aspen stands, attacked by forest tent caterpillar; oak forests, subject to attack by walkingsticks, *Diapheromera femorata;* stands of paper birch, attacked by various defoliators; forests predominantly balsam fir, attacked by the spruce bud-worm; and pure pine stands, attacked by several species of sawflies.

Animals, both wild and domestic, have also been responsible for unde-sirable changes in forest composition; for example, the elimination of particularly palatable tree species, such as yellow birch, elm, and bass-wood, by deer browsing in localities where overzealous protection has

FIGURE 40. Wind-thrown trees in a bog-seepage forest in northern Michigan following the storm of October 10, 1949. Excessive increase of noxious insects was prevented by prompt salvage of fallen trees. A similar catastrophe in the same swamp in 1940 was followed by an out-break of the northern spruce beetle that built up in the wind-thrown trees.

permitted these animals to increase excessively; also the disruption of the normal distribution of age-classes in various forest types where overgraz-ing by domestic stock has been permitted. In each case the trend toward pure stands and a single-age-class has increased the danger of insect out-breaks.

REGULATION OF DENSITY

In addition to the regulation of forest composition there are a number of other silvicultural means by which the harmful activities of forest insects may be reduced. One of these is the regulation of forest density. One of the objectives of regulating density in the interest of insect con-trol is to maintain thrifty growth. Thrifty, rapidly growing trees are gen-erally far less subject to insect injury than are slow-growing, unthrifty individuals in a comparable situation.

Thinning to Stimulate Vigor. If young trees are standing too close together to permit satisfactory growth of dominant and codominant trees, removal of part of the stand by thinning or partial cutting will often ensure vigor and thereby lower the danger of insect devastation. Thinning is usually accomplished by use of the axe and the saw. The economic justification for such operations is apparent if the materials cut can be marketed for a price sufficient to cover the cost of the operation. If the products cut are not salable, thinning might entail an outright expenditure of from $20 to $30 per acre, the justifiability of which might logically be questioned. Some authorities have recommended a less expensive method of thinning certain forest types, namely, controlled or regulated burning. Unrestricted burning cannot be condoned, but controlled burning properly planned and executed can be a useful silvicultural tool (Weaver, 1947).

The age at which a stand requires thinning varies with the species and with the amount of water available in the soil. Before the crowns of a young stand have closed, the evaporating leaf surface is so small that the trees can grow well in locations where the available moisture is relatively low. Later, when the trees have closed together, the evaporating leaf surface is greatly increased while at the same time interception of precipitation by the crowns reduces the amount of water reaching the soil surface. Therefore, a stand of large seedlings or small saplings may grow well during their early years and suffer later from water deficiency. On dry sites this condition may develop long before the trees reach merchantable size, whereas on moister sites water shortage may never occur.

When severe competition for water develops, the growth rate and vigor of the trees are reduced, whereupon they become increasingly subject to attack and injury by pests. On the drier sites, this competition for water may develop at such an early age that the stand will fail to break up into the normal distribution of crown classes. As a result it becomes stagnant. On better sites, individual trees will gain dominance over the others, so that ultimately they will eliminate their smaller competitors. In the latter case, thinning to regulate density is seldom necessary. In the former it is essential if the trees are to be brought to commercial maturity. The age when thinning should be done and the intensity of thinning required will, as we have said, depend upon the amount of available water.

From this discussion it is evident that, on sites with adequate water, trees can grow in dense stands whereas on the drier sites only scattered groups or individual trees, separated from their neighbors, can reach maturity.

Encouraging Straight Growth. Although wide spacing may be desirable for trees above sapling size, seedlings and saplings are often benefited by growing in dense stands. This is especially useful in preventing injury from insects that damage the leading shoots. Obviously, young trees should never be grown so close together that satisfactory growth is impossible; on the other hand, they should be grown in sufficiently dense stands so that side shade will stimulate straight growth, thus maintaining the excurrent habit. This will cause trees injured by such insects as the white-pine weevil, *Pissodes strobi;* the Sitka-spruce weevil, *Pissodes sitchensis;* the reproduction weevil, *Cylindrocopturus eatoni;* and the European pine shoot moth, *Rhyacionia buoliana,* to outgrow injury (Graham, 1926; Miller, 1950). Furthermore, the white-pine weevil and most other shoot insects decline in numbers soon after the crowns close in a dense stand.

Eliminating Alternate Hosts. Density also has an important influence upon insects that require herbs or shrubs as alternate hosts. For example, the Saratoga spittlebug, *Aprophora saratogensis,* is dependent upon certain shrubs and herbs for food during the nymphal stage. Only in the adult stage does it attack and damage the young pines. The favored food plants for the nymphs are sweetfern and blackberries. When these intolerant shrubs are killed by shade, the source of infestation to the pines is eliminated.

Influencing Physical Factors. Forest density influences the physical conditions found in the forest by modifying such factors as light, evaporation, air movement, and temperature. Although the effect of these factors is evident from general observations, specific information concerning their influence on insect life in the forest is very scarce. It is known that many of the sun-loving beetles are attracted only to those trees or parts of trees that are exposed to the direct rays of the sun; for instance, the work of the two-lined borer, *Agrilus bilineatus,* is almost entirely confined to individual ornamental trees, to trees in open stands, or to the few exposed branches in fully stocked and stagnating stands (Chapman, 1915). The same is more or less true of the bronze birch borer, *Agrilus anxius;* the hemlock borer, *Melanophila fulvoguttata;* and many other species.

The effectiveness of predators is often affected by density of the forest. In open, abused forests they are likely to be less numerous than in denser stands (Bess, 1947). Fully stocked stands, therefore, afford an increased possibility of insect control through predatory insects.

Adaptation to Site Conditions. Site conditions have strikingly important influences on the susceptibility of trees to insect injury. Trees growing under site conditions to which they are adapted are thrifty and relatively resistant to insect injury. For example, Craighead (1925) has shown that balsam fir is much more resistant to injury by the spruce budworm when it is growing on a favorable site than when it is growing under poor conditions. He goes so far as to recommend growing this species in pure stands, on sites where the tree grows rapidly, in spite of the budworm menace. Whether or not such a recommendation should be accepted has been questioned, but the fact remains that vigorous trees survived an outbreak when growing on favorable sites whereas less vigorous trees in the same locality were almost all killed.

FIGURE 41. Pine root-collar weevil. Larva slightly longer than adult. Pupa about the same length as adult. Adult about ⅜ to ½ inch long. This weevil has caused much injury to planted pines in the Lake States. First observed in New York it has become a major pest in the Lake States in pine plantations growing in poor sites.

Temporary Intolerant Types. From observations in Minnesota and in Michigan (Hall, 1933), it appears that thrifty forests are, as a rule, immune to the bronze birch borer. This insect is usually secondary, but sometimes it becomes primary. In a fully stocked birch forest, after the rate of growth has been reduced because of overmaturity or competition, especially under poor site conditions, this insect will attack branches and the upper parts of the bole of somewhat decadent trees. At first the larvae may fail to survive and their tunnels will be overgrown. But after a number of years, repeated injury appears to reduce the tree's vigor until it dies. Thus openings in the stand are created. Then the exposed trees on the edge of the openings eventually become infested and die, thus enlarging the openings. Once this condition is reached, the borer population grows rapidly and the infestation may change from a secondary to a primary status. Stands of white birch growing on poor sites are almost certain to deteriorate in this manner before they reach a diameter of 6 inches. On better sites a similar deterioration does not occur until the trees reach an age of 75 to 100 years. Much of the second-growth white birch in the Northeastern forests is growing on poor soils, and for this reason agrilus may prevent most of these stands from reaching full development.

Site, therefore, must be considered seriously in formulating plans for handling stands of white birch. White-birch forests should always be utilized before they begin to deteriorate. On poor soils, especially, provision should be made to convert temporary birch forests to other species better suited to the site.

Similarly, stands of aspen and other temporary forests of intolerant species growing on poor sites will deteriorate at an early age. Insect pests are often associated with this deterioration. Therefore, all such species require silvicultural treatment similar to that suggested for birch. Site conditions should be a primary consideration in formulating the silvicultural plans.

Susceptibility to Bark-beetle Attack.   In the West, site is of considerable importance in determining the susceptibility of trees to bark-beetle attack. In stands of the same physiological age and character, the number of trees attacked will be higher on poor than on good sites. Moisture is the most important site factor responsible for this condition; therefore, the above statement fails to apply at high elevations, where temperature is the chief limiting factor. Also during seasons of unusually severe drought conditions, trees on good sites are affected even more than those on poor sites, the latter being better adjusted to water deficiency than stands usually more favorably located. Therefore, during periods of drought, outbreaks of bark beetles may develop on the better sites, and the forester must be prepared to control them by direct means.

Physiological Maturity.   Western white pine in the Inland Empire region of Idaho and Montana exhibits conspicuous reaction to site. According to information received from J. C. Evenden, in white-pine stands on poor sites growth is slow and the trees become subject to pest attack at an earlier age than those on good sites. In this case, moisture appears to be the controlling factor in the development of physiological maturity.

On the poorer sites, therefore, susceptibility to pests might be reduced by thinnings or partial cutting that would make more water available for the residual trees.

We may conclude that adaptation to site conditions may be accomplished in a variety of ways: (1) by converting off-site temporary types to types better suited to the site, (2) by encouraging species suited to the site, (3) by adopting appropriate thinning and cutting practices designed to adjust residual stands to site conditions.

REGULATING WATER LEVEL

Stimulating Growth. When unfavorable site conditions are due to water level, man can often make needed improvements. Sometimes a site is poor because of an excess of surface water. This may result in producing an acid soil and other conditions that inhibit growth. In some cases these conditions may be improved by the construction of a superficial drainage system to carry off the surplus water. Such operations, if they result in the stimulation of growth and the improvement of the tree's vigor, may justify their cost by the resulting reduced susceptibility to insect injury.

Modifying Ground Cover. Another effect that drainage may have in the case of swamp forests is to change the character of the ground cover. There is evidence that such a change will have an effect upon the overwintering stage of pests that hibernate in the layers of duff or in the surface vegetation (Graham, 1938). For instance, if certain tamarack swamps were superficially drained, the surface vegetation of moss and sedge would give way to other plants and become more varied. This, in turn, would bring about improved conditions for mice and shrews—animals that destroy large numbers of larch-sawfly cocoons. Furthermore, hibernation of the sawfly is most successful in the sphagnum hummocks that are so common in tamarack swamps. Therefore, a change from sphagnum ground cover to one more characteristic of drier land would increase the hazards of hibernation for the sawfly.

Raising Water Level. Removal of superficial water by drainage produces permanent changes conducive to lessening unfavorable insect activities, but sometimes these same results can be secured by temporarily raising the water level. This technique can be used to advantage against the larch sawfly. If the water level in a tamarack swamp is raised at the time of cocooning, the number of available spots suitable for this activity will be reduced. The cocoons then become concentrated in places where predators can more easily find and attack them. The opportunity to raise water levels is rare and hence not of so much importance as is surface drainage in the control of insect pests.

IMPROVEMENT OF PLANTING STOCK

Whenever reproduction is obtained by planting, it would be ideal if the forester could use stock that would produce a forest free from insect attack. Unfortunately this cannot be accomplished. Only occasionally can stock that is resistant to even one insect be found. The desirability of breeding insect-resistant strains of trees has long been recognized, and the possibilities of doing this are evident from the resistant individuals occasionally observed in the field. Unfortunately, little breeding of this sort has been done.

Breeding Trees for Resistance. Breeding trees for resistance is not easy. It is both expensive and time-consuming. Unfortunately, from the viewpoint of forest entomology, almost all tree-breeding work has been for other purposes than insect control. Undoubtedly, breeding for insect resistance could produce valuable results.

Occasionally breeding designed for other purposes produces strains having a high degree of insect resistance. For instance, a hybrid of Jeffrey and Coulter pine, developed at the U.S. Forest Service, Institute of Forest Genetics, proved to be very resistant to the highly injurious plantation weevil. The presence in the field of resistant individual ponderosa and Jeffrey pines indicates that resistant varieties of either species might be obtained by selection; however, the hybrid affords an immediate source of a limited quantity of resistant seed.

In discussing this hybrid, Miller (1950) points out that resistance is apparently accomplished in part by walling off the attacked areas in the bark before the larvae reach the vital cambium and in part by the production of large quantities of resin. The former reaction is indicated by a thick layer of cork cells surrounding the necrotic areas. The latter is evidenced by a great concentration of resin ducts inside the cambium and also by the flow of the resin from these ducts into the bark. A similar condition is evident in resistant individuals of both Jeffrey and ponderosa pine.

Selection from Desirable Parents. Although the possibilities of tree breeding are recognized, we cannot expect to obtain many resistant varieties in the near future. Therefore, at least for the present, the production of resistant planting stock must depend upon the selection of seed from especially desirable parent trees. Selection from resistant individual trees has one glaring inadequacy. It is made on the basis of the desirability of only one parent. The characteristics of the pollen-bearing parent might be either good or bad. The chance of collecting seed from good parent stock on both sides could be improved by removing all undesirable individuals from seed-collection areas. When it comes to determining whether a tree will be good or poor for the production of insect-resistant offspring, there are certain guides to help us. These

FIGURE 42. Cross sections of pines exhibiting resistance reactions to attacks of the reproduction weevil. *A* illustrates the reactions of a resistant ponderosa pine to attack. Necrotic areas in the bark have been walled off by a layer of cork 1 year following the attack. *B* shows the cross section of the resistant Jeffrey-Coulter pine hybrid 2 years after attack. Necrotic areas in which the larva mined are being sloughed off. Concentration of resin ducts is evident in the wood produced the season of attack. (U.S. Dept. Agr. Forest Service.)

detectable characteristics of insect-resistant trees were discussed in Chap. 4 and will not be repeated here. The problems inherent in selection and breeding with a view to producing insect-resistant stock for planting purposes offer a real challenge to the enterprising forester.

Selection from Suitable Habitats. Although the development of tree varieties resistant to insect attack has not often been accomplished by man, nature, in every locality, has been selecting through the ages those individuals best fitted for survival. Observations indicate clearly that trees are especially subject to insect attack when they have been taken from their native habitat and grown under different conditions. This rule applies not only to species but almost as much to varieties of species. Care should, therefore, be exercised that planting stock is grown from seed collected in a climatic area similar to the place where it is to be planted (Isaac, 1949). The importance of this from the viewpoint of forest entomology cannot be overemphasized.

MAINTAINING THRIFT BY LOGGING

Control of forest insects by silviculture is by no means limited to practices aimed at the regulation of composition and density, to the adaptation of forests to site, or to the development of desirable varieties. These practices are concerned chiefly with the developing forest. Other equally important practices can be applied to the mature forest to create safe conditions until the trees are utilized.

Use of Tree Classifications. As soon as a forest reaches merchantable size, it may be clear cut; usually foresters find that the removal of the trees in a series of partial cuts is not only more desirable silviculturally but also more profitable. In planning for a partial cutting the question immediately arises as to which trees should be cut and which left. A number of tree classifications have been devised that make it possible for the forester to decide which trees should be removed first and which should be left for a later cut. Keen's classification of ponderosa pine on the basis of age and vigor, as indicated by bark and foliage characteristics, is a useful tree classification for silvicultural purposes (Keen, 1943). By application of this classification it is possible to select trees from those classes that possess the lowest growth capacity and the highest incidence of bark-beetle infestation. The classification applies especially to the interior or east-side type of ponderosa pine. A similar classification has been devised for eastern hemlock based on age and crown characteristics (Graham, 1943). Generally speaking, the oldest trees with the poorest crowns are likely to be most subject to injury and, therefore, should be cut first. The location of the line between the best trees and the worst, above which the trees should be reserved and below which they should be cut, depends upon the plan of management for the particular stand. The shorter the cutting cycle, the fewer will be the classes in which cutting is done.

A PONDEROSA PINE TREE CLASSIFICATION
For comparison of barkbeetle susceptibility
Classes based on age and vigor

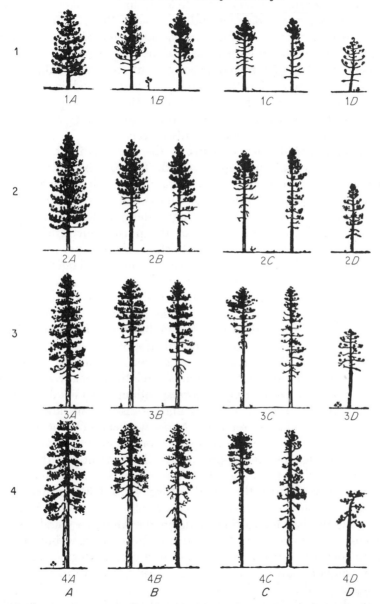

FIGURE 43. Keen's tree classification for ponderosa pine. (U.S. Dept. Agr. Forest Service.)

Removing High-risk Trees. Within any class some trees may be in better health than others (Keen and Salman, 1942). When a stand is marked for partial cutting, any sick trees should usually be cut regardless of their class, since these subnormal individuals are most likely to succumb to the attack of insects (Salman and Bongberg, 1942). Therefore, it is desirable to take current health into consideration when using a tree classification. Keen accomplishes this by applying a penalty system by which each tree may be scored according to its health. This penalty system may be compared with the risk rating discussed in Chap. 6 as follows: Penalty score 0 corresponds to risk-rating class 1; penalty scores 1 and 2 correspond to class 2; penalty scores 3 to 5 correspond to class 3; and penalty score 6 or over corresponds to class 4.

The fundamental difference between the tree-classification and the risk-rating systems must be kept in mind. The first is based upon the actuarial probability that trees in a certain class will survive until the next cutting. The second rates each individual tree according to its current health. Applying the risk-rating system, sanitation-salvage cuts are being made in ponderosa pine for the purpose of removing trees immediately subject to bark-beetle attack. Such an operation reduces the hazard of bark-beetle attack to a point where it is hoped that losses will not occur for a period of from 5 to 10 years. After that, a second sanitation-salvage cut may be made if enough trees have reached a condition of high risk. Ordinarily, however, the second cut will have special silvicultural objectives leading to the establishment of reproduction for the next tree generation and the normal distribution of age-classes.

In Montana, the risk-rating system is used in marking overmature stands of ponderosa pine. In these stands a relatively heavy cut is made, and the period between cuttings is correspondingly extended, sometimes to 30 years. All the trees in the two highest risk classes and a few of those in classes 1 and 2 are removed. Many workers feel that cuts based only on current health must be repeated more frequently than every 30 years in overmature ponderosa-pine types. They point out that, within a 5-year period, some trees may shift from one risk class to another and that, within 10 years after the initial cutting, hazard will probably have increased to a degree requiring another cutting. On the other hand, it is possible that the heavier cutting made in the Montana stands will not only remove the trees currently in the high-risk classes but will also reduce competition in the residual stand to a greater degree than would the light sanitation-salvage cuttings. As a result, the health of the stand might improve rather than deteriorate.

In this chapter on control by silvicultural practices, various principles have been considered. In the following chapters, these principles will be referred to frequently when specific pests are discussed and sometimes details that apply to particular species will be added.

PRACTICES THAT FAVOR PESTS

In spite of the fact that certain silvicultural practices reduce the injury to forests by insects pests, many forests are still handled in ways that encourage dangerous infestations. The reasons given by foresters for these practices may or may not justify the risks inherent in them.

But if a forester decides that the risks are worth-while economically, after due consideration of the probable cost of controlling resultant outbreaks of pests, one can take no issue with him. Only time can tell whether or not he is correct. If, on the other hand, he decides to use certain practices because they promise immediate financial advantages, but fails to evaluate the risk of injury from pests that such practices entail, he should not be surprised if losses instead of profits are the end result of the operations.

The importance of balancing the *damage that pests may cause* against the *advantages of some silvicultural and logging practices designed to reduce immediate cost* justifies a discussion of practices that tend to encourage outbreaks of pests. The importance of balancing advantages against disadvantages should be emphasized. Also, we should emphasize that each case is an individual problem, and a practice that in one case is undesirable because it favors pests may in another be desirable when measured in economic terms.

Disregarding Site Quality. All too often site quality has been disregarded in establishing forest plantations of pine and other trees. For example, in the North red pine has all too frequently been planted on sites that can support only jack pine, or Scotch pine has been used on sites that are unsuitable for that species. The result has been outbreaks of spittlebugs, shoot moths, scale insects, and other pests that would not have occurred in stands growing on suitable sites.

In the Southeast, large areas of slash pine have been planted on sites unsuited to that species. Similarly, loblolly pine has been planted off site. Shoot moths, scale insects, spittlebugs, and bark beetles may be expected in these off-site plantations.

Developing Single-species Forests. The single-species even-aged forest is undoubtedly easier to manage than the mixed forest. Therefore, foresters tend to favor large-scale pure-stand silviculture over practices that grow trees in mixture, in rotations that alternate species, or in diversified age and size classes. In the past this has led to encouraging pests that under primitive forest conditions were unknown.

For example, the following insects may be mentioned as having recently appeared in injurious numbers in man-made pure stands, insects that were previously almost unknown: (1) the jack-pine sawfly, (2) the Saratoga spittlebug, (3) the jack-pine budworm, (4) several soft scales of pines, (5) the white-pine weevil on red pine. Pure stands of hard maple have been almost completely destroyed by a combination of pests when the mixed northern hardwoods have been converted through years of individual tree selection to pure maple.

Other similar situations in almost every locality could be mentioned, and still other outbreaks of new pests are certain to develop in localities where pure stands are replacing naturally diversified types. Some examples are oaks in New England, yellow poplar and cottonwood in the Southeast, even-aged ponderosa pine in the Black Hills.

Using Injurious Logging Practices. Some logging practices, such as high-lead skidding, full-length skidding, and the use of heavy equipment in cutting operations, have contributed much to the economy of logging. When, however, similar heavy equipment is used in forests where partial cuttings are being made with the expectation of returning later for another crop, disastrous outbreaks of pests are almost certain to occur.

Full-length skidding has become popular in some localities and is resulting in an excessive amount of basal scarring of the trees. On pines these scars attract several bark beetles, notably the black turpentine beetle in the Southeast; several pitch moths; ambrosia beetles; carpenter ants; and other insects that cause deterioration of the butt log or in some instances a serious amount of mortality.

Heavy tractors and trucks in partial cuttings may affect the growth of residual trees and make them more subject to pest attack by compacting the soil. Especially on soft ground, such equipment may break the roots of residual trees, thus creating infection courts for fungi and conditions favorable for root-eating weevils that later will damage nearby seedlings. Similar mechanical damage may lead to bark-beetle outbreaks and to disastrous insect-fungus infestations that can completely destroy residual stands needed for a later cutting.

A point that is frequently overlooked is that practices known to favor pests that can be killed with pesticides also favor pests that cannot thus be controlled under forest conditions. For example, many insects can be killed only if a pesticide contacts their bodies. Therefore, because they cannot be contacted with pesticides effectively, control in the forest of scale insects or other sucking pests is virtually impossible with pesticides. The same is true for most shoot moths except where several heavy applications can be made from the ground.

All the practices mentioned above and others that might be mentioned under the heading of careless operations are conducive to insect injury. Unless these effects are understood and are carefully regulated, the practices can easily wipe out the expected profit from a forest operation.

In the preceding chapters some general principles concerning the population dynamics of forest insects have been presented. Also various forces that regulate these populations and some of the procedures that man can use to protect his forests against excessive depredations have been discussed. The division of this presentation into formal chapters and sections has been essential to orderly presentation. Nevertheless the degree of catagorization can be misleading unless we bear in mind that in nature the actions, reactions, and interactions between insects and their environment are all going on simultaneously and that the regulation of a forest insect population is seldom if ever attributable to the operation of any single factor.

In the following chapters accounts of specific insects illustrating various ecological groups will be presented, together with control recommendations.

BIBLIOGRAPHY CHAPTER 14

Balch, R. E., 1934. Cultural practices and forest insects, *Sep. 65th Ann. Rept. Entomol. Soc. Ontario.*

Behre, C. E., A. C. Cline, and W. L. Baker, 1936. Silvicultural control of the gypsy moth, *Mass. Forest Park Assoc. Bull.* 157.

Bess, H. A., et al., 1947. Site conditions and the gypsy moth, *Harvard Forest Bull.* 22.

Brues, C. T., 1947. Changes in insect fauna of a New England woodland following application of DDT, *Harvard Forest Papers,* 1: 1–18.

Burbridge, D., and R. R. Lejeune, 1950. Effect of moisture on larch sawfly cocoons, *Can. Dept. Agr., Forest Insect Invest., Bimonthly Progr. Rept.* 6, p. 2.

Chapman, R. N., 1915. Life history of *Agrilus bilineatus, J. Agr. Res.,* 3: 283–294.

Craighead, F. C., 1919. Protection from the locust borer, *U.S. Dept. Agr. Bull.* 787.

————, 1925. Relation between the mortality of trees attacked by spruce budworm and previous growth, *J. Agr. Res.,* 30: 541–555.

Crosley, D. J., 1949. Reproduction of white spruce following disturbance of forest floor, *Can. Dept. Mines Res., Dominion Can. Forest Serv., Res. Note* 90.

Dunning, Duncan, 1928. A tree classification for the selection forests of the Sierra Nevada, *J. Agr. Res.,* 36: 755–770.

Evenden, J. C., 1938. Insect damage resulting from zero-margin selective cutting of ponderosa pine, *Appl. Forest Notes, Northern Rocky Mt. Forest Range Expt. Sta.,* 84.

Graham, S. A., 1926. Biology and control of white-pine weevil, *Cornell Agr. Expt. Sta. Bull.* 449.

————, 1938. Relation of insects to forest types, *J. Forestry,* 36: 998–1004.

————, 1943. Causes of hemlock morality, *The Univ. Mich. School Forestry Conserv.* (now *Natural Resources*) *Bull.* 10.

————, 1951. Developing forests resistant to insect injury, *Sci. Monthly,* 73: 235–244.

————, 1956. Forest insects and the law of natural compensations, *Can. Entomologist,* 88: 45–55.

————, 1963. Making hardwood forests safe from insects, *J. Forestry*, **61**: 356–359.

————, and L. G. Baumhofer, 1927. Pine tipmoth in Nebraska National Forest, *J. Agr. Res.*, **35**: 323–333.

Hall, R. C., 1933. Post-logging decadence of northern hardwoods, *The Univ. Mich. School Forestry Conserv.* (now *Natural Resources*), *Bull.* 3.

————, 1942. Control of the locust borer, *U.S. Dept. Agr. Circ.* 688.

Hartley, Carl, 1927. Forest genetics with particular reference to disease resistance, *J. Forestry*, **25**: 667–686.

Hodson, A. C., and P. J. Zehngraff, 1946. Budworm control in jack pine by forest management, *J. Forestry*, **44**: 198–200.

Isaac, Leo A., 1949. "Better Douglas Fir from Better Seed," University of Washington Press.

Johnson, P. C., 1951. Risk-rating Inland Empire ponderosa pine, *Northwest Sci.*, **25**: 32–38.

Keen, F. P., 1943. Ponderosa pine tree classes redefined, *J. Forestry*, **41**: 249–253.

————, 1950. Influence of insects on ponderosa pine silviculture, *J. Forestry*, **48**: 186–188.

————, and K. A. Salman, 1942. Progress in pine beetle control through tree selection, *J. Forestry*, **40**: 854–858.

Miller, J. M., 1950. Resistance of hibrids to pine reproduction weevil, *U.S. Dept. Agr., Calif. Forest Range Expt. Sta., Forest Res. Notes* 68.

Milne, A., 1959. Weather, enemies, and natural control of insect populations, *J. Econ. Entomol.*, **52**: 532–533.

Prebble, M. L., 1951. Forest entomology in relation to silviculture in Canada, *Forestry Chron.*, **27**: 1–32.

Roeser, Jacob, Jr., 1926. Importance of seed source and possibilities of breeding, *J. Forestry*, **24**: 38–51.

Salman, K. A., and J. W. Bongberg, 1942. Logging high-risk trees to control insects in pine stands of northeastern California, *J. Forestry*, **40**: 533–539.

Turner, N., 1963. The gypsy moth problem, *Conn. Agr. Expt. Sta. Bull.* 655.

Weaver, Harold, 1947. Fire as a thinning agent in ponderosa pine, *J. Forestry*, **45**: 437–444.

————, 1943. Fire as an ecological and silvicultural factor in ponderosa pine, *J. Forestry*, **41**: 7–15.

Westveld, Marinus, 1930. Management of spruce stands in the Northeast, *U.S. Dept. Agr. Circ.* 134.

CHAPTER 15

LEAF-EATING
INSECTS

The foliage of trees furnishes food for a host of insect species, many of them dangerous forest pests, but the majority of the leaf-eating insects usually occur in comparatively small numbers. When they are not numerous, they scarcely affect the welfare of the trees because thrifty trees always have a greater amount of foliage than is actually required for their maintenance. When, on the other hand, a leaf-eating species multiplies so rapidly that it outstrips environmental resistance, then it may attain tremendous numbers and so create a menace. The resultant defoliation will seriously injure or even kill the trees attacked.

DEFOLIATION

Sometimes outbreaks of defoliators arise with amazing suddenness. For instance, epidemics of the spruce budworm, *Choristoneura fumiferana;* the larch sawfly, *Pristiphora erichsonii;* the forest tent caterpillar, *Malacosoma disstria;* and pine sawflies, *Neodiprion* sp., have appeared to erupt over wide areas in the same year. Actually, in most instances, the insect numbers had been building up unnoticed over several seasons. Failure to observe increasing injury caused by growing numbers of insects produces the impression that the outbreak has developed from one season to the next.

Failure to observe defoliation is not surprising because in moderate amounts it is inconspicuous. If evenly distributed over the crown of a tree, defoliation would have to be from 50 to 75 percent before the tree would appear abnormal. Even the concentrated defoliation of gregarious leaf eaters escapes the attention of the casual observer until the injury is severe.

The only way to be prepared to control defoliator epidemics is to anticipate them at least a season in advance. This can be done by annual observations on the status of potentially dangerous pests. If these observations are made correctly, they will sound a warning of approaching danger before they begin to record the first evidences of actual injury. They will reveal disturbances in the biotic balance favoring the increase of defoliators. They will also record any rare flights from localities which hold potentialities of danger into areas where highly favorable conditions prevail.

Effects of Defoliation. Defoliation injures trees by reducing photosynthesis, by interfering with transpiration, and by interfering with the processes of translocation of food within the tree. A combination of these effects is reflected in the rate of growth. Defoliation has such a profound

FIGURE 44. Increment core from a ponderosa pine illustrating the effect of defoliation on the width of the annual rings at the base of the tree. The wide ring marked *x* was laid down during the first year of severe defoliation. This ring was followed by a somewhat narrower ring, and that by a series of very narrow rings. Recovery was slow, increasing growth rate paralleling the replacement of foliage in the crown. (U.S. Dept. Agr. Forest Service.)

effect upon growth that it is possible to trace the history of past outbreaks of leaf-eating insects by studying the annual rings of the surviving trees. Studies of the effect of spruce-budworm defoliation upon the growth of balsam fir and spruce, made by Craighead (1924) and later verified by numerous workers, have proved that growth, taking the tree as a whole, is reduced the first year of almost complete defoliation. Growth at the top of the tree is usually very much reduced, but at the base it either appears to be approximately normal or is greater than in the years immediately preceding defoliation. The first year of heavy defoliation, therefore, is indicated by a relatively wide basal ring, combined with a narrowing of the same ring at the top of the tree. After the first year of such defoliation, the rings at the base, like the corresponding rings at the top, become successively smaller and smaller until they are often so narrow that the individual rings cannot be distinguished without the aid of a magnifier. In some cases, under conditions of very severe defoliation, there may be no wood produced for a season or more, in which case rings may be entirely absent. In other instances, wood may be laid down in certain parts of a tree and not in others. This results in the production of incomplete rings. Great care must, therefore, be exercised in assigning a definite year to a specific ring during periods of defoliation. If a tree survives defoliation, recovery is always gradual. As the foliage is gradually replaced from year to year, the width of the rings increases in similar proportion until a normal rate of growth has been attained.

In an evaluation of the effects of defoliation from the pattern of annual rings, care must be exercised to ensure correct interpretation. For example, on conifers, such as firs, spruces, and hemlocks, that hold their needles for a number of years, defoliators that prefer the new growth may destroy nearly all the foliage of the current year without materially affecting the growth pattern at the base of the tree. Not until one or two sets of young leaves have been lost will the loss of photosynthetic tissue severely affect the trees. Thus, in the case of a spruce-budworm outbreak the wider basal ring is the one laid down during the second or third year after severe feeding on the new needles begins.

This has led to conflicting conclusions. The first year of heavy defoliation, as reported by Craighead and other earlier workers, actually referred to the third year of severe loss of new foliage, whereas, as considered by some more recent workers, the first year of heavy defoliation referred to the season when nearly all the leaves of the current year were destroyed.

Another point that should not be overlooked is the fact that growth rate in a stand of trees is affected by many factors. Competition among trees, their relative position in reference to micro- or macrotopography, the genetic constitution of the individual tree, and many other characteristics influence the growth rate of each individual tree in a stand. As a result the growth pattern is relative rather than absolute. Therefore, attempts to express the growth pattern as the average of a series of absolute measurements can lead to confusion. Much more is left to be learned about how and why trees grow as they do. Nevertheless the relative growth and the resultant patterns can be observed and defoliation effects evaluated approximately.

All species of trees are not equally susceptible to injury from defoliation. Hardwoods are relatively resistant and ordinarily will successfully withstand three or more years of defoliation. This is due to their relatively large supply of stored food and their ability to replace the destroyed foliage immediately following defoliation. Two defoliations during the same season may, however, be disastrous (Giese et al., 1964). Correspondingly great resistance to injury from defoliation is also characteristic of deciduous conifers, as exemplified by the larch. Evergreen conifers, such as bal-

FIGURE 45. Hardwoods defoliated by the elm spanworm. These trees can stand several years of defoliation, but a persistent severe infestation will cause mortality. (U.S. Dept. Agr. Forest Service.)

sam fir or spruce, are more easily killed; for instance, white spruce, hemlock, and probably many others will die as a result of a single complete defoliation. More than three successive years of complete defoliation are likely to be fatal even to broad-leaved trees.

The time of year when defoliation occurs also has a material influence upon the effects of defoliation. For example, if complete defoliation of a conifer, such as hemlock, fir, or spruce, occurs before midsummer, the trees will not have formed buds for the following year. Then a single defoliation of 100 percent can kill the trees. On the other hand, if complete defoliation occurs late in the season, after buds for the next year have been formed, a new crop of leaves will be produced the following spring and even conifers will survive.

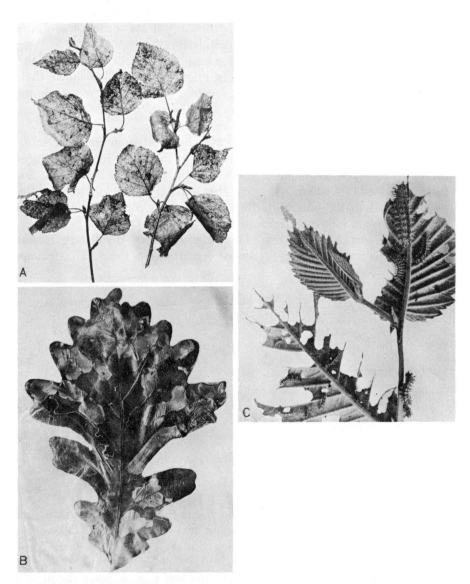

FIGURE 46. Types of defoliation. (A) Birch leaves skeletonized by the birch leaf skeletonizer, *Bucculatrix canadensisella*. (B) Blotch and serpentine mines in an oak leaf. (C) Leaves chewed by the larvae of the mourning-cloak butterfly, *Nymphalis antiopa*.

Resistance to defoliation injury varies not only with the species but also with different individuals of the same species. Dominant trees and those growing in the open without competition are less affected by defoliation than are those growing under less favorable conditions. These trees that dominate their location have larger reserves of stored food than those growing in an inferior position. Double defoliation during a single season may be especially damaging, particularly if the second one occurs before the new buds have been completely formed.

The first parts of a tree to die as a result of loss of foliage are the extremities—the twigs and small roots. Craighead (1924) has shown that, when roots of balsam fir have been severely injured, the tree is almost certain to die. Evidence has more recently been observed to show that both jack pine and hemlock suffer similarly.

Trees that have been reduced in vitality by defoliation are much more susceptible to the attack of bark beetles or borers. Frequently, trees that might survive defoliation are killed by insects of this type; for instance, stands of ponderosa pine that have been defoliated by the pandora moth or the pine butterfly are frequently killed by bark beetles during the years following defoliation.

Types of Insect Defoliators. Generally speaking, defoliating insects may be separated into three groups, according to their habits. Some

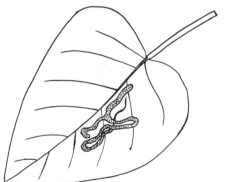

FIGURE 47. Serpentine type of leaf mine.

species, called leaf miners, feed upon the succulent interior leaf tissues while tunneling between the upper and the lower cuticula. Others eat all the leaf except the vascular portions, thus skeletonizing the leaf. These are appropriately called skeletonizers. Insects of the third group may be called the leaf chewers, for they eat all the leaf tissues. Some defoliators are miners during a part of their developmental period and skeletonizers at a later time. Others may be skeletonizers during their early stages and chewers during later stages. But there are many species that belong to only one of these three classes. Regardless of the manner of their work, all the defoliators have essentially the same effect upon the life processes of the tree. The severity of the injury is directly proportional to the amount of chlorophyll-bearing tissues destroyed.

The most important tree-defoliating species are members of three orders—the Hymenoptera, the Coleoptera, or the Lepidoptera—although a few members of other orders also feed upon the leaves of trees (Diptera and Orthoptera). Space will not permit even a brief discussion of all the destructive defoliators. In fact, merely to mention all of them would fill a volume. Therefore, only a few typical examples of the different groups will be discussed here. The species chosen for discussion will serve to illustrate the most serious types of injury and the ways in which the forester may tackle defoliator problems.

LEPIDOPTEROUS LEAF EATERS

Of all the orders of insects the Lepidoptera is the one that contains by far the greatest number of leaf-eating insects. The members of this order are, on the whole, distinctly phytophagous, and the majority are defoliators.

Spruce Budworm.   One of the outstanding defoliators of fir and spruce in our northern forests is the spruce budworm, *Choristoneura fumiferana*. This is a native insect, distributed throughout the range of its host trees.

FIGURE 48. Life-history stages of the spruce budworm. Observe the inconspicuous egg mass on the fir needle near the left edge of the picture. (U.S. Dept. Agr. Forest Service.)

For years it may remain innocuous, a rare and inconspicuous resident of the forest, but when conditions are right, it multiplies prolifically and is quickly transformed into a powerful forest devastator. The various factors that cause prolific multiplication to outbreak proportions have already been described in Chaps. 4 and 5.

The life history of the spruce budworm exhibits a number of interesting features. The eggs are deposited during late summer in elongate clusters on the needles of the host trees. These clusters are green in color and contain from 10 to 30 or more flattened eggs, overlapping one another like shingles. The young larvae that soon hatch from these eggs seek suitable places of concealment on the tree, spin a light covering of silk about themselves, and go into hibernation. The silken hibernating cases are called *hibernacula*. In the spring about the time that the buds of fir are expanding, the larvae emerge from hibernation and begin to feed. At first they mine the old needles or, in the case of the black spruce, the unopened buds. If staminate flowers are available, the young larvae prefer them to other food. Later the larvae are leaf chewers, eating the foliage of the current year. As they work, they web the needles together to form a crude shelter. The larvae develop rapidly and, under favorable conditions, are full grown in the course of 3 weeks.

During the first instars, the larvae are a pale-yellowish green with black heads and thoracic shields. Later, they become much darker until the general color is brown with black markings. They then transform to the pupal stage on the trees. No cocoon is spun; instead the pupal stage is passed within the web spun about the tip by the larva while feeding. The adult moths emerge in July and early August and soon thereafter mate and deposit their eggs. The moths have a wingspread of nearly ¾ inch and vary in color from gray to copper.

In the West, Douglas fir is a favored host of the spruce budworm, and repeated outbreaks have occurred in pure stands of that tree. Most of these outbreaks have been in the Rocky Mountains, where the budworm was active around 1937 and again around 1949. The fast-growing coast-type Douglas fir has been less susceptible to injury than the inland form; nevertheless, in 1949 outbreaks did occur in western Oregon. Little information is available concerning the ecology of the budworm in the West. Nevertheless one point seems clear. In coast-type Douglas fir (Mather, 1932) and to a lesser degree in the fir of the Rocky Mountains, the young shoots continue to elongate for several weeks following the completion of larval budworm development. Thus, after injury is completed for the season, new leaves are produced on these elongating shoots. For this reason Douglas fir appears to be less affected by budworm defoliation than the eastern firs and spruces.

The effects caused by the spruce budworm in eastern North America upon the forests of balsam fir and spruce depend upon the duration and intensity of defoliation and vary greatly from forest type to forest type and from outbreak to outbreak. For example, during the outbreak that occurred between 1909 and 1919 in eastern Canada, the injury in many localities was much more severe than that reported by Macdonald (1962) for the recent outbreak in New Brunswick. In central and western Quebec, where balsam fir in 1909 was the species in a dominant position, the mortality of balsam fir was well over 95 percent, whereas in other localities where fir was in a more subsidiary position in mixture with hardwoods the mortality was less than 50 percent (Graham, 1919, unpublished report).

Macdonald presented data on balsam-fir mortality in New Brunswick between 1952 and 1961 on representative areas selected for intensive study. In an unsprayed area reserved for comparison with a surrounding sprayed forest, the mortality in large- and small-diameter classes was "very severe" but in the diameter classes ranging between 4 and 7 inches mortality was only about 50 percent. In neither outbreak did excessive mortality in spruce occur directly as a result of defoliation, although wind throw following defoliation was locally high.

Direct control of the spruce budworm by spraying infested areas with DDT from the air has been a frequent practice since about 1948 in both the United States and Canada. Such treatments have been justified by the values involved. The objective has been to save mature timber from destruction, timber that will be needed to meet economic demands before a new crop of trees can grow.

In eastern Canada and in the western United States the objectives have differed somewhat. In New Brunswick, for example, the objective has been to prevent tree mortality by a minimum amount of spraying until natural control factors reduce the pest populations to low levels. In the western United States the objective has been to reduce the population to as near the zero point as possible by a single treatment. Both approaches have, according to reports, been successful (Webb et al., 1961; Whiteside, 1958). Neither treatment has resulted in changing the conditions that made possible the outbreaks in the first place.

Timing the chemical treatments so that they will accomplish the objective to a maximum degree is important. If minimizing defoliation pending natural reduction of the outbreak is the objective, spraying as early as practicable in the life of the larvae is desirable even though a smaller proportion of the total population is killed. If, on the other hand, the treatment is intended to accomplish as complete a kill as possible, the spray should be applied when the greatest proportion of the larvae are in a vulnerable position, that is, in the fifth and sixth instars. By that time much defoliation has been done.

In either case the stage of larval development at a given time must be determined by either direct or indirect field evaluations. Bean (1959)

points out that the diameter of frass dropped by the larvae is correlated
with the instar of the larvae ejecting it. Thus when samples of frass are
examined, the predominant larval stage can be determined without collecting samples of larvae from the trees.

In the Northeast, forest entomologists have studied the spruce budworm intensively, and recommendations for its control by silvicultural
methods can be made with reasonable confidence (Graham and Orr,
1940). If in eastern Canada or the northeastern part of the United States
the host trees of the budworm were to grow in pure stands, it is probable
that the budworm would never become epidemic on any species other
than balsam fir. This association of budworm with balsam fir is the
result of close synchronization of budworm habits with the phenology
of its favored host. The emergence of the overwintering larvae is synchronized with the expansion of balsam-fir buds. The balsam, then, provides suitable food at the right times, whereas the later developing black
and red spruce furnish less food of poorer quality. In them, the larva
must mine the needles or unopened buds until fresh expanding shoots
are available. White spruce, like balsam fir, is synchronized well with
emergence of the larvae, but the needles harden quickly and, therefore,
become undesirable food before the budworm completes development.

This close connection between budworm activities and balsam fir is
reflected in the effects of an outbreak on a mixed forest.

Table 9 shows that in outbreaks in Canada the balsam fir died within
4 years after defoliation became excessively severe whereas red spruce
died much later. This situation reflects the fact that defoliation on spruce
is not so severe as on balsam fir and also that the spruce continues to die
from secondary effects after the outbreak ends. These data are the result

TABLE 9   Tree Mortality from a Budworm Outbreak

YEARS AFTER EXCESSIVE DEFOLIATION	PERCENTAGE DYING EACH YEAR	
	RED SPRUCE	BALSAM FIR
1	0	9
2	0	32
3	0	29
4	0	18
5	0	0
6	8	0
7	12	0
8	15	0
9	25	0
10	10	0
Total	70	88

of studies by a number of Canadian workers in New Brunswick and Quebec and indicate what may be expected from a very severe outbreak in a mixed stand of balsam fir and red spruce.

Young vigorous stands of balsam fir are almost never severely damaged by budworms. This is, in part, due to the vigor of the trees but may also be due to the less favorable conditions for the budworms in young stands. One of the probable conditions influencing the susceptibility of different ages is the presence or absence of staminate flowers. Bess and others have observed that early-stage larvae are larger than usual when they feed on pollen-bearing buds. These flowers are most abundant on overmature dominant trees and those that are growing under unfavorable conditions. In contrast, they are least numerous on vigorous fast-growing individuals. Undoubtedly, outbreaks of the spruce budworm occur most frequently in stands that contain a large proportion of stamen-bearing trees.

The control of the budworm by silviculture is based upon a knowledge of its life history and the correlation of its habits with the phenological and other characteristics of the host trees. The principles involved were covered in Chap. 14 and need not be repeated. If we know the conditions that are conducive to outbreaks and those that are not, we can adopt those practices that will avoid dangerous conditions and encourage safe ones.

Conditions Favorable and Unfavorable for Spruce Budworm Outbreaks

Conducive to Outbreaks	*Not Conducive to Outbreaks*
1. Slow-growing or mature stands of pure balsam fir	1. Thrifty sapling and seedling stands of pure balsam fir without balsam overstory
2. Mature or nearly mature stands of mixed fir and spruce	2. Thrifty sapling or small-pole stands of mixed fir and spruce
3. Mature balsam fir mixed with smaller spruce. The higher the percentage of balsam, the greater the hazard	3. Fir mixed with spruce and overtopping hardwoods
4. Dominant fir, predominant in number, mixed with hardwoods, with or without spruce	4. Dominant fir, subsidiary in number, mixed with spruce and hardwoods
5. Large contiguous areas of any of above especially conducive to outbreaks	5. Areas containing balsam broken into small units so arranged that those in the same age-classes are separated from one another
6. Very dense stagnated stands of pole-size trees.	

From an examination of this summary the following practices discussed in Chap. 14 suggest themselves:

1. Conducting logging operations on small scattered units of not more than 40 acres.

2. Favoring spruce over balsam fir and encouraging mixture with intolerant hardwoods by summer logging or scarification.

3. Marketing balsam fir as soon as it reaches commercial maturity and spruce on a longer rotation.

4. Planting spruce following logging where natural regeneration of that species fails.

Eradication of balsam fir to control budworm has frequently been suggested. Even though this undertaking could be accomplished, it would be an economically unsound procedure. Balsam fir is a valuable tree that can be grown on a short rotation. It almost always finds a ready market. It reproduces well and grows rapidly. Therefore, efforts should be directed toward its continued production in reasonable quantities, but under conditions that are not conducive to outbreaks.

The Jack-pine Budworm. The jack-pine budworm, *Choristoneura pinus*, was previously considered to be a form of the spruce budworm but now is recognized as being a distinct species. This budworm, instead of being grayish in color as is the spruce budworm, tends toward the coppery shades.

The life history of the pine form of the spruce budworm is identical with that of the fir-spruce form, but it seems to be more dependent upon pollen for rapid increase. Only on Scotch pine do outbreaks build up without the presence of pollen-producing trees. An abundance of staminate flowers frequently occurs on overmature, round-topped trees (Graham, 1935), on scattered orchard-type trees, or on suppressed trees. This is because the carbon-mineral ratio is especially favorable for flower production, especially following dry seasons. Thrifty fully stocked stands seldom produce many staminate flowers.

Silvicultural control of the budworm, therefore, calls for the following practices:

1. Growing hard pines in fully stocked stands or groups.
2. Eliminating large-crowned "wolf" trees.
3. Utilizing the trees before they become overmature.
4. Encouraging species suited to the site.

Control of the spruce budworm by silvicultural practices is certainly the most desirable solution of the budworm problem. Nevertheless, there may be times when these preventive practices have not been applied and serious infestations develop in valuable timber. Then it may be necessary to resort to insecticides, as described in Chaps. 9 and 10. In controlling the budworm by chemicals, the materials must be applied after the larvae cease to mine the needles or buds but before they pupate.

Gypsy Moth. The gypsy moth, *Porthetria dispar,* is one of the many destructive insect pests that has come to America from foreign lands. It was accidentally introduced at Medford, Massachusetts, in 1869, and since that time has spread into all the New England states. It is particularly injurious to broad-leaved trees, although pines in mixture with hardwoods are by no means immune.

The eggs are laid during July in clusters of 400 or more. Since the heavy-bodied female moth is unable to fly, the eggs are usually deposited on or near the cocoon. The eggs hatch the following spring. The larvae feed in the first stage upon the foliage of susceptible trees such as oak, basswood, and aspens; later they may also feed upon chestnut, hemlock, pine, and spruce. If the infestation is severe, the trees may be completely defoliated by the end of June. When full grown, the larvae pupate, either on the tree or in other convenient places, and after a pupal period of about 10 days, the adults emerge. The male moth is brown in color, whereas the female is white with black markings. Unlike the female, the male is a good flier.

At first, it might seem that a species whose adult females were unable to fly would have little chance of spreading from one locality to another and would, consequently, be confined to a restricted area and there very easily be controlled. Unfortunately this has not proved to be the case. One of the important means of distribution for the gypsy moth is wind. The first-stage larvae are clothed with long hairs which greatly increase the surface area of the body in proportion to its weight. The larvae at this stage are so light that they can be carried long distances by air currents. How far they can be blown in this way can be only a matter of conjecture, but it is known that they have been carried for a distance of more than 20 miles. Other means of dispersal are of a more or less accidental character; for example, egg masses or larvae may be carried on persons or vehicles leaving the infested area.

The effect of climatic factors upon the gypsy moth is of great importance both directly and indirectly. A temperature of $-20°F$ is sufficient to kill the overwintering eggs, and as a result, in severe winters only those eggs that are beneath the snow line or in other protected locations survive. This, of course, has an important effect upon the abundance of the species during the following season. Cool, moist conditions followed by warm weather during early June are favorable to the development of the wilt disease which is an important natural check of this moth.

Parasites and predators of the gypsy moth have been introduced into the infested area, as described in Chaps. 12 and 13. They have brought about a condition similar to that which obtains in the native home of the pest where the parasites help to prevent outbreaks but do not, by any means, prevent them altogether.

Because of the differences in susceptibility of various tree species, the regulation of forest composition by the application of silvicultural principles promises to be a most effective method of protecting forests from the gypsy moth (Behre, Cline, and Baker, 1936). If the most susceptible species are eliminated, a forest may be made comparatively safe. Much further work along this line is necessary before completely satisfactory methods can be developed.

Unfortunately, many forest lands in New England are especially suited to oak, the favored food of the gypsy moth. Such lands cannot always be converted to other forest types. Studies in these oak types have shown that all of them are not equally subject to injury. On abused woodlands that have been repeatedly burned, heavily grazed, or trampled and on areas where the stands are poorly stocked, outbreaks are frequent. On areas where desirable forest practices have resulted in good stocking, normal distribution of age-classes, and the development of a ground cover of young trees, outbreaks seldom occur. On the lands where good forest practices have been applied, the predatory and parasitic insects are also far more effective than in the abused types (Bess, 1947).

When outbreaks occur in valuable timber, they can easily be suppressed by aerial spraying. This method has almost supplanted the high-powered ground sprayers except for use on ornamental trees. Both DDT and lead arsenate have been successfully used, and the mechanical device of banding has also proved useful in controlling this pest.

Experimental tests are under way to find nonresidual insecticides for controlling the gypsy moth which would be less objectionable than DDT in their possible side effects. Sevin is one material recommended for use where spraying is done near fish-producing water.

The Elm Spanworm. The elm spanworm, *Ennomos subsignarius,* sometimes called the snow-white linden moth, is a serious defoliator of forest hardwoods. The species is widely distributed from Canada and the Atlantic states to Colorado. It attacks elm, basswood, and many other species of hardwoods that are characteristic of fertile forest lands. A severe outbreak of this species started about 1954 in the Great Smoky Mountain region and has spread eastward involving more than 2 million acres in three states. Interestingly enough this same area was involved in a similar outbreak of the same insects just prior to 1880, and since then the population has been very low until recently (Drooz, 1960; Drooz and Solomon, 1961 and 1962; Drooz, 1963; Davis, 1960). Although a vast area is involved, only about 7 percent of the infestation is truly serious.

Other members of the family Geometridae also defoliate forest trees. Among the best known of these are the cankerworms: *Alsophila pometaria,* the fall cankerworm, and *Paleacrita vernata,* the spring cankerworm. They defoliate elms, oaks, basswood, and other hardwood trees in spring and early summer. Because their outbreaks are periodic and because the trees promptly put out a new crop of leaves after defoliation,

FIGURE 49. The elm spanworm, eggs, larvae, pupae, adults. (U.S. Dept. Agr. Forest Service.)

they are not ordinarily serious forest pests in spite of the public attention that they attract. The hemlock looper, *Lambdina fiscellaria*, and closely related species called by the same common name are probably the most serious forest insects belonging to the Geometridae. This looper is capable of killing hemlocks in a single season by completely defoliating them in midsummer. In localities where hemlocks are of major economic value, the direct control of the looper becomes imperative.

During the early nineteen twenties the hemlock looper killed large areas of hemlock in Michigan and Wisconsin. At that time one of the earliest attempts was made to control a forest insect by the application of an insecticide from the air (Fracker and Granovski, 1927).

A more recent severe outbreak in the state of Washington threatened to destroy a tremendous acreage of valuable hemlock but was controlled by aerial application of pesticides. Careful planning, supervision, and evaluation of results in terms both of pest control and of possible deleterious side effects have demonstrated that, with due precautions, pesticides can be used to control forest insects without serious deleterious effects even under very difficult situations (Anon., 1963; Johnson, 1963).

The Douglas-fir tussock moth, *Hemerocampa pseudotsugata*, is a destructive defoliator of Douglas fir and true fir in the northern Rocky Mountains. Since 1918 when it was first discovered, it has periodically defoliated extensive areas. Outbreaks occur only in areas where Douglas fir or true firs predominate. An especially extensive infestation occurred

FIGURE 50. Larvae of the fir tussock moth, *Hemerocampa osleri*. (U.S. Dept. Agr. Forest Service.)

FIGURE 51. Egg masses of the fir tussock moth deposited on the cocoons from which the wingless females had emerged. (U.S. Dept. Agr. Forest Service.)

in 1946 and 1947 in Idaho and eastern Oregon, where it threatened to destroy valuable timber on more than 400,000 acres. In 1947, DDT was applied from the air with outstanding success. Evenden and Jost (1947) estimated a saving from this operation of $4,280,000 in timber at a cost of less than one-fifth that amount.

The moths are drab-colored, gray-buff insects with a body length of ½ inch or less. The males are winged; the females are smaller and wingless. The eggs are deposited in a mass, usually on the cocoon from which the female emerged, and pass the winter without hatching. The larvae feed through June and July, spinning their cocoons in early August and emerging as adults late in that month.

The larvae are strikingly marked insects with red spots and tufts of cream-colored hair on the dorsum, two hornlike pencils of hair behind the head, and two longer similar black pencils near the posterior end. The sides are marked with somewhat broken, narrow, orange stripes.

At least five other species of tussock moths are injurious in various localities. Most of them feed on broad-leaved trees, but several eat the leaves of conifers. The white-marked tussock moth, *Hemerocampa leucostigma* (Houser, 1918), feeding mostly on hardwoods, is the best-known species of tussock moth in the East. The pine tussock moth, *Dasychira plagiata*, is an injurious forest pest throughout the Northeastern states, feeding upon all species of two- and three-leaved pines.

Other Lepidopterous Defoliators. Other lepidopterous defoliators that should also be mentioned are (1) the pine tube moth, *Argyrotaenia pinatubana*, a widely distributed species that attacks white pine in the East (Craighead, 1950) and lodgepole pine in the West; (2) the lodgepole needle miners, *Evagoria milleri* and *E. starki* (Yuill, 1942; Stark, 1952); (3) the lach casebearer, *Coleophora laricella*, an introduced spe-

FIGURE 52. Aspen defoliated by the Great Basin tent caterpillar, *Malacosoma fragilis*, Carson National Forest, New Mexico. (U.S. Dept. Agr. Forest Service.)

cies that is spreading westward; (4) the forest tent caterpillar, *Malacosoma disstria*, a serious pest of aspen, oak, sugar maple, and other hardwood trees (Hodson, 1941); (5) the pine butterfly, *Neophasia menapia*, an occasional defoliator of western white pine (Evenden, 1940); (6) the pandora moth, *Coloradia pandora*, a moth with a 2-year life cycle that periodically defoliates ponderosa pine (Wygant, 1941).

Numerous other species of Lepidoptera are responsible for defoliation of forest trees, sometimes of a very serious nature. All of them can be controlled by insecticidal treatments. The justification for chemical control will hinge upon consideration of the economic and aesthetic values involved and the probable side effects, deleterious or otherwise, that may result. These decisions are rarely simple and call for balancing of the values involved and the exercise of wise judgment by responsible foresters.

COLEOPTEROUS LEAF EATERS

The leaf-eating insects that belong to the order Coleoptera are almost all members of a single family, the Chrysomelidae, although the members of the genus *Phyllophaga* (*Lachnosterna*) and several other genera of the family Scarabaeidae are defoliators in the adult stage. The Japanese beetle, *Popillia japonica*, is an introduced pest that defoliates trees in the beetle stage; also *Pachystethus oblivia*, commonly called the anomala beetle, seriously defoliates jack pine in the Lake States; and various species of May beetles also are scarabaeid defoliators. The larvae are all root eaters and will be treated in a later chapter.

Leaf Beetles. The leaf beetles are capable of causing severe defoliation, and at times their work is conspicuous. As forest pests, however, they are far less injurious as a group than are the Lepidoptera. Therefore they will be considered only briefly, using two examples.

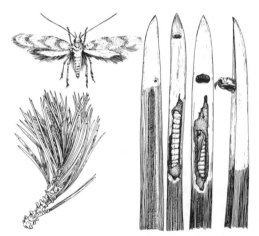

FIGURE 53. Lodgepole needle miner, *Evagoria milleri*. (U.S. Dept. Agr. Forest Service.)

The elm leaf beetle, *Galerucella xanthomelaena*, has attracted more attention than any other leaf beetle. It is an introduced pest that first appeared in Baltimore, Maryland, about 1834. Since then it has spread throughout the United States, reaching almost every area where elms are grown. Occasionally pure stands of elm are attacked severely, but for the most part the elm leaf beetle is an ornamental-tree pest. Many municipalities are compelled to spray their trees regularly in order to control this beetle.

Like most chrysomelids, the elm leaf beetle passes the winter as an adult, emerging from hibernation in the spring to feed upon and to oviposit on elm foliage. The yellow eggs are laid in groups on the underside of the leaves. The larvae are flattened dark grubs with well-developed legs. Working gregariously, they first skeletonize and later chew holes in the leaves. After completing their development in 2 or 3 weeks, the larvae drop to the ground where they pupate, unprotected by cocoons. In this stage they are very vulnerable to small mammalian predators. In a week or 10 days the adults emerge to repeat the life cycle, several times during a season in the South but only once in the North.

FIGURE 54. Hemlock looper larva in the position char-acteristic of the family. (U.S. Dept. Agr. Forest Service.)

The cottonwood leaf beetle, *Chrysomela scripta,* defoliates any species of poplar or willow and at times becomes excessively numerous. The greatest damage from this insect is to basket-willow plantations, where defoliation seriously affects the growth of willow wands. The life history is similar to that of the elm leaf beetle. This beetle is widely distributed in North America wherever its host trees grow. When necessary, it can be controlled by the usual spraying practices.

HYMENOPTEROUS LEAF EATERS

By far the greater proportion of all the leaf-eating Hymenoptera be-long to the families Tenthredinadae and Diprionidae. The adults of these families are called sawflies because of the sawlike ovipositor of the female. The larvae of most species are very similar to caterpillars of the Lepi-doptera and are called false caterpillars. Most of the common species may be distinguished from the true caterpillars by the presence of at least six pairs of prolegs on the abdomen.

The sawflies attack both coniferous and broad-leaved trees. Some are leaf miners, some are skeletonizers, but the most important are leaf chew-ers. From the economic viewpoint, those that attack conifers are of paramount interest. Many of the larvae are similar in appearance, but some are far more injurious than others. Foresters are often puzzled about the identity of the sawfly larvae observed in the field. In order to help them in recognizing the harmful species, Tables 10 and 11 have been pre-

TABLE 10   Recognition of Sawfly Larvae on Conifers Other than Pine

SPECIES	HOST	LARVAL SEASON	DISTINCTIVE CHARACTERISTICS
European spruce sawfly, *Diprion (Gilpinia) hercyniae*	Spruces	May–Sept.	Dark green with five white lines. Lines disappear in last instar. Solitary
Balsam-fir sawfly, *Neodiprion abietis*	Fir	June–Aug.	Head black. Body dull green, lighter beneath. Six longitudinal dark stripes
Spruce sawfly, *Neodiprion* sp.	Spruces	June–Aug.	Same appearance as *N. abietis*
Larch sawfly, *Pristiphora erichsonii*	Larch	June–July	Head black. Body grayish-green, darker above. No stripes
Two-lined larch sawfly, *Platycampus laricis*	Western larch	June–Aug.	Body brownish-green with two narrow dark-green stripes on the sides
Western-larch sawfly, *Platycampus laricivorus*	Western larch	June–Aug.	Body brownish-green with single dorsal green stripe
Yellow-headed spruce sawfly, *Pikonema alaskensis*	Black spruce preferred	June–July	Yellow head. Body dark yellowish-green above, lighter beneath, marked with gray-green stripes
Green-headed spruce sawfly, *Pikonema dimmockii*	Spruce	June–July	Head and body green
Eastern cedar sawfly, *Monoctenus milliceps*	Cedar and juniper	June–July	Head light brown with black eye spots. Body dull green with three longitudinal dark stripes
Western-hemlock sawfly, *Neodiprion tsugae*	Western hemlock	July–Aug.	Green, about 1 inch long. Cocoons spun either on needles or in litter on ground

TABLE 11   Recognition of Sawfly Larvae on Pine

SPECIES	HOST	LARVAL SEASON	DISTINCTIVE CHARACTERISTICS
Red-headed pine sawfly, *Neodiprion lecontei*	Hard pines	May–Oct.	Head reddish-brown. Body yellowish with six rows of irregular black spots
Abbott's sawfly, *Neodiprion pinetum*	Eastern white pine	May–Oct.	Head black. Body yellowish-white with four rows of irregular black spots
Loblolly pine sawfly, *Neodiprion americanum*	Loblolly pine	May–June	Head reddish-brown with black eye spots. Body greenish-white with dull longitudinal stripe and row of black spots on each side
Dyar's sawfly, *Neodiprion dyari*	Hard pines	May–June	Head and legs black. Body yellowish-green with longitudinal dark stripe on each side and broken stripe or spots along spiracular line
Jack-pine sawfly, *Neodiprion banksianae*	Jack pine	May–June	Similar to above but not spotted
Solitary pine sawfly, *Diprion frutetorum*	Red and Scotch pine	May–Sept.	Head reddish-brown with black blotch. Body light green with narrow stripes on each side of dark longitudinal stripe
Brown-headed jack-pine sawfly, *Neodiprion dubiosus*	Jack pine	May–July	Head brown. Body greenish
Swaine's pine sawfly, *Neodiprion swainii*	Jack pine	May–July	Head brown. Body faintly striped
Pitch pine sawfly, *Neodiprion pinae-rigidae*	Pitch pine	May–Oct.	Head reddish-brown. Body dull green with double longitudinal dorsal line and broken lateral line, below which a double row of spots may occur

TABLE 11   Recognition of Sawfly Larvae on Pine (Continued)

SPECIES	HOST	LARVAL SEASON	DISTINCTIVE CHARACTERISTICS
Red-pine sawfly, *Neodiprion nanulus*	Red pine	May–June	Head black until last instar then brown. Body dark above, light below. Three light-green stripes on the dorsum and dark stripe at base of legs
European pine sawfly, *Neodiprion sertifer*	Red and Scotch pine	May–June	Head black. Body grayish-green with light dorsal stripe and dark lateral stripe bordered by narrow lighter stripes
Introduced pine sawfly, *Diprion similis*	White pines	Apr.–Oct.	Head black. Body yellowish-green with double dorsal stripe and sides mottled with yellow and black
Lodgepole-pine sawfly, *Neodiprion burkii*	Lodgepole pine	June–Sept.	Head brown with black eye spots. Body greenish-gray with double dorsal stripe and heavy lateral stripe
Monterey-pine sawfly, *Itycorsia* sp.	Monterey pine	March–Sept.	Head black. Body green or brown. Web needles together as they feed
Pine false webworm, *Acantholyda erythrocephala*	Red and white pines	July–Aug.	Head yellow dotted with brown. Body green with dorsal, ventral, and lateral stripes. Gregarious web spinner
Nesting pine sawfly, *Acantholyda zappei*	Hard pines	July–Aug.	Head brown. Body green with darker dorsal stripe. Solitary. Webs needles together

pared. The distinctive characteristics presented therein apply to the larger larvae. In many instances, the distinctive markings do not appear until the larvae reach the third or fourth instar; therefore, the smaller sizes are not always easy to recognize, but neither are they likely to be observed. The descriptions apply to those stages that are most conspicuous.

Larch Sawfly. One of the most serious defoliators of larch, in both Europe and America, is the larch sawfly, *Pristiphora erichsonii*. In America, this pest was first reported in the early eighties in New England, where it was responsible for much damage to the native larch. Since this early outbreak, the species has played a prominent part in defoliating larch throughout the range of eastern larch.

Packard and Felt assume that it is one of our uninvited guests and that it was introduced into America prior to 1880. Hopkins, on the other hand, maintains that it is a native of America. The first historical record of larch-sawfly injury in Michigan was in the year 1906; in Minnesota, it was during 1909. A study of the annual rings of living tamaracks, however, shows that reduction from defoliation has occurred from time to time throughout the life of the oldest trees. In addition to the period of reduced growth around 1910 to 1918, there have been two other periods of heavy defoliation: one starting just previous to 1880 and another older one about 1840. Other minor defoliations occurred between 1855 and 1860, one about 1870 and another in the late nineties. This evidence shows that a defoliator, probably the larch sawfly, has repeatedly been epidemic on tamarack and supports the contention of Hopkins that the larch sawfly is native.

The life cycle of the larch sawfly is quite similar to that of many other sawflies. The eggs are deposited alternately in a double row of slits cut along one side of a rapidly expanding young shoot. When first deposited, they are translucent and very small. They soon swell, however, as a result of water adsorption until they protrude from the slit in which they are placed. The oviposition injury usually results in killing one side of the shoot, while the other side continues to grow. This type of injury causes shoots to twist, sometimes forming a complete loop. The number of these twisted twigs can be used as an idex of sawfly abundance.

The eggs hatch in about a week, and the larvae work gregariously, completely defoliating one branch before moving to another. Full growth is reached by midsummer, when the larvae drop to the ground and spin their tough, brown, oval cocoons in the moss or litter beneath the trees. The larvae remain in the prepupal stage within these cocoons until the following spring, at which time the majority of them transform to the pupal stage and emerge as adults. The remainder hold over in the prepupal stage until the second spring after cocooning, when they, too, transform to the adult stage. The adult sawfly is a handsome black insect somewhat over ⅜ inch in length with a bright-orange band about the base of the abdomen.

The larch sawfly, being very sensitive to moisture conditions, is adversely affected at time of cocooning by either high or low water. Under drought conditions, the larvae burrow deeply into the accumulations of sphagnum beneath the trees, sometimes a foot or more beneath the sur-face. There they are certain to be drowned within their cocoons when the water rises to a normal level. Droughts during the summers of 1928 and 1929 resulted in the almost complete elimination of sawfly through-out the Lake States. Regulation of water level, where it can be accom-plished practicably, offers a means of control for the larch sawfly.

Pine Sawflies. A large number of sawflies are injurious defoliators of pine. Some, such as the jack-pine sawfly, *Neodiprion banksiana,* attack the older trees, while others, such as the red-headed pine sawfly, *Neo-diprion lecontei,* attack the younger trees.

FIGURE 55. Larvae of the Virginia pine sawfly feeding on needles. (U.S. Dept. Agr. Forest Service.)

Other pine sawflies are ponderosa pine sawfly, *Neodiprion fulviceps;* Colorado pine sawfly, *Neodiprion gillettii;* western white-pine sawfly, *Neodiprion edwardsii;* and pinyon pine sawfly, *Neodiprion rohweri.* Still others are listed in Table 11.

All the members of this group deposit their eggs in slits cut in the edge of living pine needles. Some species pass the winter in the egg stage with the young larvae hatching out in the spring; others pass the winter in the prepupal stage within the cocoon. Most species have a divided emergence similar to that of the larch sawfly; that is, a part of the adults emerge in the fall or spring following cocooning, whereas part of them remain in diapause or dormancy for a year or longer. This habit protects the species against such seasonal catastrophes as may arise directly or indirectly from adverse weather conditions.

The genus *Neodiprion,* to which most of the pine sawflies belong, con-tains species that are very similar in both appearance and habits. Furthermore, the larval markings vary from instar to instar. Therefore, some of these species are easily confused in the field. Table 11 provides information that will be helpful in distinguishing some that are frequently encountered.

The jack-pine sawfly is one of this group that is a serious defoliator of jack pine, often in conjunction with the jack-pine budworm. When the two work simultaneously, the sawfly feeding on the old needles and the budworm on the new growth, the result is serious mortality of the jack pine. The greatest damage is to mature or nearly mature stands. The adults appear in the autumn. The sexes are so different in appearance that they might easily be mistakenly identified as different species. The males are only about ¼ inch in length, black in color, with featherlike antennae. The females are almost ⅜ inch in length, yellowish-brown in color, and the antennae are threadlike.

The winter is passed in the egg stage in the jack-pine needles. Hatching in May, the larvae feed gregariously, completing their growth in 4 to 5 weeks. The cocoons are spun in the litter beneath the infested trees, where the larvae remain in the prepupal stage until late August or September. Then a part of them transform to pupae and later to adults, while the others remain in diapause until the following autumn.

The causes for the increase of this insect since 1920 and the application of silvicultural control methods were discussed in Chaps. 13 and 14. Insect parasites, although numerous, are unable to check outbreaks. Apparently the most important factors regulating the abundance of this sawfly are weather conditions. For example, during one season heavy rains washed many newly hatched larvae from the trees. During another season, cool moist weather followed by hot weather and an outbreak of a wiltlike disease checked a threatened outbreak. In still another season, an early spring followed by late frosts caused the death of many larvae. Outbreaks of this sawfly are usually associated with warm dry weather in early May and June. Whenever these favorable conditions prevail during several seasons, outbreaks may be expected in localities where large areas of mature or nearly mature jack pine prevail.

In contrast to the jack-pine sawfly that injures large trees, several pine sawflies concentrate upon trees in smaller size classes. These species usually disappear after the stand becomes closed. One of the most important is the red-headed pine sawfly, *Neodiprion lecontei*. This species has always been a common enemy of young pines, but since 1934 it has become increasingly serious. The effects of extensive, even-aged plantations in bringing about this increase are discussed in Chap. 14.

The adults of the overwintering generation of the red-headed pine sawfly begin to appear in May and continue to emerge through June. They deposit their eggs in slits cut in the edge of the needles, as do the other pine sawflies. The larvae feed gregariously, stripping one branch at a time until they reach full development in about 5 weeks. Then they drop to the ground and spin their cocoons.

In the northern part of its range, the red-headed pine sawfly passes through a single generation per season, whereas in the South, two or more are completed. According to Craighead (1950), many larvae that mature prior to July 15 are able to pupate and emerge during late summer and produce another generation. In contrast, those that develop after that time do not emerge until the following spring. Apparently some controlling force prevents the transformation to adults when lateness of season would endanger completion of their progeny's development.

The cocoons are spun in the litter beneath the trees and are similar in appearance to those of other sawflies. Within the cocoon, the prepupae pass the winter, transforming to pupae and then to adults the following spring.

European Spruce Sawfly.   The European spruce sawfly, *Diprion* (*Gilpina*) *hercyniae,* was discovered near Ottawa, Ontario, in 1922 (Craighead, 1950). Later in 1929 it was found in New Hampshire. How or when it reached this side of the Atlantic from its native home in Europe is not known (Balch, 1936, 1939). This sawfly has slowly spread westward, being found for the first time in Michigan and Minnesota in 1950.

Serious outbreaks have occurred in the Gaspé Peninsula, New Brunswick, and the northern New England states. They were brought to an end by a virus disease that appeared in New England in 1940 and spread throughout the entire area. During the initial epidemic in the Gaspé Peninsula and in scattered localities in other parts of Quebec, the sawfly killed more than one-half of the merchantable spruce. In most other localities, the damage was less severe.

Whether or not an outbreak of equal severity will occur at a later time no one can say. This outbreak may have been the result of the insect's reaction to a new environment where it met greatly reduced environmental resistance. If that is the case, we may never have another serious outbreak of the pest. On the other hand, we know that this sawfly causes injury from time to time in its native land. Therefore, we may logically expect it occasionally to cause trouble in the future. A disastrous outbreak of the intensity of the Gaspé epidemic would, however, be surprising, considering the fact that the insect will be subject to the controlling influence of the parasites that are now well established in America. Morris in New Brunswick and other workers in New England found that small mammals—especially mice, voles, and shrews—were active predators on the sawfly in the cocoon stage. These animals are most abundant in mixed and diversified forests and may be encouraged by silvicultural practices designed to maintain or produce these desirable conditions.

The adult of the European spruce sawfly is about ⅜ inch in length, thick-waisted, and, like the other members of this family, provided with a sawlike ovipositor. In color it is black with yellow markings on the abdomen, thorax, and head. It is a parthenogenetic species, and males are seldom found. This, of course, adds materially to its potentialities for reproduction.

According to Balch, the adult females emerge in the spring from the oval, brown cocoons that were spun by the larvae in the duff layer beneath the trees. They lay their eggs in slits cut in the needles with the ovipositor. The larvae that hatch from these eggs pass through six instars, during the first three of which they are a pale green in color. During the fourth and fifth instars, they become striped with five longitudinal white stripes that again disappear in the sixth and final instar.

The eggs are laid in the old needles of all species of spruce. White spruce is especially favored. On hatching, the larvae feed on the old needles until the current year's needles are mature, after which some feeding may occur on them. They are not gregarious like so many sawflies but feed singly, at first chewing notches in the needles and later consuming the entire needle. This feeding habit makes their injury inconspicuous until it has reached serious proportions. Their presence is indicated by a thin appearance of the foliage and the presence of frass dropped by the caterpillars under the trees.

In the Gaspé Peninsula only one generation occurs, but in parts of New England as many as three may be completed. When full grown, the larvae drop to the ground and spin cocoons in the duff above the mineral soil. Some of the larvae may lie dormant within the cocoon for several years, but most of them will transform to pupae and adults the spring following cocooning.

The Town Ant.   The town ant, *Atta texana,* is sometimes referred to as the Texas leaf-cutting ant. It is a representative of the family Formicidae. Most ant species living in temperate localities are not defoliators of trees. Some feed upon other insects, the honeydew excreted by aphids and scale insects, fungi, fruit, or seeds, and some upon low-growing vegetation. All of them live in colonial nests constructed according to the species of ant in the soil, beneath the bark of fallen trees, or in many other situations.

The town ant is a soil-inhabiting species that constructs nests with a ramification of galleries and many chambers with hundreds of openings to the surface. The galleries penetrate deeply into the soil, sometimes to a depth of 15 feet or more. The numerous openings distributed over a considerable area of ground have given rise to the name "town ant."

These ants defoliate trees and carry the leaves into the nest, where the leaves are chewed into bits and formed into fungus culture beds in special chambers excavated for this purpose. The fungus grown in these beds provides the only known food of the insects. It is grown in virtually pure culture.

In their harvesting activities the ants march in a column to and from the tree or other vegetation that they are defoliating. Each ant on the return trip carries above it a bit of leaf. This habit has earned them the local name umbrella ant.

Although a large colony of these ants is capable of defoliating a 4-inch tree in a single day, the greatest damage is to forest reproduction during the fall and early spring when other green vegetation is scarce. In eastern Louisiana and eastern Texas they are serious pests of young pine plantations. Pines with relatively small buds, such as slash pine, are killed outright when both the needles and buds are cut off and the bark of the stem gnawed. Because of their much larger buds, the longleaf pines are seldom killed outright but may be severely weakened.

In winter the ants tend to congregate together in chambers near the center of the nest. At that time they can be controlled by fumigation. Methyl bromide has been recommended for this purpose, the gas being injected through a tube inserted to a depth of 2 feet into the central part of the colony through a principal tunnel. A pound of the fumigant is said to be enough to kill all or almost all the ants in an average-size colony. However, the treatment is likely to be only temporary because rapid reinfestation by ants from adjacent locations usually occurs. Because it is a serious pest of planted pines, the town-ant problem is currently a major subject for investigation at the Southern Forest Experiment Station of the U.S. Department of Agriculture Forest Service.

The defoliators discussed in the foregoing pages are only a few of the multitude of insects that can defoliate trees, any one of which may become numerous if their resistance factors are reduced. They do, however, illustrate most of the characteristic types of injury caused by this group of insects. References to additional species will be found in the bibliography.

BIBLIOGRAPHY CHAPTER 15

Bagworm, *Thyridopteryx ephemeraeformis* Haw:
  Howard, L. O., and F. H. Chittenden, 1916. *U.S. Dept. Agr., Bur. Entomol., Farmers' Bull.* 701.
Birch leaf miner, *Fenusa pusilla* Klug:
  Friend, R. B., 1933. *Conn. Agr. Expt. Sta. Bull.* 348.
  Lindquist, O. H., 1962. *Can. Entomologist*, 94: 524–530.
  Peirson, H. B., 1936. Biology and control, *Maine Forest Serv. Bull.* 11.
Birch leaf mining sawfly, *Profenusa thomsoni* (Konow):
  Martin, J. L., 1960. *Can. Entomologist*, **92**: 376–384.
Birch skeletonizer, *Bucculatrix canadensisella* Chamb.:
  Friend, R. B., 1927. *Conn. Agr. Expt. Sta. Bull.* 288.
  Lintner, J. A., 1893. Insects of New York, *8th Rept.*, 133–140, 1891.
Black-headed budworm, *Acleris variana* (Fern.):
  Crouter, R. A., and E. H. Vernon, 1959. *Can. Fish Culturist*, **24**: 1–18.

McCambridge, W. F., and G. L. Downing, 1960. *U.S. Dept. Agr. Forest Pest Leaflet* 45.

Silver, G. T., 1959. *J. Forestry,* **57**: 203–205.

———, 1960. *Can. Entomologist,* **92**: 401–410.

Brown-tail moth, *Nygmia phaeorrhoea* (Donov.):

Britton, W. E., 1914. *Conn. Agr. Expt. Sta. Bull.* 182.

———, et al., 1919. *Conn. State Entomol. Rept., Bull.* 211, pp. 272–290.

Burgess, A. F., 1917. *U.S. Dept. Agr. Farmers' Bull.* 845.

———, and W. L. Baker, 1938. *U.S. Dept. Agr. Circ.* 464.

California oakworm, *Phryganidia californica* Pack.:

Burke, H. E., and F. B. Herbert, 1920. *U.S. Dept. Agr. Farmers' Bull.* 1076.

Essig, E. O., and W. M. Hoskins, 1944. *Calif. Ext. Bull.,* 87 rev., p. 89.

Cankerworms:

Balch, R. E., 1937. Effectiveness of banding, 68*th Rept. Entomol. Soc. Ontario.*

Hartzell, A., and W. J. Youden, 1935. Efficiency of banding, *Contrib. Boyce Thompson Inst.,* **7**: 365.

Jones, T. H., and J. V. Schaffner, 1953. *U.S. Dept. Agr. Leaflet* 183.

Catalpa sphinx, *Ceratomia catalpae* (Bdvl.):

Houser, J. S., 1908. *Ohio Agr. Expt. Sta. Bull.* 332, pp. 238–241.

Howard, L. O., and F. H. Chittenden, 1907. *Dept. Agr. Bur. Entomol., Circ.* 96.

Cottonwood leaf beetle, *Chrysomela scripta* (Fab.):

Felt, E. P., 1906. *N.Y. State Museum, Mem.* 8, pp. 317–321.

Douglas-fir tussock moth, *Hemerocampa pseudotsugata* McD.:

Eaton, C. B., and G. R. Struble, 1957. *Pan-Pacific Entomologist,* **33**: 105–108.

Evendon, J. C., and E. J. Jost, 1947. *U.S. Dept. Agr. and Other Co-op. Org., Dept.* Unnumbered, mimeographed.

Roberts, P. H., and J. C. Evenden, 1949. *U.S. Dept. Agr. Yearbook,* pp. 436–445.

Wickman, B. E., 1963. *U.S. Dept. Agr., Res. Paper* PSW-7.

Elm leaf beetle, *Galerucella xanthomelaena* (Schr.):

Britton, W. E., 1932. *Conn. Agr. Expt. Sta. Circ.* 84.

Herrick, G. W., 1911. *Cornell Agr. Expt. Sta. Circ.* 8.

Elm leaf miner, *Fenusa ulmi* (Sund.):

Chrystal, R. N., 1919. *Agr. Gazette Can.,* **6**: 725–728.

Slingerland, M. V., 1905. *Cornell Agr. Expt. Sta. Bull.* 233, pp. 51–57.

Elm spanworm, *Ennomos subsignarius* Hbn.:

Davis, R., 1960. *Proc. Entomol. Soc. Wash.,* **62**: 247–248.

Drooz, A. J., 1960. *Southern Lumberman,* December.

———, 1963. *U.S. Dept. Agr. Res. Note* S.E. 12.

———, and J. D. Solomon, 1961. *U.S. Dept. Agr. Res. Note* S.E. 173.

———, and ———, 1961. *J. Forestry,* **54**: 1060–1061.

Fedde, G. F., 1963. *U.S. Dept. Agr. Forest Pest Leaflet* 81.

Solomon, J. D., 1962. *J. Econ. Entomol.,* **55**: 269–270.

European spruce sawfly, *Diprion* (*Gilpinia*) *hercyniae:*

Baird, A. B., 1937. Biological control, *Pulp Paper Mag. Can.*

Balch, R. E., 1936. *Can. Entomologist,* **68:** 23–31.

———, 1939. *J. Econ. Entomol.,* **32:** 412–418.

———, 1940. *Can. Dept. Agr., Forest Insect Invest., Spe. Circ.*

MacAloney, H. J., 1936. *J. Forestry,* **34:** 125–127.

Reeks, W. A., and G. W. Barter, 1951. Growth reduction and mortality of spruce, *Forestry Chron.,* **27:** 1–16.

Fall webworm, *Hyphantria cunea* (Drury):

Tothill, J. D., 1922. *Can. Dept. Agr. Tech. Bull.* 3, pp. 3–107.

Oliver, A. D., 1964. *J. Econ. Entomol.,* **57:** 314–318.

Forest tent caterpillar, *Malacosoma disstria* Hbn.:

Batzer, H. O., and W. E. Waters, 1956. *U.S. Dept. Agr. Forest Pest Leaflet* 9.

Blais, J. R., R. M. Prentice, W. L. Sippell, and D. R. Wallace, 1955. *Can. Entomologist,* **87:** 1–8.

Hodson, A. C., 1941. *Univ. Minn. Agr. Expt. Sta. Tech. Bull.* 148.

———, 1945. *Univ. Minn. Agr. Expt. Sta. Tech. Bull.* 170.

Schaffner, J. V., 1950. *Soc. Am. For., N. E. Sec., Tree Pest Leaflet* 5.

Sippell, W. L., 1962. *Can. Entomologist,* **94:** 408–416.

Slingerland, M. V., 1899. *Cornell Agr. Expt. Sta. Bull.* 170, pp. 557–564.

Green fruitworm, *Lithophane antennata* (Walker):

Felt, E. P., 1912. *N.Y. State Museum Bull.* 155, pp. 48–52.

Green-striped mapleworm, *Anisota rubicunda* (Fabr.):

Wilson, L. F., 1963. *U.S. Dept. Agr. Forest Pest Leaflet* 77.

Gypsy moth, *Porthetria dispar* (L.):

Behre, C. E., A. C. Cline, and W. L. Baker, 1936. Silvicultural control, *Mass. Forest Park Assoc. Bull.* 157.

Bess, H. A., S. H. Spurr, and E. W. Littlefield, 1947. *Harvard Forest Bull.* 22.

Brown, R. C., et al., 1944. *J. Forestry,* **42:** 393–407.

Burgess, A. F., and W. L. Baker, 1938. *U.S. Dept. Agr. Circ.* 464.

Campbell, R. W., 1963. *Can. Entomologist,* **95:** 426–434.

Conklin, J. G., 1950. *Soc. Am. Foresters, N. E. Sec., Tree Pest Leaflet* 25.

Dowden, P. B., 1959. *U.S. Dept. Agr. Forest Pest Leaflet* 41.

Nichols, J. O., 1962. *Penn. Dept. Agr. Misc. Bull.* 4404.

Smith, D. M., 1962. *Proc. Conn. Forest and Park Assoc.,* pp. 7–10.

Turner, N., 1963. *Conn. Agr. Expt. Sta. Bull.* 655.

Hemlock looper, *Lambdina fiscellaria* Guen.:

Anon., 1963. *News Pesticides Rev., Natl. Agri. Chem. Assoc.,* **21:** 8–9.

Fracker, S. B., and A. Granovski, 1927. *J. Econ. Entomol.,* **20:** 287–295.

Johnson, N. E., 1963. *Weyerhaeuser Co. Forest Res. Note* 55.

Kinghorn, J. M., 1954. *Forestry Chron.,* **30:** 380–400.

Richmond, H. A., 1947. *Can. Dept. Agr. Bimonthly Progr. Rept.* 3, pp. 3–4.

Schaffner, J. V., 1950. *New Eng. Sec. Soc. Am. Forestry Tree Pest Leaflet* 51.

Thomson, M. G., 1957. *Forest Chron.,* **33:** 141–147.

Jack-pine budworm, *Choristoneura pinus* Freeman:

Dixon, J. C., and D. M. Benjamin, 1963. *J. Econ. Entomol.,* **56:** 266–270.

Freeman, T. N., 1953. *Can. Entomologist,* **85:** 121–127.

Graham, S. A., 1935. On pine, *Univ. Mich., School Forestry Conserv. Bull.* 6.

Hodson, A. C., and P. J. Zahngraff, 1946. *J. Forestry*, **44**: 198–208.

MacAloney, H. J., and A. T. Drooz, 1956. *U.S. Dept. Agr. Forest Pest Leaflet* 7.

Larch casebearer, *Coleophora laricella* Hbn.:

Britton, W. E., 1924. *Conn. Agr. Expt. Sta. Bull.* 256, pp. 288–291.

Felt, E. P., 1933. *J. Econ. Entomol.*, **26**: 46–47.

Larch sawfly, *Pristiphora erichsonii* (Htg.):

Buckner, C. H., 1954. *Proc. 10th Intern. Congr. Entomol.*, **4**: 353–362.

Drooz, A. T., 1960. *U.S. Dept. Agr. Tech Bull.* 1212.

Graham, S. A., 1956. *Forest Sci.*, **2**: 132–160.

Heron, R. J., 1960. *Ann. Entomol. Soc. Am.*, **53**: 476–481.

Ives, W. G. H., 1959. *Can. Entomologist*, **91**: 513–519.

———, 1963. *Can. Entomologist*, **95**: 887–892.

LeJeune, R. R., 1951. *Can. Entomologist*, **83**: 152–156.

———, 1955. *Can. Entomologist*, **87**: 111–117.

Turnock, W. J., 1960. *Can. Entomologist*, **92**: 500–516.

Large aspen tortrix, *Archips conflictana* (Walker):

Prentice, R. M., 1955. *Can. Entomologist*, **87**: 461–473.

Locust leaf miner, *Chalepus dorsalis* Thunb.:

Dominick, C. B., 1938. *J. Econ. Entomol.*, **31**: 186–189.

Lodgepole needle miner, *Evagoria milleri* Busck. and *Evagoria starki* Freeman:

Henson, W. R., and R. F. Shepherd, 1952. *Can. J. Zool.*, **30**: 144–153.

———, R. W. Stark, and W. G. Wellington, 1954. *Can. Entomologist*, **86**: 13–19.

Patterson, J. E., 1921. *J. Agr. Res.*, **21**: 127–142.

Stark, R. W., 1952. *Forestry Chron.*, **28**: 57–60.

———, 1959. *Can. J. Zool.*, **37**: 753–761.

———, and J. A. Cook, 1957. *Forest Sci.*, **3**: 376–396.

Struble, G. R., 1958. *U.S. Dept. Agr. Forest Pest Leaflet* 22.

Yuill, J. S., 1942. *J. Econ. Entomol.*, **35**: 16–20.

Maple Blight:

Giese, R. L., D. R. Houston, D. M. Benjamin, J. E. Kuntz, J. E. Kapler, and D. D. Skilling, 1964. *Univ. of Wisconsin Research Bull.* 250.

Maple leaf cutter, *Paraclemensia acerifoliella* (Fitch):

Herrick, G. W., 1923. *Cornell Agr. Expt. Sta. Bull.* 417.

Mourning-cloak butterfly, *Aglais (Euvanessa) antiopa* (Linn.):

Felt, E. P., 1906. *N.Y. State Museum Mem.* 8, pp. 158–162.

Oak caterpillars:

Hitchcock, S. W., 1961. *Conn. Agr. Expt. Sta. Bull.* 641.

Wickman, B. E., 1962. *U.S. Dept. Agr. Forest Pest Leaflet* 72.

Wilson, L. F., 1961. *U.S. Dept. Agr. Forest Pest Leaflet* 67.

Orange-striped oakworm, *Anisota senatoria* (Abb. and Sm.):

Houser, J. S., 1918. *Ohio Agr. Expt. Sta. Bull.* 332, pp. 249–251.

Pandora moth, *Coloradia pandora* Blake:

Burke, H. E., 1932. *U.S. Dept. Agr. Circ.* 224.

Wygant, N. D., 1941. *J. Econ. Entomol.*, **34**: 697–702.

Pine butterfly, *Neophasia menapia* Felder:

Cole, W. E., 1961. *U.S. Dept. Agr., Forest Pest Leaflet* 66.

Evenden, J. C., 1940. *J. Forestry,* **38**: 949–955.

————, 1926. *J. Agr. Res.,* **33**: 339–344.

Pine sawflies:

Benjamin, D. M., 1955. *U.S. Dept. Agr. Tech. Bull.* 1118.

————, and J. E. Kapler, 1960. *Forest Sci.,* **6**: 253–268.

Bird, F. T., 1955. *Can. Entomologist,* **87**: 124–127.

Buckner, C. H., 1955. *Can. Entomologist,* **87**: 121–123.

Coyne, J. F., 1959. *U.S. Dept. Agr. Forest Pest Leaflet* 34.

Ewan, H. G., 1957. *U.S. Dept. Agr. Forest Pest Leaflet* 17.

Ghent, A. W., 1960. *Behavior,* **16**: 110–148.

MacAloney, H. J., 1957. *U.S. Dept. Agr. Forest Pest Leaflet* 14.

Ross, H. H., 1955. *Forest Sci.,* **1**: 196–209.

Pine tube moth, *Argyrotaenia pinatubana* Kearf:

Burke, H. E., 1932. *U.S. Dept. Agr. Circ.* 224.

Pine tussock moth, *Dasychira plagiata* (Walker):

Banash, S. E., et al., 1963. *Proc. North Central Branch Entomol. Soc. Am.,* **18**: 70.

Walgenbach, D. D., and D. M. Benjamin, 1963. *Proc. North Central Branch Entomol. Soc. Am.,* **18**: 15–16.

Satin moth, *Stilpnotia salicis* (Linn.):

Burgess, A. F., 1927. *U.S. Dept. Agr. Bull.* 1469.

Collins, C. W., 1931. *U.S. Dept. Agr. Circ.* 189.

Glendenning, R., 1924. *Can. Dept. Agr. Pamphlet* 50 *n. s.*

Silver-spotted tussock moth, *Halisidota* spp.:

Silver, G. T., 1958. *Can. Entomologist,* **90**: 65–80.

Spruce budworm, *Choristoneura fumiferana* (Clem.):

Balch, R. E., 1958. *Can. Dept. Agr. Forest Biol. Div. Publ.* 1035.

Bean, J. L., 1959. *Ann. Entomol. Soc. Am.,* **52**: 605–608.

————, 1961. *U.S. Dept. Agr. Forest Pest Leaflet* 58.

Blais, J. R., 1952. *Can. J. Zool.,* **30**: 1–29.

Brown, R. C., 1944. *U.S. Dept. Agr. Leaflet* 242.

Craighead, F. C., 1924. *Can. Dept. Agr. Bull.* 37.

Dowden, P. B., H. A. Jaynes, and V. M. Carolin, 1953. *J. Econ. Entomol.,* **46**: 307–312.

Elliott, K. R., 1960. *Forestry Chron.,* **36**: 61–82.

Graham, S. A., and L. W. Orr, 1940. *Minn. Agr. Expt. Sta. Tech. Bull.* 142.

Greenbank, D. O., 1956. *Can. J. Zool.,* **34**: 453–476.

Heller, R. C., J. L. Bean, and J. W. Marsh, 1952. *J. Forestry,* **50**: 8–11.

Macdonald, D. R., et al., 1962–1963. *Can. Dept. Agric. Forest Entomol. Pathol. Branch Inform. Repts.* XVII and XVIII.

Mather, W. G., 1932. The spruce in British Columbia, *Forestry Chronicle,* **8**: 154–157.

Morris, R. F., et al., 1963. *Mem. Entomol. Soc. Can. No. 31.*

Webb, F. E., 1955. *Forestry Chron.,* **31**: 342–352.

————, 1960. *J. Econ. Entomol.,* **53**: 631–633.

————, J. R. Blais, and R. W. Nash, 1961. *Can. Entomologist,* **93**, 360–379.

Wellington, W. G., et al., 1950. *Can. J. Res.,* **28**: 308–331.

Whiteside, J. M., 1958. *Proc. 10th Intern. Congr. Entomol.*, 4: 291–302.

Spruce needle miner, *Encordylea ducharmei* Freeman:

McLeod, J. M., 1963. *Can. Entomologist*, **95**: 443–447.

Town ant (Texas leaf-cutting ant), *Atta texana* (Buckley):

Bennett, W. H., 1958. *U.S. Dept. Agr. Forest Pest Leaflet* 23.

Moser, J. C., 1062. *Forests and Pooplo,* **12**: 12–13, 40–41.

————, and M. S. Blum, 1963. *Science*, **140**: 1228.

————, 1963. *Ann. Entomol. Soc. Am.*, **56**: 286–291.

Walkingstick, *Diapheromera femorata* (Say):

Graham, S. A., 1937. *The Univ. Mich., School Forestry Conserv., Circ.* 3.

Shepherd, K. R., 1957. Forest Commission, New South Wales, Australia, pp. 1–18.

Wilson, L. F., 1964. *U.S. Dept. Agric. Forest Pest Leaflet* 82.

Walnut caterpillar, *Datana integerrima* Grote and Rob.:

Felt, E. P., 1905. *N.Y. State Museum Mem.* 8, pp. 303–305.

White-marked tussock moth, *Hemerocampa leucostigma* Abb. and Sm.:

Ruggles, A. G., 1917. *Minn. State Entomol. Circ.* 46.

Swaine, J. M., 1918. *Can. Dept. Agr. Entomol. Branch Circ.* 11.

Yellow-headed spruce sawfly, *Pikonema alaskensis* (Roh.):

Wilson, L. F., 1962. *U.S. Dept. Agric. Forest Pest Leaflet* 69.

CHAPTER 16

SAP-SUCKING
INSECTS

All the insects discussed in the preceding section feed upon the tissues of trees by ingesting the solid parts, and all of them have mandibulate mouth parts. In addition to these chewing insects, there is a large and important group of insects that live upon sap. Their mouth parts are of the sucking type in which the mandibles and maxillae have become slender bristlelike organs enclosed in a sheath, the labium. The mouth parts thus form a beak, used to pierce the tissues and suck the fluid therefrom. The sucking insects attacking trees belong to two orders: the Hemiptera and the Homoptera.

The effect of sucking insects upon trees is much less conspicuous than is the effect of defoliators. Only a few species seem able to kill trees directly, but nevertheless, the trees suffer distinctly injurious effects. Because their work is not conspicuous, the sucking insects of forest trees have received comparatively little consideration. On orchard and ornamental trees, however, they are acknowledged to be exceedingly important enemies. As the intensity of forest management increases, the importance of these insects will doubtless receive more consideration. Unquestionably sucking insects do as much actual damage to forest trees as they do to orchard and ornamental trees.

Sucking insects may injure plants in a number of ways: (1) directly, by sucking the sap, thus robbing the plant of a part of its supply of food and water and at the same time producing necrotic spots in the growing tissues, and (2) indirectly, by disseminating plant diseases. It has been demonstrated that certain disease-causing organisms are carried from tree to tree by sucking insects, phloem necrosis of elm for instance. In some cases the insects are, evidently, mechanical carriers, but in others they are essential intermediate hosts. For example, the mosaic diseases are transmitted from plant to plant by sucking insects; in some cases, this is the only way by which these diseases can be carried from one host to another. How important the insect-borne diseases may ultimately prove to be in the forest time alone can tell.

A third way in which sucking insects may injure trees is mechanically, by ovipositing in them. In fact some species, for example, certain tree-hoppers (Membracidae), do not generally feed upon trees at all, but they may still seriously injure or even kill trees by filling the branches with egg slits.

FIGURE 56. Scars on an aspen stem resulting from injury caused by the oviposition of tree hoppers, insects that feed chiefly upon the sap of herbaceous plants.

The species of sucking insects that attack trees are so numerous that space will not permit a full consideration of this important group. Therefore, the discussion will be confined to a few representative types of the more important families. References to others will be found in the bibliography.

HEMIPTEROUS SAP-SUCKERS

The order Hemiptera embraces a large number of sucking insects. The members of this order are the true bugs, and it is only to this group that the name bug can be correctly applied.

Plant Bugs. The members of one family of the Hemiptera, the Miridae, are known as the plant bugs and contain many tree species. Every tree of every species is infested with its share of these insects, but they seldom occur in sufficient numbers to be serious pests of forest trees. Some of them, however, are always sufficiently abundant to be conspicuous wherever their host trees are abundant, and they are sometimes very injurious in nurseries. An example of these potentially injurious plant bugs is the tarnished plant bug, *Lygus oblineatus*. The boxelder bug, *Leptocoris trivittatus*, of the family Corixidae is another common member of the Hemiptera that feeds on trees. The eggs of these plant bugs are deposited in slits cut by the females with their ovipositors in the twigs and small branches of the trees. The young bear a close resemblance to the adults, except that they have no wings. They run about actively on the leaves and twigs, obtaining their food by puncturing the tissues and sucking the sap. Unlike the Miridae the boxelder bug feeds upon the developing seeds. Therefore this insect is a pest of only the female boxelders. Like other Hemiptera, the metamorphosis of these insects is gradual. With each succeeding molt, the nymphs become more and more like the adults until the final molt, when they appear as winged imagoes. No satisfactory control of these insects had been developed until the advent of DDT and other synthetic organic insecticides. Where spraying the foliage of the trees is practicable and safe, most species of plant bugs can now be controlled.

Lace Bugs. Another important family of the Hemiptera is the Tingidae, or lace bugs. These insects are small in size, usually not more than $\frac{1}{8}$ inch in length, but they are very striking in appearance. The hemelytra are thin, almost gauzelike in appearance and marked with a network of fine lines. These, combined with the similarly lacelike lateral expansions of the prothorax, give the insects a decidedly lacelike appearance.

Unlike the leafhoppers, which are very active in all stages, the lace bugs lead a very sedentary life. Their entire developmental period may be spent upon a single leaf. Injury done by them is much more likely to be observed than that caused by the plant bugs, in part because it is usually more localized and in part because the insects themselves are more easily seen.

The lace bugs sometimes occur in extremely large numbers and in some years may, over extensive areas, destroy practically all the foliage of their host trees. They are not, however, tree killers. They attack trees of all sizes but appear to prefer saplings or small poles. Drake (1922) considers one of the tingids, *Corythuca pallipes*, to be "the most injurious leaf-feeding insect on yellow birch" in certain parts of New York State. These insects are sometimes very seriously injurious to hardwood trees growing in nurseries. Birch is one of the common hosts for a number of lace bugs, but other hardwood species, for example, ironwood, sycamore, oak, maple, willow, and basswood, are also heavily attacked. As a result of heavy lace-bug attack, the injured leaves fade in color and later turn brown, producing an effect similar to defoliation.

The life history of the lace bug is in some ways quite similar to that of other Hemiptera. The eggs are deposited in the veins on the underside of leaves of the host tree, sometimes singly but usually in groups. No definite pattern is followed in arranging the groups. The eggs are dark in color, rather elongate, and slightly curved in form, with the upper end somewhat constricted and closed with a lighter colored cap or lid. Those of the summer generation hatch in about 10 days after deposition.

The young nymphs insert their probosces into the leaf tissues to suck out the sap. During the early nymphal stages, they are usually gregarious. When they become mature, they generally scatter. The adults feed on both the upper and lower surfaces of the leaves, whereas the nymphs practically always feed only on the lower side.

Almost all the lace bugs have two generations per year in the latitude of New Jersey. Farther north, they probably have only a single generation, whereas farther south, they probably have more. Most of the species pass the winter in the egg stage, although a few hibernate as adults. These overwintering adults hide themselves under loose bark, in the litter beneath the trees, or in other sheltered places. The control of lace bugs may be accomplished on ornamental trees and in tree nurseries with relative ease, since spraying with a contact insecticide is usually effective. Where water is available, the insects may be held in check by washing the foliage thoroughly with a forcible stream of water from a garden hose. Seldom if ever is direct control under forest conditions necessary.

CERTAIN HOMOPTEROUS SAP-SUCKERS

Many members of the Homoptera are important enemies of both forest and ornamental trees; in fact almost every family of the order has representatives that feed upon trees. The most important groups, from the viewpoint of forest entomology, are the aphids or plant lice, the chermes, and the scale insects, but members of other families are sometimes injurious, for instance, certain species of leafhoppers and spittlebugs. In addition to these, there are the jumping plant lice, which are particularly injurious to orchard trees, sometimes even killing them. Since about 1940, some of these homopterous insects have become serious pests of forest plantations.

Periodical Cicada.   The more common species of the Cicadidae are well known to almost everyone, because those who do not know the insects by sight are familiar with the strident, rattling song of the male, so often heard on warm summer days. They are called harvest flies and sometimes, incorrectly, termed locusts. One of the most injurious and best-known members of this family in the periodical cicada, *Magicicada septendecim.*

The periodical cicada has an astonishing life history which is, indeed, stranger than fiction. The full-grown nymphs, sometimes called pupae, emerge in spring and early summer from the ground, where they have been entombed while passing through the developmental stage. During emergence years, large areas of ground are literally peppered with their exit holes. In places there may be as many as 100 holes per square foot of surface. The nymphs, heavy-bodied with broad abdomens and powerful legs, leave their burrows and climb upon any convenient object to transform to adults. In years when cicadas are abundant, their cast skins may be observed almost everywhere in the locality where they are emerging: on trees, fences, poles, shrubbery, and the sides of buildings.

The adult is dark brown to black in color with red eyes. In a resting position, the wings are folded over the back like a tent. The head and thorax are broad, and the abdomen is tapering. The female is armed with a strong ovipositor that might be compared with a pair of chisels. By means of this organ, she gouges out slits in twigs and small branches in which to deposit her eggs. It is this oviposition injury that constitutes the chief damage to the trees rather than the sap sucking of the nymphs. After about a week in the egg, the young nymphs hatch, drop to the ground, and promptly burrow into the soil. There, at a depth of about 2 feet, each one hollows out an individual cell next to a small root of some woody plant, inserts its beak, and begins its long period of sedentary feeding.

The periodical cicada lives for 17 years in the nymphal stage, the longest nymphal stage for any sucking insect. Most other insects with long life cycles have overlapping broods, some of which emerge each year, but this is not true of the periodical cicada. All the individuals in a locality emerge simultaneously. The broods of this insect are well known to entomologists. Each one is numbered, and the time and geographic distribution of each emergence can be accurately forecast. In the

South there is a race which has a somewhat shorter life cycle than usual, only 13 years being required for its development. Some entomologists believe it to be a different species.

From time to time, the periodical cicada appears in great swarms, particularly in the regions of eastern North America that are heavily wooded with hardwood trees. At such times every available twig will be filled with egg slits. As a result, many twigs and branches will be killed. This is not particularly injurious to mature forest trees, but to young stands or trees in nurseries it is very serious.

The control of this insect by direct means is unnecessary in the forest. In limited areas, as in a nursery, the population of cicadas could be reduced by pruning off and burning all twigs containing egg slits before the eggs hatch. Natural enemies are important aids in reducing the number of cicadas. Birds, particularly those of the blackbird group, are very fond of the newly emerged adults and consume them in large quantities. Many other birds feed heavily upon them at times when they are emerging. Immediately prior to emergence, when the nymphs are close to the surface of the ground, they are found and destroyed by scratching birds, skunks, moles, and hogs.

Spittlebugs.   Spittlebugs, or as the adults are called, froghoppers, are very common insects. The great majority of them feed upon herbaceous plants and shrubs, but a few attack trees. Two species attacking pine have received much attention: the pine spittlebug, *Aphrophora parallela*, and the Saratoga spittlebug, *Aphrophora saratogensis*. The pine spittlebug attacks all pine species but seldom causes recognizable injury to any except Scotch pine growing in plantations. It is a pine pest in all stages. The Saratoga spittlebug, on the other hand, feeds on pine only as an adult, but during that brief period it causes severe injury to the trees, especially to plantations of red and jack pine.

The feeding of the adults on the pine twigs produces a necrotic spot in the cambium region wherever the beak is inserted. When these spots are numerous, the injured twigs die, producing the characteristic brown "flags" of dead foliage. In cases of severe infestation this injury may involve the entire tree and cause its death.

The eggs of the Saratoga spittlebug are laid on the pine twigs. On hatching, the nymphs drop to the ground, where they may feed on any of a number of shrubs and herbs. Blackberry and sweetfern are the favored hosts, and only where there is a combination of one or the other of these shrubs with the pine can enough adults develop to cause injury to the pines. The nymphs feed beneath the surface of the litter near the root collar of the alternate host. Therefore, they may easily escape attention. However, when the litter is pushed aside, the foamy masses of spittle containing the nymphs are clearly observable.

On reaching full growth in July, the nymphs transform to adults, leave the sweetfern, and move to the pines where they feed and oviposit on the twigs. At each point where an adult inserts its beak through the bark a necrotic spot develops. When these spots become numerous, the twig dies and the needles turn red. In the course of several years, the "flagging" of twigs may involve the entire tree and cause its death. More often, however, the tree becomes deformed but still lives. The feeding punctures are invaded by a fungus that some believe contributes to the death of the tree. Anderson (1947) has demonstrated experimentally that the spittlebugs independently can cause flagging and death of trees.

Since the Saratoga spittlebug requires an alternate host, usually sweetfern, rapid crown closure will shorten the time that a plantation is susceptible to injury. Before crown closure, the insect can be effectively controlled with DDT—at 1 pound per acre applied while the adults are in flight. However, repeated spraying may be required until the alternate host has been destroyed by shading.

FIGURE 57. Frothy mass of "spittle" covering the nymphs of the pine spittlebug. Injury by this insect is often associated with dry weather or by stagnation in too dense stands.

The eggs of the pine spittlebug are also deposited in the twigs of the host. In early spring they hatch and the nymphs suck the sap from the twigs and small branches. Their favorite feeding place is on the growth of the previous year. The nymphs secrete a foamy fluid, resembling spittle, that covers and hides them. This white spittle on the twigs is the most conspicuous feature of their attack. When the nymphs are excessively abundant, the dripping of liquid from the trees often resembles the sound of rain.

At each point of attack, a necrotic spot develops in the growing tissues; this later becomes infiltrated with resin, thus preserving in the wood a permanent record of the injury. When these necrotic areas are numerous, they obstruct the normal flow of sap and the trees fade, lose foliage, and sometimes die.

Mortality resulting from pine-spittlebug injury is usually confined to overdense stagnating stands. Thinning plantations before the trees begin to stagnate will prevent mortality.

Aphids. Among the homopterous sucking insects the family Aphididae stands out prominently as an injurious group. The members of this group are called aphids or plant lice. They are abundant in numbers, both of individuals and of species, and they are so generally distributed that it is scarcely possible to find a tree of sapling size or larger which is not infested by them to a greater or lesser degree.

The aphids are usually very small, soft-bodied insects with pear-shaped bodies. The legs are long and slender, and most species possess on the dorsal side of the abdomen, near the caudal end, a pair of cornicles. These are tubelike structures, sometimes erroneously called honey tubes. Aphids may be either winged or wingless. When wings are present, all four of them are transparent, delicate, and provided with a few simple or branched veins.

When aphids occur in comparatively small numbers, the direct injury caused is comparatively slight; when they become very abundant, as they frequently do under favorable weather conditions, their injury to the trees is often great. They are not tree killers, however, and the injury that they cause usually results only in a reduced rate of growth and in a generally unthrifty condition. Trees injured by aphids may succumb to secondary insects or fungous diseases that they could have resisted when in vigorous health.

Various aphids have different habits. Some of them live on the bark of the trunk and large branches, others confine their feeding activities to the leaves and green tips, whereas still others feed upon the roots of trees. Some cause the formation of galls, particularly on the leaves. These live within the galls, and thus the tree provides them with both food and shelter. Other species provide shelter for themselves by causing the leaves on which they feed to curl about them. Still other live unprotected on the surface of the trees. Some aphids are provided with glands which secrete a flocculent, waxlike material, which collects over the insects and affords them some protection from their enemies and from the weather.

Some of these, so-called woolly aphids, are especially serious enemies of trees. One of these observed in Michigan, presumably an undescribed species of *Prociphilus*, attacks trembling aspen. Aggregations of these insects covered with white wax are conspicuous. The injury causes the bark to die beneath the areas where the aphids are feeding. If the aggregations encircle the trunk a tree can be killed (Graham, Westell, and Harrison, 1963). Some evidence indicates that insecticidal treatment using DDT can encourage infestation by this insect.

All aphids excrete a sweet material called honeydew, which is highly

FIGURE 58. Aphid colonies are often very large. This one is *Cinara pseudotaxifoliae* on Douglas fir. Note the ants tending the aphids to obtain honeydew, a sweet fluid excreted by the insects. (Weyerhaeuser Co.)

prized for food by ants and other insects. For this reason, it is a common sight to see ants busily collecting this sweet liquid. In some instances interesting symbiotic relationships have arisen between ants and aphids. The ants care for the aphids and in return receive honeydew. It is because of this relationship that aphids are sometimes called ant cows.

Although the habits of the various species of aphids vary greatly, the general features of the life cycle are quite similar for most of the common species. The true aphids pass the winter in the egg stage on the host tree. In the spring, with the appearance of green vegetation, parthenogenetic females, called stem mothers, hatch. The stem mother, or *fundatrix,* is wingless in most species. The young are all agamic females which in their turn reproduce parthenogenetically and are called wingless agamic forms or *spuriae apterae.* From these may be produced a number of generations of similar forms, each generation giving birth to living young. Reproduction is very rapid. In from 5 to 7 days after an individual is born, she will, in her turn, begin to produce living young. It is not surprising, therefore, that the aphids build up rapidly in numbers as the season progresses.

In certain generations another type usually appears. These are winged agamic females and are known as migrants, or *spuriae alatae.* Frequently, both winged and wingless forms are present in the same generation. These forms are often produced by the *spuriae apterae* at a time when the food plant has become crowded. In certain species, the migrants are produced directly from the stem mother. These migrants leave the plant upon which they have been feeding to seek fresh food. Some species seek out plants of the same species as that which they left, but a large number of aphids have an alternate host. When this is the case, the host upon which the stem mother and the succeeding generations are produced is called the primary host; the host species to which the migrants fly is termed the secondary host.

On the new host, the migrants give birth to winged or wingless agamic forms. A number of generations of these usually occur. On a secondary host the wingless agamic forms may or may not resemble the form on the primary host. Sometimes they are so different that they have been regarded by entomologists as distinct species until a careful study of their life history has disclosed their identity. The members of the last generation of this series give rise to the true sexes and are therefore known as *sexuparae.* In those species that have alternate hosts, this generation is winged, at least in part, whereas species which always remain on the same host may be wingless.

The winged *sexuparae* which are to produce the sexually perfect females fly from the secondary host back to the primary host. There they give birth to the oviparous females, which appear only at this stage in the life cycle. The males are usually produced by *sexuparae* on the secondary host. They migrate to the primary host, where mating and oviposition occur. In some species, each female produces only one fertilized egg, whereas in others, several eggs may be laid.

The control of aphids is practically the same for all species. In the forest no control is practiced, in spite of the serious injury that they may cause. Undoubtedly the practices that encourage vigor, discussed in Chap. 14, are of value in preventing aphid damage. Only in nurseries, in young plantations, and on ornamental trees does aphid control receive much consideration. There, spraying is the surest and best means of checking outbreaks of these insects on standing trees. During the growing season, contact insecticides usually give satisfactory control, and the overwintering eggs may be destroyed by a dormant spray of lime sulfur or oil (Chap. 10). Stock that is infested in the nursery should not be set out, either in the forest or in ornamental plantations, without its first being treated to destroy the aphids. Effective treatment may be accomplished either by dipping or by fumigating.

Chermids. The chermids are close relatives of the aphids and belong to the family Chermidae (Adelgidae). They differ from aphids in several important respects. For instance, the chermes have no cornicles, and both the parthenogenetic and sexually perfect females lay eggs. Because the bodies of the chermes are, in certain stages, covered with a flocculent mass of white waxy threads, the common name woolly aphid is frequently applied to them. However, they should not be confused with the true aphids, some of which are covered with a similar waxy covering.

The chermes all feed upon coniferous trees, and in some instances they are responsible for much injury. They are definitely more injurious than the true aphids, particularly to trees growing under unfavorable conditions. The life cycle of these insects is even more complicated than that of the true aphids. Some of them produce leaf galls resembling cones on the expanding shoots of spruces. These insects are usually called sprucegall aphids. In order to complete their sexual cycle they require an alternate host, a fir, Douglas fir, a larch, or a pine, depending upon the insect species. However, on either the primary host (spruce) or the secondary host, the insects may pass through the asexual cycle year after year. With some species such as the eastern spruce gall aphid, *Chermes abietis*, the secondary host is unknown in America (Wilford, 1937). Similarly the primary host of the white-pine adelgid, *Chermes pinicorticis*, is unknown. In Fig. 60 the complete life cycle of a typical chermid is illustrated.

Cooley's spruce gall aphid is a common and troublesome pest of spruces and Douglas fir wherever these trees are grown close together. If the galls are clipped from small spruces, infestations can be eliminated, if reinfestation from Dougles fir is prevented. Usually this species is not considered to be a dangerous forest pest either in the United States or

FIGURE 59. The balsam woolly aphid on Fraser fir, Mt. Mitchell, North Carolina. Conspicuous accumulation of waxy threads indicates a heavy infestation. (U.S. Dept. Agr. Forest Service.)

in Canada. However, Chrystal (1922) reports mortality of planted Douglas fir caused by the secondary cycle.

The balsam woolly aphid, *Chermes piceae*, is a most injurious pest of true firs. It was introduced into the Maritime Provinces of eastern Canada, New England, New York, and New Jersey from Europe prior to 1910. Since that time it has spread northward in New Brunswick and has appeared both in the Pacific Northwest and in the southern Appalachian Mountains in Virginia and North Carolina.

On balsam fir in the Northeastern localities it attacks both the twigs and the trunk. As a result of the injury the twigs become thickened and stubby in appearance, the condition called *gouting*. On the trunks the

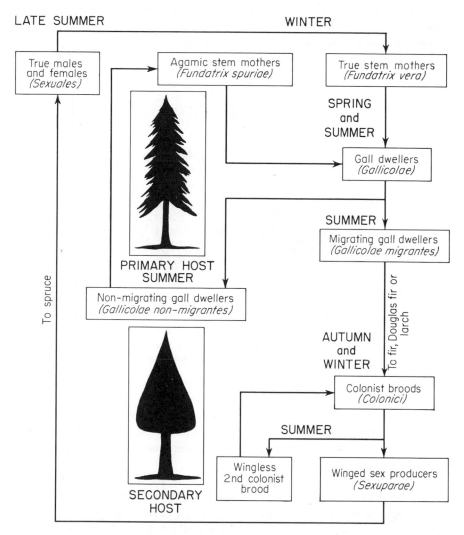

FIGURE 60. Generalized life history of a spruce gall aphid *Chermes* spp. On emerging from the galls, the dwellers are of two types. Although represented on the graph by three different rectangles, there is only one brood of gall dwellers, one group producing agamic stem mothers that remain on the primary host. Others from the same brood are winged and migrate to the secondary host. A part of this group, the sexuparae, continue the sexual cycle while the other part starts an asexual cycle on the secondary host. Thus there are three distinct cycles of development: the sexual cycle on the primary host, the asexual cycle on the primary host, and the asexual cycle on the secondary host.

sapwood beneath the infested bark becomes brown and brittle. Many trees in a heavily infested stand will die, sometimes within a single season.

The complete life history of this insect is complex, including sexual and asexual cycles. However, the sexual forms are rare and from the

FIGURE 61. Galls on blue spruce caused by *Chermes cooleyi*. (U.S. Dept. Agr. Forest Service.)

practical viewpoint have little influence upon the total population in a locality.

The balsam woolly aphid may have two or more generations each year, depending upon temperature conditions. According to Amman (1962) two somewhat overlapping generations occur in the vicinity of Mount Mitchell, North Carolina.

Although possible, the chemical control of the balsam woolly aphid seems impractical under forest conditions. Silvicultural control in the case of spot infestations has been suggested (Carroll and Bryant, 1960). Such treatment would involve not only cutting the merchantable trees but also destroying all small-size balsam firs by cutting and burning. Otherwise rapid reinfestation would occur. Favoring reproduction of spruce in forests where the balsam woolly aphid has become established has been recommended by Frost (unpublished report, 1956, Newfoundland Department of Mines and Resources). He suggests reserving spruce seed trees and creating favorable conditions for spruce reproduction through burning, but objection to this treatment has been raised because of the fire hazard involved. Mineral soil necessary for successful spruce reproduction might be exposed by disking or the use of a bulldozer blade. But all these suggested procedures involve considerable expense.

The introduction and establishment of predators and parasites from Europe in order to accomplish the natural control of this insect hold distinct possibilities and are receiving much study in both the United States and Canada (Amman, 1961; Clark and Brown, 1961). The fact that the insect, although a recognized pest in Europe, does not cause such disastrous damage as it has in some localities in America is encouraging. If the natural complex of parasites and predators native to European forests is established, the American situation may be greatly ameliorated.

SCALE INSECTS

The scale insects, Coccidae, comprise another family of the Homoptera that includes many dangerous tree insects. Because they are so different in habits and appearance from the other Homoptera and because of their great economic importance, they are discussed here in a separate section. They are usually regarded as being particularly injurious to ornamental and orchard trees, although they are really equally dangerous in the forest. Their inconspicuousness, coupled with the fact that their work is often supplemented by that of other more conspicuous species, has resulted in a general underestimation of the importance of scales as forest pests. From time to time, however, severe outbreaks in forests have been reported. For instance, the black pine leaf scale, *Aspidiotus californicus* Coleman, has been responsible for heavy injury in parts of the Lake States and has also been injurious in California forests, and several tortoise scales have been responsible for severe injury to forest plantations of pine.

The scale insects are peculiar. No one on seeing these creatures for the first time would guess that they were insects. In fact, it is doubtful if, on cursory examination, a person unfamiliar with them would even regard them as living organisms. They are, for the most part, small to the point of minuteness, and many of them appear as tiny scales of wax adhering to the leaves or bark. Others look like small galls, whereas still others appear to be accumulations of granular waxy material or masses of resinous exudation. Although this group includes many important pests, some very useful insects are also members of the family. For instance, the lac insects excrete over their bodies a resinous material which is an important article of commerce. This material, called stick-lac, is manufactured into shellac. Before the days of coal-tar dyes other scales were important in the production of coloring materials.

Three groups of the family contain dangerous forest- and ornamental-tree pests. These are the armored scales, the tortoise scales, and the mealybugs. The life history and habits characteristic of each group are quite different, and, therefore, a representative of each one will be discussed.

FIGURE 62. Root aphids on aspen. Attack of this aphid locally causes heavy mortality. It appears to be an undescribed species.

Armored Scales. The oystershell scale, *Lepidosaphes ulmi,* belongs to the subfamily Diaspini, the armored scale. This group is characterized by the scalelike covering beneath which the insect lies. This scale is composed in part of molted skins and in part of waxy or resinous excretions of the insect.

The oystershell scale is well known to almost everyone who works with woody plants. This insect attacks a great variety of fruit trees and deciduous forest trees and shrubs. In the forest, the ashes, poplars, willows, and maples are probably the most susceptible trees. This insect is distributed throughout the temperate regions of the world and either is native to America or was introduced in very early colonial days. It now

FIGURE 63. White-ash seedling heavily infested with oystershell scale. Seedlings of white ash growing under shady conditions are almost certain to be infested and killed. Although this scale insect is generally distributed throughout hardwood forests it usually kills only slow-growing trees of various species.

occurs throughout temperate North America from the Atlantic to the Pacific.

The oystershell scale is well named, for its general shape is that of an elongated oystershell. The full-grown scale is about ⅛ inch in length and brown in color. When these insects are abundant, the small branches of the infested trees may be almost completely encrusted with the scales. The male scales are said to be very rare. The exact proportion of males to females has never been determined, but it is so low that, according to Griswold (1925), thousands of scales may be examined without finding a male. This suggests that this species usually is reproduced parthenogenetically, although no general acceptance of such an assumption is evidenced in published writings.

In the North, the eggs are deposited in late summer or early autumn and pass through the winter without hatching. In the early spring they hatch, the time varying greatly, depending upon the latitude and the season. In general, hatching corresponds in time to the dropping of the apple petals. The young insects creep from beneath the mother scales by the hundred and wander about on the bark of the host tree. At this time they may creep upon birds, other insects, or anything else that comes in contact with the trees. In this way they may be carried from tree to tree or even from locality to locality.

After wandering aimlessly about over the bark for some time, the young settle down in a suitable place, insert their mouth parts, and proceed to feed upon the sap of the tree. The secretion of the scale then begins. The female scales never move again. As the insect grows, the scale is increased in size so that the body is always entirely covered. When mature, the female has lost both legs and eyes. She is little more than a reproductive sack with sucking mouth parts through which the food is drawn. The male, on the other hand, undergoes an entirely different type of metamorphosis, and, after passing through a stage resembling the pupal stage, he emerges as a tiny two-winged insect, with antennae, compound eyes, and the mouth parts replaced by a second pair of rudimentary eyes. The adult male takes no food and is short-lived, but during his short life he presumably fertilizes many females.

By the time the female is full grown, her body is filled with eggs. As she lays them, her body shrinks in size until almost the entire cavity beneath the scale is occupied by eggs, and in consequence the mother is crowded into a small portion of the anterior part. Shortly after oviposition, the female dies; consequently, by late autumn there are no females alive. The number of eggs deposited by each female varies from 20 to slightly more than 100. In the North, there is only one generation each year, whereas in the South, where there are two generations, the eggs of the first brood are deposited early and hatch during the month of July.

Other important species of armored scales pass through life cycles similar to that of the oystershell scale. The scurfy scale, *Chionaspis furfura,* and the pine-needle scale, *Phenacaspis pinifoliae,* both develop in a manner quite comparable to that of the oystershell scale. Some other members of the group pass the winter in a partly grown condition and complete their development the following spring. In some of these scales, the eggs hatch within the body of the female and the young are born alive.

Tortoise Scales. The tortoise scales are as a rule larger and more conspicuous than the armored scales. Some of them secrete very little wax and are, therefore, called naked scales; others, such as the cottony maple scale, *Pulvinaria innumerabilis,* secrete enough wax to form an egg sack, whereas others secrete wax in abundance. Unlike the armored scales, the legs of many tortoise scales are not reduced to the point of uselessness, at least not until the female becomes filled with eggs; there-

FIGURE 64. White, waxy egg cases of the cottony maple scale, *Pulvinaria innumerabilis.*

fore, the insects can change their location when partly grown. Many of these scales excrete large quantities of honeydew, which coats the leaves and branches of the infested trees. A fungus growing in this honeydew gives the trees an unsightly black appearance and is an aid in the identification of infestations at a distance.

The cottony maple scale is a good example of the tortoise-scale group. It attacks maples, particularly soft maples, throughout the range of its host trees and, when abundant, sometimes kills trees. Previous to cold weather, the female is fertilized and spends the winter in a partly developed condition on the small branches of the host. With the arrival of spring, these females complete their growth, reaching maturity early in the summer. Then they are over $\frac{1}{8}$ inch in length and broadly ovate in form. Each female deposits a tremendous number of eggs beneath a white covering of wax threads, the so-called egg sack. The specific name *innumerabilis* describes well its fecundity. A comparatively unproductive female will lay 500 eggs, whereas some may produce several thousand. The reproductive potential of such a species is stupendous. In the absence of environmental resistance, this species would reproduce at an unbelievable rate.

The white egg sacks mentioned above are extruded from beneath the caudal end of each mother scale. These white masses standing out prominently against the blackened bark of the trees attract much attention. Some other members of the tortoise-scale group, instead of laying their eggs in sacks, lay them beneath their arched bodies, whereas still others produce living young.

The tiny scales leave the egg sacks in July or August and make their way to the leaves. There they settle down and feed until fall. Most of them locate on the underside of the leaves along the large veins. The males develop much more rapidly than the females and emerge as winged adults in late summer or autumn. At that time, mating takes place even though the females are not fully developed. After fertilization and before the leaves drop in the fall, the females move from the leaves and make their way back to the twigs and small branches where they pass the winter, complete their development, lay their eggs and die.

Mealybugs. Some members of the mealybug group are serious enemies of trees, especially in warm regions. Even in cooler climates, however, some members of this subfamily are injurious tree pests. Instead of secreting waxy threads, the mealybugs cover or partly cover themselves with a powdery wax. This flourlike secretion gives them their common name. The European elm scale, *Gossyparia spuria*, will serve to illustrate this group.

When first introduced into America, the European elm scale caused much mortality among the elms attacked and was considered to be one of the most dangerous of the forest mealybugs. It was first reported in the United States from New York State in 1884, but apparently it had been established for a number of years prior to that time. In 1894, it was reported from California and now is widely distributed throughout the United States and Canada wherever its host trees are present.

Now that it has become thoroughly established in its new environment, the elm scale, although still an injurious pest, does not cause so much mortality among the elms as it did when first introduced. This situation can be explained in part by the increased activities of parasites and predators and in part by the increased resistance of the surviving elms. This pest serves as one more illustration of the principle that a newly introduced pest is likely to be more injurious when first introduced than it will be later.

The rapid spread of the elm scale throughout the United States is surprising. It might have been carried in some instances by birds, but in most cases it was carried to new localities on infested nursery stock. The overwintering scales may be carried easily in this way. The popularity of elm as a shade tree and the lack of inspection and certification of nursery stock during the period when it was becoming generally distributed were doubtless factors of importance contributing to its rapid spread.

The body of the European elm scale is ovate in form. In the second stage this species secretes a powdery wax like that of other mealybugs. The third-stage females are brown in color and without any dorsal waxy covering. They do, however, secrete a white waxy fringe called the semicocoon, which curves upward from the ventral side and partly encloses the body. The males, between the second stage and the adult, are enclosed in white waxy cocoons.

The life cycle of this insect is similar in many ways to that of the other scales discussed. The winter is passed on the branches of host trees in the second instar. Their covering of powdery wax serves to protect them to some degree against both excessive desiccation and moisture. Very early in the spring or even in late winter, the males molt to the third stage and spin their waxy cocoons, after which they molt again. This fourth stage, the prepupal, is a quiescent stage within the cocoon. In the course of a week or more the prepupa molts again. It is then a pupa. After another quiescent period, the adult males emerge from the cocoon. The first males to emerge are wingless; the later emergents are winged. Between these two extremes are insects with all stages of wing development.

In the meantime the females have also been undergoing a certain change. About the time that the adult males are ready to emerge from their cocoons, the females molt for the last time. The males emerge and mating takes place. The fertilized females then seek out a suitable location, usually on the underside of a branch, and settle down for the last time. They then begin to excrete the semicocoon. During this third period, the female excretes large quantities of honeydew, which covers the branches, the foliage, and the ground beneath the trees with a sticky coating. In this sweet material a sooty fungus grows, and soon the infested trees assume an inky-black appearance.

By late spring, the females are fully grown and have completed their semicocoons. They are then ready to lay their eggs. The egg-laying period of most insects is brief, but this insect takes her time in performing this important process; oviposition may last for several months. The eggs are held in the body of the mother until they are about ready to hatch. The vulva opens ventrally so that the eggs are deposited beneath the mother's body, where they are protected until hatching has been accomplished. Each female lays a large number of eggs, although by no means as many as does the cottony maple scale.

In less than an hour after the eggs are laid, the nymphs hatch and leave the mother. They migrate to the leaves, where they settle down to feed. During this stage little wax is secreted, and, except for the pubescence of the leaves, they are without protection. Some 6 weeks after hatching, they molt for the first time. In this stage a powdery wax covers the body. With the approach of autumn, most of the young scales move from the leaves and locate upon the branches and trunk. Those that fail to do this drop with the leaves, and most of them probably starve. Some are said to creep up the trunks of convenient trees, where they establish themselves. Thus the insect may be spread from tree to tree on wind-blown leaves.

Control of Scale Insects.   Scale insects are very difficult to control even on ornamental and nursery trees. For that reason, it is particularly important that every possible precaution be taken to prevent the introduction of scales into uninfested localities. Planting stock should be carefully inspected, and if scale infestation is found, the stock should be rejected, because no treatment of infested stock will give perfect results.

When once infested with scales, a forest will always remain infested, and only by means of natural factors can these pests be held in check. Fortunately, there are many valuable agencies of natural control. Unfavorable weather conditions, for example, heavy washing rains during the migration of the young scales, may reduce the numbers of the insects materially. In 1925, heavy rains during June checked a dangerous infestation of the black pine leaf scale, *Aspidiotus californicus* in the jack-pine region of Minnesota.

Like most other insects, competition among themselves appears to be a limiting factor. When the suitable parts of a tree become heavily encrusted with scales, the fecundity of the individual is apparently much reduced. In still more severe cases, the death of leaves or twigs upon which the scales are feeding may bring about an acute food shortage and ultimate starvation for many scales.

Predaceous insects, such as the lady beetles, feed upon scales. The adults and the larvae of these beetles both participate in this valuable work. The larvae of the lacewing flies, Chrysopidae, are also important enemies of scales. Among the most important of the predatory groups that feed upon scales are the mites, although all mites that are observed under or near scales are not necessarily predaceous. Some of them are scavengers but many of them, like *Hemisarcoptes malus,* are important predatory forms. This mite feeds upon the oystershell and San Jose scales and is at times very effective in controlling these pests. Tothill (1919) reports that this is by far the most important agency of control of the oystershell scale in eastern Canada.

Certain small hymenopterous parasites are also important in keeping scale insects in check. *Aphelinus mytilaspidis* is one of the important parasites of the oystershell scale.

In some cases, it has been possible to regulate the activities of some of these biotic factors of control and thus use them directly against a specific pest. For instance *Rodolia (Vedalia) cardinalis,* a coccinellid, has been used in California for the control of the cottony-cushion scale, *Icerya purchasi,* and has proved very effective. The beetles have been reared and liberated where they were most needed. Tothill suggests that hemisarcoptes might be handled in a similar manner to control the oystershell scale. But as we have seen in a previous chapter, we are not yet able to make full use of these biotic factors of environmental resistance in direct control work.

Chemical methods of direct control must often be resorted to. Spraying and fumigating are the two most important means of coccid control at our disposal. These methods are not, of course, applicable in the forest, but they can be used to advantage on nursery stock. Several suitable materials for this purpose are discussed in Chaps. 9 and 10. DDT, however, is not very effective against scale insects.

BIBLIOGRAPHY CHAPTER 16

Aphids:
   Jones, T. H., and C. P. Gillette, 1918. *J. Agr. Res.,* 14: 577–593.
   Palmer, M. A., 1952. The Thomas Say Foundation, V.
   Patch, E. M., 1915. *Maine Agr. Expt. Sta. Bull.* 241.
   ———, 1920. *Ann. Entomol. Soc. Am.,* 13: 156–167.
   ———, 1923. *Maine Agr. Expt. Sta. Bull.* 313.
Balsam woolly aphid, *Chermes piceae* (Ratz.):
   Amman, G. D., 1961. *U.S. Dept. Agr. Southeast Forest Expt. Sta. Res. Note* 153.
   ———, 1962. *J. Econ. Entomol.,* **55**: 96–98.

Balch, R. E., 1952. *Can. Dept. Agric. Publ.* 867.

Carroll, W. J., and D. G. Bryant, 1960. *Forestry Chron.*, **36**: 278–290.

Clark, R. C., and N. R. Brown, 1958–1961. *Can. Entomologist,* **90**: 657–672, **93**: 1162–1168.

Mitchell, R. G., N. E. Johnson, and J. A. Rudinsky, 1961. *Can. Entomologist,* **93**: 794–798.

————, 1962. *Oregon State Univ. Tech. Bull.* 62.

Beech scale, *Cryptococcus fagi* (Baer):

Brower, A. E., 1949. *J. Econ. Entomol.,* **42**: 226–228.

Hawbolt, L. S., 1944. *Acadian Naturalist,* **I**: 137–146.

Shigo, A. L., 1962. *U.S. Dept. Agr. Northeast For. Expt. Sta. Paper* 168.

Lace bugs:

Barber, H. G., and H. B. Weiss, 1922. *N.J. Dept. Agr., Bur. Stat. Insp., Circ.* 54, pp. 3–21.

Drake, C. J., 1922. *N.Y. State Coll. Forestry Tech. Pub.* 16, pp. 111–116.

Wade, Otis, 1917. *Okla. Agr. Expt. Sta. Bull.* 116.

Periodical cicada, *Magicicada septendecim* (L.):

Felt, E. P., 1905. *N.Y. State Museum Mem.* 8, pp. 231–237.

Marlatt, C. L., 1907. *U.S. Dept. Agr. Bur. Entomol., Bull.* 71, pp. 5–181.

Pineus:

Hoffman, C. H., 1947. Needle droop, *J. Econ. Entomol.,* **40**: 229–231.

Plant bugs:

Anderson, R. F., 1947. Saratoga spittlebug, *J. Econ. Entomol,* **40**: 695–701.

Eaton, C. B., 1955. *U.S. Dept. Agr. Forest Pest Leaflet* 3.

Ewan, H. G., 1961. *U.S. Dept. Agr. Tech. Bull.* 1250.

Kerr, Jr., T. W., 1956. *J. Econ. Entomol.,* **49**: 426.

Lintner, J. A., 1895. Insects of New York, *Rept.* 10, pp. 432–439.

Speers, C. F., 1941. *N.Y. State Coll. Forestry Tech. Bull.* 54.

Ursinger, R. L., 1945. Ash plant bugs, *J. Econ. Entomol.,* **38**: 585–591.

Red pine scale, *Matsucoccus resinosae* Bean & Godwin:

Bean, J. L., 1956. *U.S. Dept. Agr. Forest Pest Leaflet* 10.

————, and P. A. Godwin, 1955. *Forest Sci.,* **1**: 164–176.

Scale insects:

Blackman, M. W., and W. O. Ellis, 1916. Cottony maple-scale, *N.Y. State Coll. Forestry Bull.* 16, pp. 26–107.

Brown, C. E., 1958. Pine needle scale, *Can. Entomologist,* **90**: 685–690.

Comstock, J. H., 1883. *Cornell Agr. Expt. Sta. Second Rept.*

Dozier, H. L., 1925. Obscure scale, *Fla. State Plant Bd., Quart. Bull.* 9, pp. 129–133.

Gillette, C. P., and G. S. Langford, 1925. *Colo. State Entomol. Circ.* 46.

Glenn, P. A., 1920. *J. Econ. Entomol.,* **13**: 173.

Griswold, G. H., 1925. Oyster-shell scale, *Cornell Agr. Expt. Sta. Mem.* 93.

Herbert, F. B., 1920. Cyprus bark-scale, *U.S. Dept. Agr. Bull.* 838.

————, 1924. European elm-scale, *U.S. Dept. Agr. Bull.* 1223.

Hough, W. S., 1925. Comstock's mealybug, *Va. Agr. Expt. Sta. Tech. Bull.* 29.

MacAloney, H. J., 1961. Pine tortoise scale, *U.S. Dept. Agr. Forest Pest Leaflet* 57.

McKenzie, H. L., et al., 1948. *Matsucoccus vexillorum* Morrison, *J. Agr. Res.*, **76**: 33–51.

Rabkin, F. B., and R. R. LeJeune, 1954. Pine tortoise scale, *Can. Entomologist*, **86**: 570–575.

Spruce gall aphids:

Chrystal, R. N., 1916. *Ontario Entomol. Soc. Rept.* 1916, pp. 123–130.

———, 1922. *England Forestry Comm. Bull.* 4.

Cumming, M. E. P., 1962. *Can. Entomologist*, **94**: 1190–1195.

Plumb, G. H., 1950. *New Eng. Sec., Soc. Am. Foresters, Tree Pest Leaflet*, 1.

Wilford, B. H., 1937. *The Univ. Mich. School Forestry Conserv.* (now *Natural Resources*) *Circ.* 2.

CHAPTER 17

MERISTEMATIC
INSECTS

The meristematic tissues, as compared with other portions of a tree, are high in protein content and are, therefore, among the parts held in favor by many insect species. In number of species, the meristem eaters are exceeded only by the leaf eaters. The term *meristematic tissue* is here interpreted to include not only the cambium layer proper and the growing tips but also the adjacent soft portion of the xylem and phloem.

GROUPS OF MERISTEMATIC INSECTS

In a discussion of insects feeding upon the meristematic tissues, we may group them according to their taxonomic position, the condition of their host, or the part of the tree on which they feed.

On the Basis of Taxonomic Position. Among the meristematic insects are representatives of several orders. In the Diptera there are a number of cambial miners that find their nourishment in living trees. These dipterous miners do not kill trees, but their activities are responsible for certain minor defects of birch and maple, called pith flecks. Only occasionally are these insects numerous enough to be of economic importance. Some of the Chironomidae, called pitch midges, feed upon the cambium and phloem of coniferous trees. The pitch exuding from the tree covers the larvae and serves as a protection for them. Although numerous, this group contains no dangerously injurious species. There are also numerous dipterous species that inhabit the cambium and phloem region of dead trees or logs without being true meristem eaters. Either they feed upon fungi or other microorganisms, or as in the case of the snipe flies, they are predaceous upon the true meristem eaters. Thus the Diptera living in meristematic tissue is not a very important group economically.

Among the Lepidoptera, on the other hand, are many important meristematic insects. Certain species of the family Aegeriidae, the clear-winged moths, for example, feed upon the meristematic tissues of the trunk and branches. Some of them that attack conifers are known as pitch moths because of the mass of pitch which exudes from the injured tissues. When these masses become overgrown by wood, pitch pockets are formed. These defects, when numerous, materially reduce the merchantable value of lumber. The superfamily Tortricoidea also contains a number of typical meristematic insects. The tip moths and bud miners furnish many illustrations of this group.

Of all the meristem eaters, those that feed on the cambium and adjacent soft tissues of the xylem and phloem are by far the most injurious. These insects have been called cambium insects, but their activities extend beyond the thin cambium layer. Because most of their tunneling is in the phloem, current usage tends toward the name phloem insects for this group. Of the phloem insects the larger proportion belong to the order Coleoptera. The families of beetles most commonly feeding upon phloem are the Curculionidae, the Scolytidae, the Cerambycidae, and the Buprestidae. Each of these families contains species that are highly specialized for life in the phloem, and many spend their entire developmental period there. Others require the succulent and nourishing tissues only during the early developmental stages and later are able to complete their development in solid wood.

In the following brief review of meristematic insects only a few species can be considered. References to some others are included in the bibliography for the convenience of those who wish to expand their study of these insects.

On the Basis of Host Condition. Meristem-eating insects are often divided into two groups: primary and secondary. Unfortunately, these terms have been used rather loosely in entomological work, and therefore it is important that their meaning as used herein be made clear. A primary insect is one that is able to attack a healthy, living tree and complete its normal development therein. A secondary insect, in contrast, is one that is incapable of attacking and completing normal development in a healthy tree. The practical application of these two terms is sometimes difficult because an observer may fail to recognize that a tree has ceased to be healthy and has become decadent. As a result, confusion has arisen and different observers may arrive at different conclusions concerning the same tree. Nevertheless, the terms primary and secondary are valuable and will be used as defined above.

On the Basis of Feeding Place. Grouping the meristematic insects according to the part of the tree affected seems most convenient for discussion purposes. These divisions are:

1. Insects feeding on the terminal parts of trees:
   a. On twigs, tips, or shoots.
   b. On small roots.
   c. On seeds and cones.
2. Insects feeding only in the phloem region of the trunk and branches.
3. Insects attacking both phloem and wood.

In this and the succeeding two chapters, these groups will be discussed separately.

INSECTS FEEDING ON THE TIPS

This group contains a multitude of insect species, comparatively few of which are sufficiently abundant to be serious pests. They seldom kill the trees, but they can reduce the rate of terminal growth or cause deformities that affect the merchantable value of timber. In some cases, they cause a reduction in both growth and quality. Only when tip destroyers are active year after year, killing all or nearly all of the new growth each year, can they kill trees.

Nantucket Pine Moth. One of the injurious tip eaters is the Nantucket pine moth, *Rhyacionia (Evetria) frustrana.* This species was first reported by Scudder in 1876 from Nantucket Island, where it was said to be killing pines 20 to 30 years old. A few years later Comstock reported it upon Virginia scrub pine near Washington, D.C. Since that time it has been found generally distributed throughout the pine forests of North America. It attracted little attention in the East between 1876 and 1925, because the only damage it caused was a periodic reduction in the growth of small trees. In 1925, a severe outbreak, similar to that on Nantucket Island, developed on Cape Cod.

The middle-western variety, *Rhyacionia frustrana bushnelli,* has done very little damage in some localities, whereas in others it has been very injurious, especially to ponderosa-pine seedlings and small saplings. Some entomologists consider the two varieties to be distinct species. However, their life cycles and appearance are so similar that they will be considered together.

In the Lake States and the Black Hills, the Nantucket pine moth can be found in practically every stand of young pine, but it has never caused serious injury. On the other hand, in the sand-hill plantations of the Nebraska National Forest, in Ohio Valley plantings, and farther south, it has been a most serious pest.

The number of generations per season varies with latitude. Only one generation occurs in the Lake States and the Black Hills, but in the South there may be three, or possibly five. In the latitude of Nebraska there are two generations. This variation is, doubtless, one reason for the difference in economic importance of this species in different localities.

FIGURE 65. Adults of the Nantucket pine moth, *Rhyacionia frustranae bushnelli* (this variety, bushnelli, is regarded by some as being a distinct species), and the larger southwestern moth, *Rhyacionia neomexicana*, an associate of the smaller species in the Nebraska National Forest.

In the Lake States and the Black Hills, where there is only one generation, little economic injury results; whereas in Nebraska and farther south, where two or more occur, the injury to young pine is severe. It is doubtful if this insect will ever be an important pest under climatic conditions that permit the development of only one generation per year.

The life history of the insect in the East and in the West is very similar but varies somewhat more than is usually the case with the same species. The adult moths of both are small, with a wingspread of less than ½ inch; the front wings are marked with conspicuous copper-colored bands and spots. They emerge in the early spring and deposit their eggs on the tips of the young trees. After the eggs hatch, the tiny pale-brown larvae mine the buds or needles and also the expanding growth.

In the latitude of Nebraska, they complete their growth by the latter part of June. They then transform to the pupal stage, which is spent in a thick silken cocoon within the tunnels that they have mined in the tips. During the first part of July, the adults emerge. These moths of the first generation then deposit eggs on the young pine tips for the production of a second generation. This second brood is much more numerous than the first and does a correspondingly greater amount of injury. When the larvae of the overwintering generation reach maturity, they spin a cocoon in which to pass the winter. The eastern variety passes the winter in the tips, while the larvae of the western variety, when full grown, drop to the ground to spin their cocoons in the soil beneath the trees.

The history of the Nantucket pine moth in the Nebraska National Forest illustrates well the danger of shipping planting stock without fumigation from one region to another. This forest is composed entirely of plantations isolated from native stands of pine. Therefore, if clean stock had been used for planting, the plantations would, in all probability, have reached considerable size before pine pests could have invaded them. Instead, forest-pulled seedlings from Minnesota, the Black Hills, and the Southwest were used in the original plantings. With the seedlings from the North came the Nantucket pine moth. Although innocuous in its original localities, this insect became an exceedingly serious pest in its new home.

The infestation of Nantucket pine moth in Nebraska illustrates two other points mentioned previously: (1) control by introduction of an effective parasite, *Campoplex frustranae*, and (2) the fundamental principle that a niche left vacant will soon be occupied by an organism similar to the previous occupant. The use of campoplex for a time was highly effective in controlling the Nantucket pine moth. Following its reduction, however, another closely related species took over. This southwestern pine moth, *Rhyacionia neomexicana*, was presumably introduced on the original planting stock but was unable to compete with the Nantucket moth. Unfortunately, control by campoplex has not continued to be effective.

In the Gulf Coast and South Atlantic states, where four or five generations occur each season, the moth has caused great concern especially in stands of loblolly and shortleaf pine. Yates (1962) has demonstrated that the oleoresin from loblolly and shortleaf pine will crystallize within a short period after flow commences owing to larval feeding. In contrast, no such effect on either slash or longleaf pines could be demonstrated. He feels that this difference may explain the relative resistance of the latter two species to injury by the moth. The larvae can cope with the relative dryness of the crystallized resin whereas they cannot survive a covering of uncrystallized resin.

Injury by the moth is especially severe on pines growing on poor sites. There the stand may be ruined. In contrast, on the good sites the trees continue to make height growth in spite of injury, new growth appearing promptly at the base of the killed bud or tip, usually from dormant buds within the leaf fascicles. Under these favorable situations the trees close together and grow above the height where they are most susceptible to attack and injury.

Chemical control is possible using either DDT or benzene hexachloride, either in emulsion or in oil solution. These are effective using ground equipment; applications from the air have been unreliable. The need for a number of treatments during the season and the necessity for accurate timing of application, if success is to be attained, coupled with the difficulty of access into many infested areas discourage the use of chemical control of this insect in the forest.

European Pine Shoot Moth. In recent years, the European pine shoot moth has received much attention because of the serious injury that it has caused in pine plantations, especially on red pine. The pest has now spread to the Pacific Northwest. Much fear has been felt that this insect, which has now spread into much of New England and westward through Illinois, might invade the stands of native pine in northern New England and the Lake States. This danger seemed remote when it was shown that the insect is unable to withstand successfully the severe winter temperatures characteristic of most of the natural northern pine areas. A minimum temperature of $-18°F$ results in the nearly complete destruction of the shoot moth.

Nevertheless in Michigan the species occurs far beyond the expected limit, having been spread far and wide on nursery stock. Once established, its persistence is explained by the protective snow covering that in most winters shelters the insect in young plantations or on certain ornamentals planted along the highways such as mugo pine. Sooner or later a severely cold period without snow cover will almost certainly destroy the outposts beyond the insect's normal range.

The European pine shoot moth probably will continue to be a serious pest in pine plantations in southern New England and other localities with a similar climate. It can be controlled by spraying the trees in midsummer with one of the chlorinated hydrocarbon insecticides such as DDT, but the required dosage is very high. Such control is practical only on areas of limited size, in Christmas tree plantations, and on ornamentals.

Heikkenen (1963) has demonstrated that trees growing on good sites will outgrow an infestation with little permanent injury, whereas on poor sites the trees may be stunted for many years.

Pales Weevil. Another important meristematic pest of young pines, particularly in the Eastern states, is the pales weevil, *Hylobius pales*. This weevil is normally a secondary pest of mature pine, but the adults may be extremely injurious to seedlings (Peirson, 1922). It is a small brown snout beetle with light-colored markings on the elytra. It breeds in freshly cut logs, stumps, and injured trees, depositing its eggs in the bark during the early spring months. The larvae, resembling the young of the bark beetles, develop in the cambium region. When full grown, they form pupal cells by cutting depressions in the surface layers of the sapwood and roofing them over with shredded wood. This type of pupal case is often called a chip cocoon. The adults emerge in the spring months, and before ovipositing, they require fresh phloem of pine for nourishment. In cutover pine areas, the small seedlings provide almost the only fresh phloem available. For this reason, the young trees are attacked in the spring and sometimes entirely destroyed by hungry adult weevils.

Speers (1958) points out that the weevils feed not only upon young or newly planted seedlings but also upon the twigs of older trees. In the Southeast, cutting operations have resulted in a great increase in the numbers of these beetles until they have become a major problem. The weevils are attracted to new cuttings, where they deposit their eggs in stumps and large pieces of slash and weakened trees. On emergence they may kill most of the seedlings resulting from either natural reproduction or planting within 300 feet of infested cuttings.

If planting is delayed for a season after a cutting is made, the weevils will have emerged and left the locality. If a cutover area must be planted immediately after logging, the stumps should be treated to prevent infestation or the planted seedlings should be protected by an insecticide. Dipping the tops of planting stock in a 2 percent emulsion of aldrin or heptachlor is recommended and is perhaps the least expensive procedure. To spray the seedlings after planting with the same materials is said also to provide protection, but the cost will be many times as great, perhaps as much as twenty-five times.

White-pine Weevil.   One of the conspicuous meristematic insects of the eastern white pine in the sapling stage is the white-pine weevil, *Pissodes strobi*. This pest does not kill trees, but by killing the terminal shoot of the main stem, it causes the trees to grow forked and crooked and may, under some conditions, render them unmerchantable for lumber (Graham, 1926; MacAloney, 1930).

The weevils are brown snout beetles somewhat smaller than the pales weevil and with more sharply distinct white markings on the elytra. They pass the winter in the litter beneath the trees. In the spring, they emerge from hibernation to feed for a time upon the buds and inner bark of the leading shoots of young white pines. They then deposit their eggs in chambers hollowed out of the inner bark, one to three eggs in each chamber. The grublike larvae work downward beneath the bark, destroying the phloem as they proceed. Full growth may be attained before the first whorl of branches is reached, but in some instances the larvae may pass below the second or even the third whorl before reaching full development. When full grown, the larvae construct pupal cells in the pith or wood, there transforming to pupae. In late July and August, the young adults emerge and after feeding for a short time upon the inner bark of the new growth, they seek hibernation quarters beneath the trees.

Although the white-pine weevil is primarily a pest of sapling pines, its activities are not confined entirely to such trees. Occasionally, large trees may be attacked, but the injury that results is negligible. The age at which the trees are most susceptible is between 10 and 15 years. After the 20-year mark is passed, the proportion of infested leaders falls rapidly and soon becomes of little consequence in closed stands.

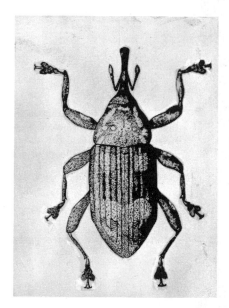

FIGURE 66. Adult of the white-pine weevil, *Pissodes strobi*.

This pest can be controlled by spraying the leading shoots in the early part of the spring. Crosby (1950) points out that, after spraying, the weevil population will require 5 years to increase to original numbers. Therefore, he concludes that two treatments, spaced 4 years apart, will carry a plantation through the susceptible period. Marty and Mott (1964) have shown that chemical treatment in white pine can be economically justified. Pruning and destroying infested shoots before emergence of the weevils are recommended as control practice. Cline (1933) points out, however, that it is too costly to be justified unless, at the same time, it prevents the injury from extending below the topmost node.

Studies in New England, New York, and Minnesota have all shown conclusively that trees growing in a dense stand are less subject to weeviling than are trees growing in open stands and, also, that in dense stands the stimulation to straight growth is so strong that practically all weevil injury is outgrown. For perfect results 1,700 trees per acre are

FIGURE 67. Diagrammatic drawing illustrating the position of eggs and newly hatched larvae of the white-pine weevil in the phloem of a white-pine shoot.

necessary in New York, whereas the standard density of 1,200 trees per acre gives adequate protection under Minnesota conditions.

It has also been shown by Peirson (1922) and others (Graham, 1918) that white pines growing under the shade of hardwoods are not attacked by the white-pine weevil. This explains why white pine that has grown with aspen or paper birch is seldom weeviled.

Many white-pine plantings have been unduly weeviled because of open spacing or other reasons. Unless this damage can be repaired, they will not produce any valuable wood. Cline and MacAloney (1931) have shown that good results may be obtained by pruning crop trees so that they will recover from weevil injury. This method of rehabilitating damaged stands has proved very profitable.

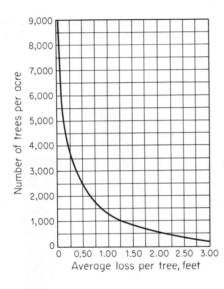

FIGURE 68. Effect of the white-pine weevil attack on the height growth of sapling pines growing at various degrees of density. The significant part of this diagram lies below the 2500 density level.

Other Tip Insects. Numerous other meristematic insects attack the terminal parts of trees. Some of them are decidedly injurious, although most of them are not usually important as pests. Several species of *Pissodes* are very injurious; for example, *Pissodes terminalis,* on lodgepole pine; *Pissodes engelmanni,* on Engelmann spruce; and *Pissodes sitchensis,* on Sitka spruce. Numerous small bark beetles belonging to *Pityophthorus, Scolytus, Pityogenes, Orthotomicus, Ips,* and buprestid or cerambycid borers, such as *Agrilus, Callidium,* and *Neoclytus* are frequently observed working in the terminal parts, but most of these are secondary and need not be considered here. References to some of the more important species will be found in the bibliography.

INSECTS FEEDING ON SMALL ROOTS

The meristematic insects considered thus far are those that injure aboveground parts. There are others that feed upon the small rootlets beneath the ground. These root-eating species are usually, but by no means always, enemies of small trees, because the roots of the larger trees penetrate into the ground below the depth at which insects normally feed. Trees growing in nurseries and seedlings in the forest suffer severely as a result of the activities of root-eating insects that eat the fine roots and rootlets. However, injury to tree roots by insects is not confined to these very small roots. For example, some species of weevils burrow as adults into the soil and deposit their eggs in the roots were the larvae feed, whereas others deposit their eggs aboveground and the larvae, on hatching, mine into the below-ground parts.

White Grubs. The most important insects feeding on rootlets belong to the white-grub group represented by the species of the genus *Phyllo-*

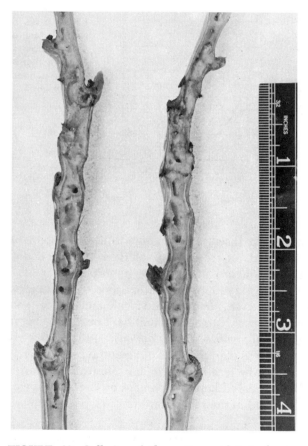

FIGURE 69. Galleries of the cottonweed twig borer, *Gypsomoma haimbachiama*. Such damage results in considerable breakage in cottonwood twigs and leaders. This is thought to be largely responsible for the crooked-growth main stem of the cottonwood trees. (U.S. Dept. Agr. Forest Service.)

phaga (*Lachnosterna*) and certain other related genera. The genus *Phyllophaga* is by far the most important. These insects are closely related to the very injurious European genus *Melolontha*. The phyllophagous white grubs are the larvae of the May beetles, of the family Scarabaeidae. These beetles, commonly called May or June beetles, are about ½ inch or more in length, heavy-bodied, awkward, and brown or black in color. They emerge from the ground in early spring to feed upon the foliage of trees. At times, the beetles are so abundant that they may completely strip oak woods.

The females deposit their eggs in the ground, close to their food plants. The degree of larval infestation depends more upon proximity to food for the adults than upon the kind of vegetative cover (Yeager, 1937). The life cycle may show some variations from species to species, but in general it is as follows: The young hatch in summer and feed for the

FIGURE 70. Larva of a white grub of the genus *Phyllophaga*. (University of Minnesota.)

remainder of the season upon organic material and roots near the surface of the soil. When winter comes, most species burrow deep into the ground and hibernate.[1] The next spring they work their way upward toward the surface and continue to feed on the roots of trees or herbaceous vegetation. With the arrival of fall, they again burrow deeply into the ground for hibernation, and the next spring they continue to feed upon roots. The larval growth, during the final season of develop-

[1] One important species in the Northern forest areas, *Phyllophaga drakii*, remains near the surface during the winter, where the soil is usually protected from freezing by a heavy leaf and snow covering.

ment, is completed by midsummer. Then the larvae make pupal cells in the ground where they transform to the pupal stage. After an interval of a few weeks, transformation to the adult takes place, but the beetles remain in the ground until the following spring. Thus three full years are usually required to complete the life cycle.

In the South, the cycle may be reduced to 2 years, but in the extreme northern part of the United States and in a large part of Canada, completion of the cycle requires 4 or possibly 5 years. Those species that have a 3-year life cycle are most injurious during the second season when the large larvae feed actively throughout the summer. During the first season, the larvae are too small to cause much damage, and in the third summer, only a brief period is spent in eating, the greater part of that season being spent in the prepupal, pupal, and adult stages. Those having a 4-year cycle are especially injurious during the second and third seasons, whereas those having a 5-year cycle feed most during the third and fourth seasons.

White grubs are sometimes exceedingly injurious in forest nurseries, particularly in transplant beds. Injury in nurseries almost always occurs in locations that are within a few hundred yards of the food plants of the adults. Oak is one of the favorite adult foods for several of the more important species. Other species feed on aspen, paper birch, juneberry, New Jersey tea, and many other woody plants, including pine in a few instances.

The beetles feed at night and pass the day in the soil where they lay their eggs. Formerly, it was thought that the beetles would oviposit only in soil that was covered by vegetation, but this is not correct, as their oviposition has been observed in nursery paths and bare areas of washed sand. Thus the former recommendation to screen the beetles from seedbeds is not effective, since the larvae can move into the beds through the soil.

A far more practical method is to destroy the favored food plants of the adults for a distance of 300 or 400 yards. Because different beetle species are injurious in different localities and each has its own food preferences, the identity of the beetles causing damage and their food preferences must be determined locally before this recommendation can be applied. Chemical control of white grubs in nurseries is covered in Chaps. 9 and 10.

In forest plantations, the damage from white grubs is sometimes tremendous. In the Lake Superior State Forest and the Marquette National Forest in Michigan the grubs have completely destroyed many plantations. In other places, periodic injury occurs. It is not at all uncommon, however, for grubs to destroy from 10 to 25 percent of the planted trees in a single season. If an insecticide is applied during the planting operation, as described in Chap. 10, damage can be greatly reduced at low cost. At the same time undesirable side effects upon wildlife will be avoided.

Various species belonging to genera of lamellicorn beetles, other than *Phyllophaga,* also feed on the roots of trees but are not nearly so dangerous (Yeager, 1937). Some of these genera are *Serica, Diplotaxis, Macrodactylus, Dichelonyx, Pachystethus,* and *Anomala.*

Root Weevils.   Several root weevils belonging to the genus *Brachyrhinus* are sometimes very injurious to coniferous trees in the nursery (Gambrell, 1938; Shread, 1950). For example, the strawberry root weevil, *Brachyrhinus ovatus,* is a general feeder that attacks many different kinds of plants. The larvae live in the soil and eat bark from the small roots. This stripping of the roots results in the death of the trees. Almost all species of conifers are attacked, but the beetles in a locality may have a special preference for certain species. Hemlock, white cedar, and various spruces are attractive to them.

The adults are small black weevils, about $\frac{1}{4}$ inch long, with the head pronged only slightly into a broad snout. They cannot fly, a fact which probably explains the spotty character of their infestations. The larvae are typical legless weevils and lie, when at rest, in a curved position in the soil.

These insects have only one generation per year. The young adults emerge from the pupal stage late in June and, after a period of feeding, begin to oviposit. A certain proportion of the adults may live over winter, about 20 percent according to Gambrell's observations. Presumably they continue to oviposit throughout the growing season, but the greater number of eggs are deposited during June and July. There is, however, considerable variation from year to year.

Poisoned baits have proved effective for control of the adult beetles. Bait should be scattered lightly on the ground in the evening, so that it will be in an attractive condition when the nocturnal beetles are abroad. Poisoning the soil is described in Chap. 10. Spraying the trees on which the beetles feed was not so effective as baiting, except in wet weather.

Other Small-root Insects.   In addition to the white grubs and weevils there are a number of insects of lesser importance that feed upon the small roots of trees. Some of the cecidomyid gall insects attack the root meristem and there produce galls. Some other members of the Diptera also attack the small roots, but they are all of minor importance from the economic viewpoint. Other soil-inhabiting insects, such as wireworms, will feed upon the small roots and, if numerous, may cause considerable injury to seedlings, either in the forest or in the nursery.

The wireworms belong to the family Elateridae of the order Coleoptera and, like the white grubs, feed in the larval stage upon vegetable material, including plant roots. The adults of this family are commonly called click beetles. They are heavily chitinized flattened beetles resembling some of the buprestids in form. The larvae are slender, elongate, and heavily chitinized, hence the name wireworm. The legs are feebly developed.

These insects are found most commonly in comparatively heavy moist soil that contains a considerable amount of undecayed plant materials. Small trees growing in such locations are most likely to suffer injury from these pests. Soil poisoning has proved to be a satisfactory way to control wireworms, but the precautions discussed in Chap. 10 should be observed.

Since root-eating insects are hidden in the soil, much of their injury escapes observation. Not until the damaged trees show aboveground evidence of their activities do foresters, as a rule, consider these insects in forest practice. This is a mistake. Direct control in the forest has limited possibilities, but if the activities of root eaters are anticipated, much can be done to avoid their effects. For example, during moist seasons moderate injury to the tree roots is repaired promptly by vigorous root growth. Then young trees are able to become established in spite of considerable injury. In dry years, on the other hand, even a slight amount of damage may be fatal. Long-range weather forecasting now permits general weather predictions a year or even more in advance, and more use should be made of these forecasts in preparing planting plans. When dry seasons are predicted, plantings should be made only in areas that are relatively free of root eaters. When moist years are predicted, infested areas may be planted with the reasonable expectation that the trees will become established in spite of some damage.

Insects Feeding on Larger Roots. Several insects closely related to the root collar weevil (Chap. 18) feed upon roots above $\frac{1}{4}$ inch in diameter. Some injure mature trees. However, the greatest amount of damage is to relatively small trees. Little is known about many of these insects, largely because of their inconspicuous habits. Doubtless many species belonging to this ecological group are still to be discovered. Some are secondary feeders upon roots and cause economically significant damage only when the adults feed upon the bark and foliage of young seedlings in a manner similar to the pales weevil.

The pitch-eating weevil, *Hylobius picivorous,* is among these (Thatcher, 1960). This weevil breeds in the roots of freshly cut pine stumps and fire-killed trees. The weevils burrow to a root where the eggs are laid and the young develop. Damage to seedlings may be prevented by delaying planting until the beetles have emerged and left the cutover area. A minimum of damage will be done to natural seedlings during their first year because they are not then attractive to the weevils. If natural regeneration is desired, therefore, cuttings should be made during the fall and early winter following a seed fall. Cutting during the summer following a seed fall would be undesirable because the beetles would emerge from the infested roots at a time when the seedlings would be in their second season and very subject to injury.

Planted seedlings may be protected from attack by dipping the planting stock as advised for the control of the pales weevil.

The rhyzophagus weevil, *Hylobius rhyzophagus,* is another root-eating weevil. It injures sapling pines in the Lake States. Unlike the pitch-eating beetle, this insect injures the trees in which it breeds. It is similar to *Hylobius radicis,* the root collar weevil, and doubtless has hitherto been confused with that insect (Millers, Benjamin, and Warner, 1963).

Although the entire life history of rhyzophagus is not known, the adults must burrow through the soil to oviposit in a root, and the larvae later tunnel toward the tree, killing the root.

The aspen root agrilus, *Agrilus horni,* attacks and kills small aspens, usually less than ¾ inches in diameter, in the Lake States. Although it was thought to be an undescribed species, this *Agrilus* is apparently identical with type specimens of *Agrilus horni* (Nord, Knight, and Vogt, 1965). The eggs are deposited during an extended period in summer. They are placed a short distance above the ground. The young larvae tunnel in the phloem downward into a root for 6 inches or more from the root crown. They then work back to the aboveground stem, cutting a spiral gallery around the root and the lower part of the stem. Then a typical agrilus-type pupal cell is formed in the wood. There the later transformations are completed. This *Agrilus* is one of the common pests of aspen suckers if they are growing either on a relatively poor site or in a stand of low density. The injury to the roots is usually associated with and supplemented by root-rotting fungi.

Chemical control is impracticable in the forest. If injury by the root agrilus is to be avoided, stand density of between 4,000 to 12,000 suckers per acre should be maintained until the trees are in their fifth year.

INSECTS FEEDING ON SEEDS AND CONES

In the natural forest seed and cone insects are relatively unimportant economically because the abundance of seed produced by most forest trees far exceeds the number required for adequate reproduction of the species. Most tree species produce heavy seed crops periodically, the heavy crops being interspersed by years when seed production is light. This periodic production appears to have a profound effect upon insect populations that feed upon seeds and cones. When their food is scarce, the insect populations become low, and generally, when a bumper crop occurs, the number of seed eaters present is too low to destroy a large proportion of the seeds.

Occasionally, however, there may be two successive seed years. When this happens, the seed eaters may build up to high numbers during the first seed year, so that the crop produced the following season may be almost completely destroyed. This was observed in northern Michigan during 1948 and 1949. The cone crop on white spruce in 1948 was heavy. In 1949 it was somewhat lighter than that of the previous season but still heavy enough to be classified as a cone year. However, cone worms and other seed eaters were so numerous during the second season that almost no sound seeds were produced in localities that we observed, a most unusual situation in a natural forest. In the long run, however, this damage was of little consequence.

In recent years much attention has been directed toward the improvement of tree varieties by breeding elite individuals and planting them in seed orchards, where they are grown widely spaced and are cultivated, fertilized, and protected from injury by stock and wild browsing animals. Such orchards are very different ecologically from natural forests. The factors naturally controlling pests are largely eliminated. Therefore, in seed orchards severe injury from insects may be expected.

Even in the specially treated seed-production areas, where good stands of a certain species are selected, the same is true to a lesser degree. Such areas are selected because the general quality of the trees is good. The stands are then further improved by cutting the less desirable individuals to release the better ones from competition in order to encourage crown development, and seed-production area is treated in much the same way as the seed orchard and will certainly require special treatments in order to control insect pests. This conclusion is supported by a preliminary study of preharvest losses in slash-pine seed-production areas in the Southeast (Hoekstra, 1956). This study suggests that losses between flowering and maturing of the cones could, without protection, reach the 60 to 70 percent level.

The number of seed and cone insects are legion and include representatives from a number of orders and families of insects. The cone moths, *Dioryctria*, and seed worms, *Laspeyresia*, are Lepidoptera. The cone beetles belonging to the genus *Conophthorus* of the family Scolytidae, the nut weevils of the family Curculionidae, and the buprestid cone borers are Coleoptera. The cone and seed midges belong to the Diptera, and the seed chalcids of the genus *Megastigmus* belong to the Hymenoptera. These groups are the ones most frequently encountered, but they are by no means the only destroyers of tree seed. For example, thrips (Ebel, 1961) and mites attack and destroy tree flowers, and infestations of aphids or scale insects may materially reduce the seed production of infested trees.

Many insects that feed upon buds and green tips also attack cones incidentally; the spruce budworm and the various pine shoot moths, especially those of *Dioryctria* species, are some of these. The *Dioryctria* species seem to vary greatly in their habits; the same species feed at times on green tips, flowers, either young or old cones; mine woody shoots; or attack the phloem on the trunk of sapling-size trees.

Dioryctria abietella is one of the species that exhibits diverse habits. The suspicion seems justified that more than one species is actually included under the name Dioryctria abietella. Therefore, we should, perhaps, refer to them as the Dioryctria abietella complex. Many of the Dioryctria species exhibit diverse habits. At present, it is not known

FIGURE 71. Cone worms. (A) Adult Dioryctria amatella, (B) adult Dioryctria abietella, (C) larva of Dioryctora amatella, (D) Dioryctria amatella, attack on first-year cone of Pinus elliottii infested with Cronartium strobilinum. (U.S. Dept. Agr. Forest Service.)

whether these variations in biology represent true species differences or are responses to environmental changes. In Southeastern states three Dioryctria species are receiving special study, i.e., Dioryctria abietella, Dioryctria amatella, and Dioryctria clarioralis, but other species are also present, seedworms of the genus Laspeyresia, for example. In the Western states another cone moth, Barbera colfaxiana, is common and sometimes very injurious to Douglas-fir cones (Hedlin, 1960).

The length of the life cycle of these cone insects varies with temperature and the length of the growing season. In the North only a single generation may be expected, whereas in the Southeastern states from three to possibly five may occur judging from the length of a single life cycle as observed under laboratory conditions (Ebel, 1959). Therefore, the cone moths may logically be expected to cause far more severe damage to the cone crop in warm than in cool localities.

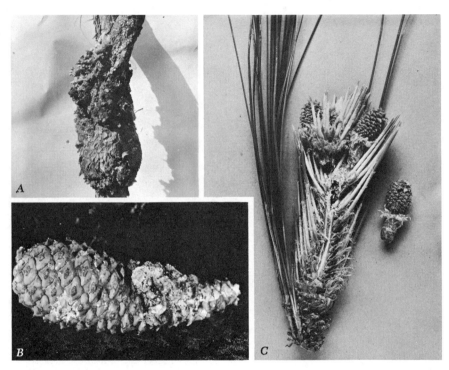

FIGURE 72. Damage by *Dioryctria* is extremely variable. (*A*) Damage associated with *Cronartium fusiforme* canker, (*B*) damage to large cones, (*C*) damage to shoot and first-year cones. (U.S. Dept. Agr. Forest Service.)

Merkel (1958) reports that first-year cones of slash pine infected with the rust *Cronartium strobilinum* are preferred food for *Dioryctria* cone moths and that second-year cones are more likely to be attacked when they are growing on branches where infected first-year cones are present.

Cone beetles, members of the scolytid genus *Conophthorus*, are frequently observed pests of cones. Some also attack shoots of pines as reported by Herdy and Thomas (1961). The adults cut egg galleries in the developing first-year cones, and the larvae develop therein, destroying the seeds. The white-pine cone beetle, *Conophthorus coniperda*, according to Craighead (1950) may occasionally destroy 50 percent of the cone crop over large areas and in limited areas 100 percent.

Nut weevils, Curculionidae, are snout beetles that attack nuts of various kinds including acorns, hickory nuts, pecans, and walnuts. They are occasionally numerous enough to destroy a forest seed crop, but in orchards they are especially injurious. They pass the winter in the soil

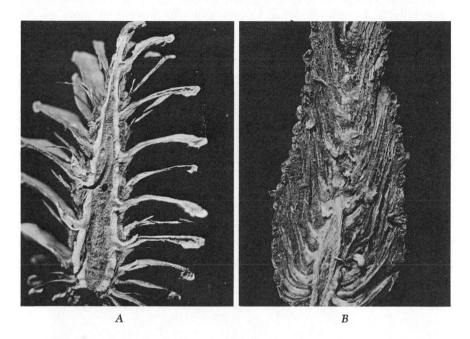

| A | B |

FIGURE 73. Damage caused by seedworms *Laspeyresia* sp. (*A*) Longitudinal section through axis of slash pine cone showing galleries in pith, (*B*) oblique section through longleaf pine cone showing larva and frass-filled seeds. (U.S. Dept. Agr. Forest Service.)

as full-grown larvae, transform to pupae and adults in midsummer, and oviposit in developing nuts. When fully grown, the larvae cut their way out of the nut leaving a circular hole. They then enter the ground, where they form hibernating cells. Infested nuts usually drop early and in orchards should be picked up and destroyed before the larvae emerge (Craighead, 1950).

Cone midges, of the family Cecidomyiidae, are common pests of Douglas-fir cones. Hedlin (1961) presents a detailed account of *Contarinia oregonensis* life history and habits. The winter is passed in or immediately beneath the litter. Johnson (1962) reports that the dead staminate cones provide the larvae with ideal situations for hibernation and that in litter containing these dead cones hibernation is more successful than in litter devoid of this constituent (Pettinger and Johnson, 1962).

The eggs are deposited in early spring near the base of a cone scale in the newly opened flower. When they hatch, the larvae tunnel into the scales, forming a small gall and destroying the nearby ovules. They leave the cones in the autumn to hibernate in the litter within a cocoon.

Seed chalcids of the genus *Megastigmus* are sometimes very abundant, especially in Douglas-fir seed. Occasionally 50 percent or more of the crop may be destroyed, although in natural stands the damage is usually

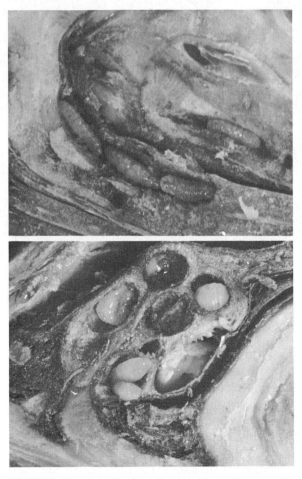

FIGURE 74. Two closely related midges (Diptera, Cecidomydae) from coniferous cones. Top: *Contarinia washingtonensis* in a cone; note lack of galls. Bottom: *Contarinia oregonensis* in a cone; note galls. (Weyerhaeuser Co.)

much less than this. The eggs are deposited directly into the ovule late in the spring, the female wasp inserting the egg by means of her long ovipositor. The larva develops within the seed, where it spends the winter. Emergence as an adult occurs the following spring. Some larvae, occasionally as many as one-half of them, may remain in diapause for a year or even longer before completing development to the adult.

The adults in appearance are similar to other familiar members of the Chalcididae. Usually they are small, heavy-bodied insects and are predominantly black, often with yellowish markings. Most of the family Chalcididae are parasitic upon other insects. These phytophagous species are therefore in the minority.

The control of seed and cone insects by the use of insecticides is a major subject for study in the Southeast and also in other localities (Merkel, 1962). Considerable research on chemical control is also being conducted in California and in the Northwest. However, the research has not reached a point that justifies final recommendations. Definite spray schedules will be published for some species this year. Koerber (1960) suggests that ultimately, in seed orchards and seed-production areas, a combination of biological and insecticidal control for these pests may be developed. But more must be learned about the insects, their parasites and predators, and the environmental factors that are operating to regulate their numbers.

BIBLIOGRAPHY CHAPTER 17

SHOOT INSECTS

Cone beetles (Twig damage):
>   Herdy, H., and J. B. Thomas, 1961. *Can. Entomologist,* **93:** 936–940.
>   Struble, G. R., 1947. *J. Forestry,* **45:** 48–50.

European pine shoot moth, *Rhyacionia buoliana* (Shiff.):
>   Carolin, V. M., and W. K. Coulter, 1963. *U.S. Dept. Agr. Res. Paper* PNW 1.
>   Friend, R. B., G. H. Plumb, and H. W. Hicock, 1938. *J. Econ. Entomol.,* **31:** 506–513.
>   Green, G. W., 1962. *Can. Entomologist,* **94:** 314–336.
>   ————, 1962. *Can. Entomologist,* **94:** 282–299.
>   ————, and P. J. Pointing, 1962. *Can. Entomologist,* **94:** 299–314.
>   Heikkenen, H. J., 1963. Doctoral Dissertation, The University of Michigan, University Microfilms, Ann Arbor, Mich.
>   ————, 1960. *J. Forestry,* **58:** 380–384.
>   Klein, W. H., and R. M. Thompson, 1962. *U.S. Dept. Agr. Pacific Northwest Forest and Range Expt. Sta., Res. Paper* 50.
>   Miller, W. E., and R. B. Neiswander, 1955. *Ohio Agr. Expt. Sta. Res. Bull.* 760.
>   ————, A. R. Hastings, and J. F. Wooten, 1961. *U.S. Dept. Agr. Forest Pest Leaflet* 59.
>   ————, and H. J. Heikkenen, 1959. *J. Forestry,* **57:** 912–914.

Parr, Thaddeus, 1937. In Sweden, *J. Forestry*, **35**: 269–273.
Gall midges:
Barnes, H. F., 1945–1947–1948. "Gall Midges of Economic Importance."
Condrashoff, S. F., 1961. *Can. Entomologist*, **93**: 833–851.
Giese, R. L., and D. M. Benjamin, 1959. *Forest Sci.*, **5**: 143–208.
Rooks, W. A., 1960. *Can. Entomol.*, **92**: 154–160.
Jack-pine eucosma, *Eucosma sonomana* Kft.:
Butcher, J. W., and A. C. Hodson, 1949. *Can. Entomologist*, **81**: 161–173.
Larch shoot moth, *Argyresthia laricella* Kft.:
Eidt, D. C., and W. L. Sippell, 1961. *Can. Entomologist*, **93**: 7–24.
Nantucket pine moth, *Rhyacionia frustrana* (Comst.)
Baumhofer, L. G., 1936. Distribution on nursery stock, *U.S. Dept. Agr., Bur. Entomol. P. Q., Mimeographed Publ.* E-366.
Graham, S. A., and L. G. Baumhofer, 1927. *J. Agr. Res.*, **35**: 323–333.
Martin, J. L., 1960. *Can. Entomologist*, **92**: 724–728.
Miller, W. E., and R. B. Neiswander, 1959. *Ohio Agr. Expt. Sta. Res. Bull.* 840.
Yates, H. O., 1960. *U.S. Dept. Agr. Southeast. Forest Expt. Sta. Paper* 115.
———, and R. H. Beal, 1962. *U.S. Dept. Agr. Forest Pest Leaflet* 70.
Oak twig girdler, *Agrilus angelicus* Horn *and A. arcuatus torquatus:*
Burke, H. E., 1920. *J. Econ. Entomol.*, **13**: 379–384.
Ruggles, A. G., 1919. *Minn. State Entomol. Rept.* 17, pp. 15–20.
Pales weevil, *Hylobius pales* (Herbst):
Ferguson, E. R., and R. C. Thatcher, 1956. *J. Forestry*, **54**: 469–470.
Finnegan, R. J., 1959. *Can. Entomologist*, **91**: 664–670.
Peirson, H. B., 1921. *Harvard Forest Bull.* 3, pp. 1–33.
Speers, C. F., 1958. *J. Forestry*, **56**: 723–726
Reproduction weevil, *Cylindrocopturus eatoni* Buch.:
Callahan, R. Z., 1960. *U.S. Dept. Agr. Pacific Southwest Forest Expt. Sta. Tech. Paper* 51.
Eaton, C. B., 1942. *J. Econ. Entomol.*, **35**: 20–25.
Hall, R. C., 1957. *U.S. Dept. Agr. Forest Pest Leaflet* 15.
Smith, R. H., 1960. *J. Econ. Entomol.*, **53**: 1044–1048.
White-pine weevil, *Pissodes strobi* (Peck):
Cline, A. C., 1933. Improvement of weeviled plantations, *Conn. Forest Park Assoc. Publ.* 24.
———, 1935. Reclamation of severely weeviled plantations, *J. Forestry*, **33**: 932–935.
———, and H. J. MacAloney, 1931. Reclaiming severely weeviled pine plantations, *Mass. Forestry Assoc. Bull.* 152.
Connola, D. P., T. McIntyre, and C. J. Yops, 1955. *J. Forestry*, **53**: 889–891.
Crosby, D., 1950. Concentrated lead arsenate, *J. Forestry*, **48**: 334–336.
Graham, S. A., 1918. *J. Forestry*, **15**: 192–202.
———, 1926. *Cornell Agr. Expt. Sta. Bull.*, 449, pp. 3–32.
Jaynes, H. A., and H. J. MacAloney, 1958. *U.S. Dept. Agr. Forest Pest Leaflet* 21.

MacAloney, H. J., 1930. *N.Y. State Coll. Forestry Tech. Publ.* 28, vol. III, no. 1.

Marty, R. J., 1959. *Forest Sci.*, **5**: 269–274.

————, and D. G. Mott, 1964. *U.S. Dept. Agr. Northeast Forest Expt. Sta. Paper* NE 19.

Peirson, H. B., 1922. *Harvard Forestry Bull.* 5, pp. 1–42.

Sullivan, C. R., 1961. *Can. Entomologist*, **93**: 721–741.

————, 1959. *Can. Entomologist*, **91**: 213–232.

Waters, W. E., T. McIntyre, and D. Crosby, 1955. *J. Forestry*, **53**: 271–274.

Zimmerman pine moth, *Dioryctria zimmermani* (Grote):

Felt, E. P., 1915. *N.Y. State Museum Bull.* 180, pp. 39–42.

Rennels, R. G., 1960. *Univ. Illinois Agr. Expt. Sta. Bull.* 660.

ROOT INSECTS

Aspen root girdler, *Agrilus horni* Kerremans:

Nord, J. C., F. B. Knight, and G. B. Vogt, 1965. *Forest Sci.*

Strawberry root weevil, *Brachyrhinus ovatus,* Linn.:

Gambrell, F. L., 1938. *J. Econ. Entomol.*, **31**: 107–112.

Shread, J. C., 1950. Control, *Conn. Agr. Expt. Sta. Circ.* 174.

Weevils:

Millers, I., D. M. Benjamin, and R. E. Warner, 1963. *Can. Entomologist,* **95**: 18–22.

Thatcher, R. C., 1960. *Forest Sci.*, **6**: 354–361.

Warren, G. L., 1956. *Forestry Chron.*, **32**: 7–10.

————, 1956. *Ecology*, **37**: 132–139.

White grubs, *Phyllophaga* (*Lachnosterna*):

Davis, J. J., 1930. *Purdue Univ. Bull.* 168.

Fleming, W. E., F. E. Baker, and Louis Koblitski, 1937. *J. Forestry*, **35**: 679–688.

Forbes, S. A., 1907. *Univ. Illinois Agr. Expt. Sta. Bull.* 116.

Luginbill, Sr., P., and H. R. Painter, 1953. *U.S. Dept. Agr. Tech. Bull.* 1060.

Schenefelt, R. D., and H. G. Simkover, 1950. *J. Forestry*, **43**: 429–434.

Speers, C. F., 1955. *Southern Lumberman,* December.

————, and D. C. Schmiege, 1961. *U.S. Dept. Agr. Forest Pest Leaflet* 63.

Stein, W. I., 1963. *Northwest Sci.*, **37**: 126–143.

Yeager, L. E., 1937. Doctoral Dissertation, The University of Michigan, University Microfilms, Ann Arbor, Mich.

Wireworms:

Arnason, A. P., 1951. *Can. Dept. Agr. Sci. Serv. Processed Publ.*, Ser. 111.

Hyslop, J. A., 1916. *U.S. Dept. Agr. Farmers' Bull.* 725.

Lane, M. C., 1925. *J. Econ. Entomol.*, **18**: 90–95.

SEED AND CONE INSECTS

Ebel, B. H., 1959. *Dioryctria abietella, J. Econ. Entomol.*, **52**: 561–564.

————, 1961. Thrips, *J. Forestry*, **59**: 374–375.

————, 1963. On slash and longleaf pine, *U.S. Dept. Agr. Southeast. Forest Expt. Sta. Res. Paper* S.E. 6.

Hard, John S., 1964. Red pine cones, *U.S. Dept. Agr. Lake States Forest Expt. Sta. Res. Paper* LS 12.

Hedlin, A. F., 1960. *Barbera colfaxiana, Can. Entomologist,* **92:** 826–834.

————, 1961. *Contarinia oregonensis, Can. Entomologist,* **93:** 952–967.

Hoekstra, P. E., 1956. *Southern Lumberman,* December.

————, E. P. Merkel, and H. R. Powers, Jr., 1961. *U.S. Dept. Agr. Yearbook,* pp. 227–232.

Johnson, N. E., 1962. Douglas-fir cone midges, *Can. Entomologist,* **94:** 915–921.

Keen, F. P., 1958. In western forests, *U.S. Dept. Agr. Tech. Bull.* 1169.

Koerber, T. W., 1960. Douglas-fir, *U.S. Dept. Agr. Pacific Southwest Forest Range Expt. Sta. Tech. Paper* 45.

Merkel, E. P., 1958. *Dioryctria, J. Forestry,* **56:** 651.

————, 1962. Insecticides, *J. Econ. Entomol.,* **55:** 682–684.

Pettinger, L. F. and N. E. Johnson, 1962. *Contarinia oregonensis, Weyerhaeuser Co. Forest Res. Note* 45.

Schaefer, C. H., 1963. *Conophthorus radiatae, Hilgardia,* **34:** 79–103.

CHAPTER 18

PHLOEM
INSECTS

Meristem insects that attack the trunks and larger branches of trees are discussed in this chapter. They live in the phloem and the soft tissues of the xylem. With certain groups, the Scolytidae for example, even the adult stage is spent in the phloem. Among the phloem insects are some of the most destructive forest pests and also many species that never kill or seriously injure healthy forest trees. Representatives of several orders live in the phloem, but the most injurious belong to either the Lepidoptera or the Coleoptera. For purposes of discussion, it is more convenient to divide the phloem insects into two arbitrary groups: the borers and the bark beetles. Insects belonging to both these groups feed on the inner bark during the development period, but the borers score the wood and often pupate beneath the wood surface, whereas the bark beetles are restricted to the phloem and bark throughout their lives.

PHLOEM BORERS

Although most of the phloem borers are members of the Coleoptera, there are some members of the Lepidoptera in this group. Most common of these, perhaps, are the pitch moths. Although there are numerous species in this group, the life cycles and types of injury are very similar for all of them. The well-known pine pitch-mass borer adequately illustrates these lepidopterous phloem insects.

Pine Pitch-mass Borer.   The adult pine pitch-mass borer, *Vespamima pini,* is one of the clear-wing moths of the family Aegeriidae. In shape and coloring, these moths suggest wasps; consequently, members of this family are frequently cited to illustrate protective coloration and mimicry. This insect does not kill the trees but causes defects that lower the value of the lumber made from them.

The adult moths appear in midsummer and deposit their eggs on the bark of the host tree, usually at the edge of a wound. The larvae, which are typical caterpillars, spend 2 or 3 years in the developmental stages. During this period they feed in the phloem and adjacent tissues, in which each larva excavates a broad chamber near the point where the egg was deposited. After the larvae have become full grown, they transform to the pupal stage in the pitch mass accumulated over the burrow. Just before the adult moth is ready to emerge, the pupa works the anterior portion of its body out of the sticky mass of resin, so that the moth may emerge without becoming entangled.

The control of pitch moths is very difficult in the forest. The systematic examination of the trees, in order to secure the destruction of larvae by mechanical means, has been recommended for certain species, but such an operation would be economically justifiable only on ornamentals or where extremely severe infestations occur in very valuable timber. Because moths seek wounds and scars for oviposition, the prevention of mechanical injury to trees or any treatment that tends to stimulate the rapid healing of wounds will reduce the amount of injury by the pitch moth. Thrifty trees growing on a suitable site are less susceptible than are trees growing on poorer sites.

Zimmerman Pine Moth.   The Zimmerman pine moth, *Dioryctria zimmermani,* is a member of the genus *Dioryctria.* Some of these were discussed under seed and cone insects. As with those species that attack cones, the Zimmerman pine moth exhibits great variation in its feeding habits, suggesting that more than a single species may be referred to by the same name. It is responsible for damage to many pine species in the United States. Although it feeds upon the branch tips, the most serious injury to the trees is along the trunk at branch whorls or between whorls. Damage may kill trees, retard the growth, or cause poor form. Mortality of the attacked trees often results from wind breakage at the points of severe infestation. The presence of larvae in the trunk is indicated by exudation of resin mixed with larval frass (Rennels, 1960).

The following recommendations will help to prevent severe damage in new plantations.

1. Plant pines at 6- by 6-foot spacing or closer.
2. Avoid planting highly susceptible species such as Scotch pine, Corsican pine, and Japanese red pine.

3. Promptly replant spots where trees die.
4. If possible, avoid planting within ½ mile of known infestations.
5. Destroy infested material and heavily infested trees.

These recommendations are mainly based on the fact that dense, closed stands are not generally infested. This pest occurs throughout most if not all of northern United States and southern Canada. Schopmeyer and Smith (1955) reported severe injury to slash pine 3 to 5 inches in diameter in some southern plantations. They suggested the use of BHC for control.

FIGURE 75. Pitch-blister moth, *Petrova albicapitana,* attack on jack pine. The larvae working in the phloem are covered by hollow blisters of pitch, protecting them from enemies and evaporation. By partially girdling the stem at a node, this insect causes breakage and deformation of young trees. Increasing quantities of planted jack pine has been followed by a corresponding increase in the incidence of this pest.

By far the greater number of the important pholem borers belong to the order Coleoptera. Some of these are Cerambycidae, long-horned or round-headed borers. Certain of these beetles are primary, whereas others are secondary. Among the former are some of our best-known forest pests. The latter play an important role in hastening the death of overmature and decadent trees (Hall, 1933) and in speeding the decay of logging waste by opening the way through the bark for fungous infection.

Sugar-maple Borer. Among the cerambycid phloem borers one of the most striking and best-known examples of a primary species is the sugar-maple borer, *Glycobius* (*Plagionotus*) *speciosus*. This insect confines almost all its larval activities to the phloem and adjacent soft tissues. Only when it reaches full growth does it penetrate into the sapwood, there to form its pupal cell.

The adults are beautiful black beetles, almost 1 inch in length, marked with yellow stripes. They emerge in midsummer and deposit their eggs in slits cut with their mandibles in the bark of sugar-maple trees, usually on the trunk. The larvae tunnel through the bark and take up their injurious labors in the phloem. There they pass the winter and in the year following accomplish the greatest injury. Since the larvae tend to tunnel around the tree rather than lengthwise of the trunk, a very few of them working close together may girdle a tree and kill it. Usually, however, the larvae are not gregarious, and consequently the infested tree does not immediately die. The killing of patches of bark opens the way, however, to the attack of other organisms. The larvae attain full growth by the end of the summer following the year of oviposition. At that time they tunnel into the wood where the pupal cell is formed; there the second winter is passed in the prepupal stage. The pupal stage occurs the following summer just previous to the emergence of the adults. Thus a period of 2 years is required for the complete life cycle of this insect.

To control this insect in ornamental trees, it is advisable to destroy badly infested trees. In moderately infested ornamentals, the larvae may be cut out and destroyed. This work should be done as early as possible in the life of the insects so that the resultant wounds may be small and, as a result, quick to heal. The presence of young larvae is indicated by the exudation of frass and sap from the egg slits. In woodlands and groves, the presence of a luxuriant undergrowth is said to reduce the danger of infestation by this beetle. The beetle is a light-loving species; hence trees in the open are more subject to attack than are trees in closed stands. This fact should be borne in mind when improvement cuttings and thinnings in hardwood forests are contemplated.

Agrilus Beetles.   Another large group of coleopterous phloem insects are members of the family Buprestidae, the metallic wood borers or flatheaded borers. Some of these species spend their entire larval period in the phloem, for example, the two-lined borer, *Agrilus bilineatus;* the bronze birch borer, *Agrilus anxius;* and the bronze poplar borer, *Agrilus liragus.* The agrilus beetles are widely distributed in the United States. The three mentioned here are similar in appearance, brown or black in color, slender, and about ½ inch in length. Adults emerge in late spring or early summer and deposit their eggs on the bark of their host trees, cementing the eggs firmly in place. These insects are light-loving. The adults like to bask in the sun; thus, they are likely to deposit eggs on trees in the open and on branches and trunks of forest trees that are exposed to the sun's rays. The larvae emerge from the eggs by boring

FIGURE 76. "Grease spot" in southern hardwoods caused by *Agrilus acutipennis*, a species not mentioned in the text but one that causes considerable damage. Top: In the log. Bottom: In a finished board. (U.S. Dept. Agr. Forest Service.)

through the part of the shell that is cemented to the bark, through the outer bark and phloem layers to the cambial region. There they typically cut winding frass-filled galleries that score the wood. The larvae are elongated flattened grubs with the head invaginated into the somewhat expanded prothorax. By autumn, having completed their growth, they tunnel into the bark and there form their pupal cells in which they pass the winter as prepupae. In the spring they transform to the pupa and in June emerge as adults. Prior to ovipositing, the beetles feed for a time on foliage of the host trees.

The two-lined borer infests chestnuts, oaks, and possibly beech. It is

FIGURE 77. Galleries of the bronze poplar borer, *Agrilus liragus,* in the cambium region of poplar. Agrilus larvae are more slender than most other buprestids. When this insect attacks a moderately vigorous tree it cuts short zig-zag tunnels close together, thus killing a spot of bark. The larva usually dies under such a situation.

often injurious to ornamental trees. In some localities, the two-lined borer frequently works with the root rot, *Armillaria mellia,* a parasitic fungus. *Armillaria,* unlike the borer, appears to attack trees growing in woodlands and kills groups of trees. Around the edges of these killings, the two-lined borer finds a desirable place and usually joins with the fungus in continuing the destruction of the trees. A tree that is heavily infested by this insect is almost certain to die; the tunnels resulting from a light attack, on the other hand, are usually overgrown in healthy vigorous trees.

There is a difference of opinion concerning the primary character of this beetle. Some believe that it attacks only decadent trees and is, therefore, secondary. Available evidence, however, indicates that, in the northern sections of the United States, trees of the black-oak group, apparently growing under normal conditions, are frequently killed by this insect. Farther south, however, conditions are more favorable for the growth of oak, and there only decadent trees are attacked.

Direct control practices should not be necessary to protect forests from this borer if oaks are maintained in a thrifty condition. However, when *Armillaria* and oak wilt are common in a locality, agrilus beetles may become excessively numerous. Then, spraying valuable trees with DDT to kill the beetles as they feed on the leaves may be advisable. The bronze

FIGURE 78. Feeding of *Agrilus* adults on trembling aspen leaves. Feeding of this sort is characteristic of many buprestid beetles.

birch borer, *Agrilus anxius*, is an especially well-known forest and ornamental-tree pest. In parts of the United States it has made impossible the growing of birches as ornamentals. Even in the forest, overmature stands, slow-growing birches on poor sites, and trees left on cutover areas are attacked and killed by this insect. Like the two-lined borer, the bronze birch borer stands on the border line between the secondary and the primary insects. On cutover lands many trees that have apparently been killed by this borer have actually died from adverse physical effects (Hall, 1933). In other instances subnormal trees that might have survived for years have been attacked and killed.

Therefore, the protection of birches from this insect depends, to a considerable degree, on maintaining the trees in a thrifty condition. The effect of exposure to the sun's rays, especially from the south and the west, deserves special comment. Birches so exposed in the course of logging operations are likely to be attacked and die within a few years. Therefore in partial cuttings, special care should be exercised to avoid leaving the trunks of birches exposed to the sun. Either birches should be cut, or they should be left shaded by trees less subject to exposure, such as sugar maple.

The bronze birch borer was discussed as a pest of birches and poplars for many years. Barter and Brown (1949) gave a new species name *Agrilus liragus* to the form infesting poplars. Thus, *Agrilus anxius* is host specific to *Betula* sp. The two species can be separated by characters of the male genitalia and by chromosome counts (Smith, 1949). Another species very similar to *Agrilus anxius* is *Agrilus horni*, which girdles the roots of aspen regeneration (Chap. 17).

Melanophila Beetles. Several buprestid species of the genus *Melanophila* have attracted considerable attention. One of these is the hemlock borer, *Melanophila fulvoguttata*. This insect is a flattened, metallic-

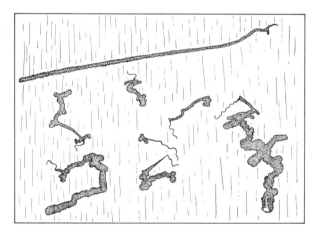

FIGURE 79. Tunnels of the hemlock borer, *Melanophila fulvoguttata*. The long transverse tunnel represents an unsuccessful attack made while the tree was alive. The others are successful attacks made immediately after the tree died.

black beetle with three small white spots on each elytron. The larvae are legless grubs with the widened prothorax characteristic of most buprestids.

The hemlock in the Lake States underwent severe attack of the hemlock looper, *Lambdina fiscellaria*, about 1922, but examination of the tree rings of the surviving trees indicated that in every case the trees had recovered by 1930. From 1932 through 1937, the excessive mortality of hemlock was attributed by some to injury by the hemlock borer. However, a check-up of conditions during these years shows that, except in 1935, drought prevailed, and examination of the tree rings revealed that the hemlock was growing at an exceedingly slow rate during that period. Investigation of the situation disclosed that drought was the chief cause of death, with the borer acting only in a secondary capacity.

Some tree killing on cutover lands has sometimes been attributed to the borer when the actual cause of death was exposure. Hemlock is a very sensitive tree; on cutover lands it is affected, as is birch, by exposure to the sun's rays and often dies as a result of exposure or a combination of exposure and borers. Also hemlock is easily injured by trampling about its roots. Such mistreatment is likely to be followed by decadence, borer attack, and death. Therefore, this tree should not be used for shade on camp or picnic grounds, neither should hemlock groves be used for such purposes.

The eggs of the hemlock borer are deposited in groups deep in the bark crevices, where they are cemented firmly. The young larvae penetrate directly through the bark to the inner phloem. If conditions are unfavorable for them, they do not reach the cambium but cut transverse tunnels in the phloem until they die without seriously injuring the tree. If conditions are favorable, they penetrate to the cambium and construct tortuous, frass-filled galleries just outside the wood until their growth is completed. Then they cut their pupal cells in the outer bark where they pass the winter as prepupae. The following summer they pupate and emerge during June and July to mate and oviposit, thus completing the life cycle.

Another species, *Melanophila californica*, is an important insect in overmature ponderosa-pine forests of California and Oregon, especially on the drier sites (Keen, 1952). It attacks apparently healthy trees in the top. Often the attack may be unsuccessful, and the attacking larvae either die before reaching the phloem or cut very short galleries before they are killed. These galleries are promptly overgrown by wood. Only when the tree becomes decadent are the larvae able to develop to maturity. Then they kill the tops of trees that might have continued to live.

The borer usually works in association with another pest such as the western pine beetle. The flat-headed borer often attacks the tree first, predisposing it to further attacks by bark beetles (Lyon, 1958). It is most common in trees of declining vigor.

Sanitation-salvage logging—a selective cutting of poor-vigor trees—is an effective method of control in merchantable stands. In young stands or special-use areas such as recreational areas, logging may not be feasible. Chemical control has proved successful with penetrating oil sprays using ethylene dibromide in diesel oil.

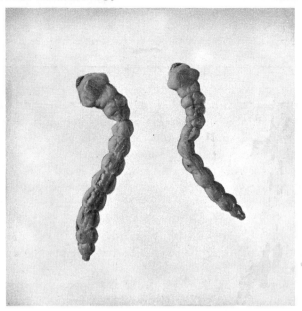

FIGURE 80. Larvae of *Melanophila californica*. Observe the widened prothorax into which the head is invaginated. This is characteristic of all buprestid larvae. (U.S. Dept. Agr. Forest Service.)

Weevils. Many weevils of the family Curculionidae are phloem-eating insects. Some of these have been mentioned among the tip and root insects previously discussed, but others feed upon the phloem of the bole. Probably the most damaging is the pine root-collar weevil, *Hylobius radicis*. Its biology is described by Schaffner and McIntyre (1944) and Finnegan (1962). Discussions of closely related species are found in Warren (1960) and Finnegan (1958, 1961). This weevil attacks many species of pines but is particularly destructive in plantations of introduced species, such as Scotch, Austrian, or Corsican pines and in some red-pine plantations growing on poor sites.

The young larvae feed in the inner bark at and below the root collar. Feeding continues in this general area, causing much resin flow from the injured bark. Gradually the soil becomes resin soaked, so that a layer of pitch-infiltrated soil may be 2 or 3 inches thick near the feeding area. Trees become greatly weakened in the root-collar area and are susceptible to wind-throw. Small trees may be completely girdled. Generally mortality is greatest in trees of 4 inch diameter at breast height (dbh) or less. The life cycle is variable in length with much overlapping of generations. Adult weevils are long-lived. Lindane or dieldrin applied directly to the soil around the base of the trees will effectively control this insect for at least 4 years (Finnegan and Stewart, 1962).

Nitidulidae. Recent studies have revealed a considerable amount of defect in lumber resulting from the work of the sap-feeding beetles, Nitidulidae. These small beetles cause a type of defect called "bark pocket" in oaks, black gums, hickories, and yellow poplar. The larvae and adults feed in sap oozing from injured bark, and the larval feeding kills patches of cambium. These areas heal over, leaving a pocket of ingrown bark and stained wood. The losses in southern bottomland oaks is second only to carpenter-moth damage and in some cases may be even more injurious. These insects often reduce the logs cut from black and tupelo gum from veneer grade to core stock grade (Morris, 1955). This means a loss of 50 to 75 percent of the potential value.

BARK BEETLES, ENGRAVERS

We now come to the second group of phloem insects, the bark beetles of the family Scolytidae. Most of both the genera and species of this family are found in North America. Each genus of this family has a characteristic manner of working, and there is much variation among the individual species as to both their characteristic manner of working and their life histories. Almost all members of this family are tree-inhabiting insects.

Certain traits and habits are common to all bark beetles. For instance, all true bark beetles excavate egg galleries in fresh phloem. The larvae work away from the egg gallery, mining in the succulent tissues of the inner bark until they are full grown. At the end of its larval gallery, each larva excavates a pupal cell, usually between the bark and the wood but sometimes in the sapwood or in the outer bark. The pattern formed by the tunnels is specific in character, an expert being able, usually, to identify the species of beetle from its work alone.

Most bark beetles are secondary in character, but some are important primary pests. Some stand in the middle ground and are usually secondary, although they may occasionally become primary. Only under favorable conditions are these intermediate forms able to attack and kill living trees. The balsam-fir bark beetle, *Pityokteines sparsus*, is an example of a bark beetle that appears never to be primary. The pine engraver, *Ips pini* and also *Ips perroti* and *Pityogenes hopkinsi* are usually secondary, but when they occur in excessively large numbers, they may kill a few young trees. Other species of *Ips*, particularly some of the western species such as the five-spined engraver, *Ips confusus*, and the four-spined engraver, *Ips oregoni*, may become primary temporarily and attack living trees, especially in the upper parts.

Western Engravers. A number of serious local outbreaks of the five-spined and the four-spined engravers have occurred in California and Oregon on ponderosa pine. These outbreaks have often been in vigorous

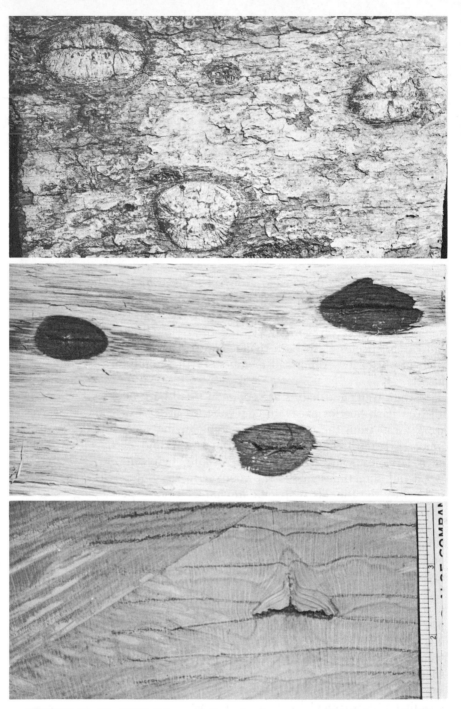

FIGURE 81. The Nitidulidae, called sap beetles, are responsible for much defect in southern oak. Top: Overgrown scars on the bark. Middle: View of inner surface of the bark. Bottom: Cross section shows permanent defect. (U.S. Dept. Agr. Forest Service.)

stands growing under favorable site conditions and almost invariably have been associated with sporadic logging operations. According to Struble and Hall (1955), the five-spined engraver passes through four or occasionally five generations during a season, the overwintering beetles emerging in the early spring, the final brood overwintering under the bark of the attacked trees or slash.

In the spring, the overwintering beetles are unable to breed successfully in living trees and, therefore, must have a supply of fresh slash if

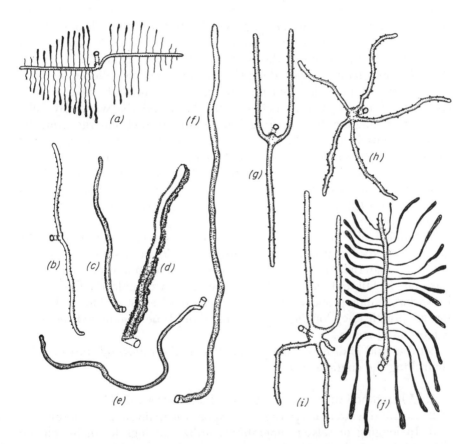

FIGURE 82. Some common forms of bark-beetle galleries. (*a*) Transverse tunnels of *Scolytus ventralis*. (*b*) *Ips perturbatus*, a species characterized by biramous tunnels. (*c*) Longitudinal tunnel of the northern spruce beetle, *Dendroctonus obesus*. (*d*) Broad and usually short gallery of *Dendroctonus valens*, the red turpentine beetle. (*e*) Sinuate gallery characteristic of the western pine beetle, *Dendroctonus brevicomis*. (*f*) Longitudinal, elongate tunnel, usually j-shaped characteristic of the northwestern pine beetle, *Dendroctonus ponderosae*. (*g*), (*h*), and (*i*) Radiate tunnels characteristic of various species of ips beetles, *Ips oregoni*, *Ips pini*, and *Ips calligraphus*. (*j*) Longitudinal tunnels of *Phloesoinus canadensis*.

they are to multiply successfully. They prefer pieces of slash ranging in size from 6 to 24 inches in diameter and cut after January 1. Fall-produced slash after lying on the ground over winter is unsuitable for breeding. When an abundance of fresh slash is available, the emerging beetles multiply rapidly.

The males cut through the bark into the phloem, where they excavate a nuptial chamber. They are there joined by females, usually four in number, each of which excavates a separate egg gallery in the phloem from the nuptial chamber. As they extend their galleries, the females push the frass into the nuptial chamber from which the male relays it to the outside. Thus the galleries of the engraver beetles are kept clear of frass. Accumulations of brown frass about the entrance holes is conspicuous evidence of the presence of the beetles beneath the bark. The eggs are deposited in separate niches along the sides of the egg galleries, and the larvae work through the phloem. On completion of their development, the larvae form pupal cells between the bark and the wood. By July, hordes of young adults, averaging 150 per square foot, emerge from the slash and seek fresh breeding places. If logging has been continued and fresh slash is, therefore, available, the emerging broods continue to work in that material. If, however, the supply of slash is limited, they attack living trees. This is possible because by July the trees, having completed their vigorous spring growth, are unable to repel an en masse attack by the beetles.

Treatment of slash in the spring and early summer is, therefore, the key to successful control of these engravers. Without a supply of freshly cut green material, large populations of the beetle cannot develop. Since slash cut in fall and early winter has become unsuitable for the beetles by spring, thinning operations, clearing for road construction, and, insofar as practicable, logging operations should be conducted between August and January.

Struble and Hall in summary recommend the following measures for controlling the engraver beetles:

1. When practicable, cut young-growth pine after July 15.
2. Lop and scatter all slash so as to expose the main stem to the sun.
3. In logging or salvage operations, utilize all logs to an 8-inch top diameter.
4. Keep accumulations of slash or green logs away from living trees, and fell trees away from dense thickets of young growth.
5. When necessary, kill broods by fire or by toxic oil applications of orthodichlorobenzene or ethylene dibromide.

The fir engraver, *Scolytus ventralis,* is an important pest of true firs, *Abies* sp., in the Western forests (Struble, 1957). Trees from pole size to mature saw timber are killed. Trees may be killed in one season or may be weakened through successive attacks. This insect has caused an estimated average annual loss in California alone of 450 million board feet. This is more than half the estimated annual net growth of firs. Like many other bark beetles the fir engraver readily attacks wind-thrown firs and green cull logs resulting from logging operations. The wide variation in injury to the host makes the possibility of effective artificial control remote. The removal of decadent and weakened firs may be the best control possibility, since vigorous, healthy stands are not usually severely affected.

Two additional species of native bark beetles are also destructive to western true firs. These are the silver-fir beetles, *Pseudohylesinus granulatus* and *Pseudohylesinus grandis* (Thomas and Wright, 1961). The beetles characteristically attack wind-thrown, felled, or injured trees, but poles and saplings stagnating in dense stands and understory trees are also commonly killed. These insects have generally been considered secondary, but an outbreak in northwestern Washington in mature Pacific silver fir resulted in the loss of 528 million board feet of timber between 1947 and 1955. Preventive control may be possible through forest management practices which utilize true fir stands while they are young and vigorous.

Eastern Engravers. Of all the eastern engravers, the pine engraver beetle is the best-known species. It is common throughout the eastern half of the United States and Canada and may occasionally become primary. Its habits and life history are very similar to that of other species of the genus. The adults are small, black beetles about ⅛ inch in length. As is the case with all the members of the genus, the caudal portion of the elytra, called the declivity, is concave and bordered on each side with spines. In the opinion of Trägårdh (1930), this modification is useful for keeping the galleries free of frass and represents a very high degree of specialization. The declivity gives the beetle the appearance of having the rear end of the body cut off sharply. The beetles attack freshly cut or unhealthy pines and, to a lesser extent, spruce. After completing their development, the young adults feed for a short time in the inner bark and then emerge to seek fresh material in which to start a new generation. In the North, there is but one generation of this engraver during a season. Thomas (1961) reports that the beetle usually has two generations a year in Ontario. Farther south, because of the longer and warmer season there may be three or possibly four generations. Some engraver beetles pass the winter under the bark of their host trees, but the pine engraver beetle hibernates in the litter on the ground.

Control of the pine engraver beetle is usually unnecessary, but occasionally it may become sufficiently numerous to require protective measures, especially during drought periods. As in the case of the western engravers, if logging is carried on periodically and not continuously, beetles of the genus *Ips* in the East may temporarily become sufficiently abundant to kill some living timber, especially seedlings and saplings. The recommendations for the control of the western engravers are equally appropriate for the eastern species. However, in the Northern states, slash cut later than October is usually suitable for infestation in the spring. Usually, materials cut between August 1 and November 1 will be unsuited for attack the following spring.

The pine engraver beetle is one of the insects that often causes the loosening of the bark on rustic pine materials. Rustic buildings and furniture may be protected from this injury by careful sun-curing or by the chemical treatments described in Chaps. 9 and 10.

In southern pine forests there are three species of *Ips* which are responsible for much annual mortality: *Ips calligraphus*, *Ips grandicollis*, and *Ips avulsus* (Thatcher, 1960). The three are similar in habits and life histories but can be readily distinguished by their size and number of elytral teeth. *Ips avulsus* is small, 2.1 to 2.6 mm long, and has four teeth on each elytron; *Ips grandicollis* is 3.0 to 3.9 mm long and has five teeth; and *Ips calligraphus* is 4.0 to 6.0 mm long and has six teeth.

Infestations in green timber are usually sporadic and of short duration. Tree killing often occurs near slash areas but spots may be found in other locations. The broods develop very rapidly during the summer, making control difficult. Broods may be emerging as the trees commence to fade. Some attacked trees may contain all three species or there may be only one or sometimes two species present. Three to five females and one male usually occupy each nuptial chamber with its series of radiating egg galleries. Many generations may occur each year in the south. *Ips avulsus* may have 10 or more, whereas the larger species may have only 6. Ips beetles seem to be attracted to any stand in which some disturbance has left fresh pine slash, stumps, and weakened or injured trees. Lightning-strikes, very frequent in parts of the Southeast, are often the centers for spot killings by ips beetles.

Bark beetles may serve as vectors for serious tree diseases. Such is the case with the Dutch elm disease, *Ceratocystis ulmi*. The two vectors are the smaller European elm bark beetle, *Scolytus multistriatus*, and the native elm bark beetle, *Hylurgopinus rufipes*. These are both secondary beetles, but in their capacity as vectors they assume primary importance. The adults of the smaller European elm bark beetle feed upon the inner bark on the twigs of healthy elms. Because of this habit it is the chief vector of the disease. The only known methods of control are directed at destruction of the vectors. Control is impossible in forest areas, so the American elm is rapidly disappearing as an important component of Eastern forests. Elms in urban areas may be saved by thorough sanitation procedures along with chemical application to destroy the vectors.

BARK BEETLES, DENDROCTONUS

The bark beetles of the genus *Dendroctonus* are by far the most important beetle enemies of living trees. The tremendous annual losses occasioned by the attack of these beetles has already been discussed. All the species of this genus are not equally injurious.

The taxonomy of this genus has been in need of revision for many years. Forest entomologists have generally recognized that the separation of many species was on an artificial basis. Wood (1963) has recently

FIGURE 83. Ponderosa pine attacked by the northwestern pine beetle. Observe the long longitudinal galleries characteristic of this beetle. (U.S. Dept. Agr. Forest Service.)

completed a revision which has greatly reduced the number of species. There is not complete agreement on all the changes, but as a whole the revision is a great improvement. Table 12 presents the revised nomenclature of Wood. His synonymization requires modification of common names currently used. The second column presents our suggested common names where changes are needed. In the remainder of the chapter the *Dendroctonus* species discussed will be referenced by the revised names, both common and scientific.

FIGURE 84. Winding egg galleries of the southern pine beetle in the phloem. (U.S. Dept. Agr. Forest Service.)

Some of these beetles, for example the red turpentine beetle, are almost always secondary. This may change with time owing to changing management or possibly changes in the habits of the insect. The black turpentine beetle was once considered a completely secondary insect. Today it is causing extensive losses throughout the pine belt of the Southern states (Smith and Lee, 1957). Most *Dendroctonus* species are pests of mature timber under ordinary circumstances, but when they

TABLE 12   The Bark Beetles of the Genus Dendroctonus Erichson

SPECIES (WOOD)	SUGGESTED COMMON NAMES	SPECIES (PRIOR TO WOOD)	COMMON NAMES (PRIOR TO WOOD)
1. *brevicomis*	Western pine beetle	*brevicomis*	Western pine beetle
		barberi	Southwestern pine beetle
2. *frontalis*	Southern pine beetle	*frontalis*	Southern pine beetle
		arizonicus	Arizona pine beetle
		mexicanus	Smaller Mexican pine beetle
3. *parallelocollis*	Rocky Mountain pine beetle	*parallelocollis*	Larger Mexican pine beetle
		approximatus	Colorado pine beetle
4. *adjunctus*	Round-headed pine beetle	*adjunctus*	
		convexifrons	Round-headed pine beetle
5. *ponderosae*	Northwestern pine beetle	*ponderosae*	Black Hills beetle
		monticolae	Mountain pine beetle
	Jeffrey pine beetle*	*jeffreyi*	Jeffrey pine beetle
6. *aztecus* (new species)	No common name		
7. *terebrans*	Black turpentine beetle	*terebrans*	Black turpentine beetle
8. *valens*	Red turpentine beetle	*valens*	Red turpentine beetle
		beckeri	
9. *micans*	European spruce beetle	*micans*	European spruce beetle
10. *punctatus*	Allegheny spruce beetle	*punctatus*	Allegheny spruce beetle
		johanseni	
11. *murrayanae*	Lodgepole-pine beetle	*murrayanae*	Lodgepole-pine beetle
		rufipennis	Red-winged beetle
12. *obesus*	Northern spruce beetle	*obesus*	Sitka-spruce beetle
		rufipennis	Red-winged beetle
		similis	
		piceaperda	Eastern spruce beetle
		engelmanni	Engelmann spruce beetle
		borealis	Alaska spruce beetle
13. *simplex*	Eastern larch beetle	*simplex*	Eastern larch beetle
14. *pseudotsugae*	Douglas-fir beetle	*pseudotsugae*	Douglas-fir beetle

* Because of biological differences, we feel that the common name Jeffrey pine beetle should be retained.

become epidemic, some will attack indiscriminately any tree above 6 inches in diameter, regardless of condition.

The most important species of the genus are the southern pine beetle, *D. frontalis,* the northern spruce bettle, *D. obesus,* on both north eastern spruces and those in the Rocky Mountain region; the northwestern pine beetle, *D. ponderosae,* and the western pine beetle, *D. brevicomis.* At times other species, for example, the Douglas-fir beetle, *D. pseudotsugae,* may become abnormally abundant and cause severe injury, especially when widespread wind throw occurs.

Character of Attack.   As each species of *Dendroctonus* has its own special habits, it is not easy to generalize concerning either their life history and habits or their economic status. Even the same species may behave differently in various parts of its range so as to require variations in control methods. On the other hand, they all have certain features in common.

One characteristic common to all important economic species is their

FIGURE 85. Mature larvae of the northern spruce beetle. Note the pupal cells in which the larvae are located. (U.S. Dept. Agr. Forest Service.)

gregarious habit of attack. They select certain individual trees or groups of trees and attack en masse. This procedure results in the prompt death of the tree and a minimum flow of resin to hamper the beetles. Although the beetles are able to cope with a moderate amount of resin for a short time, they are overwhelmed or driven from the trees by a continuous or copious flow. For this reason, not even the most aggressive species are able to attack successfully as individuals. Even when a moderately large number of beetles attack a particularly vigorous tree, the attack may not succeed. Such a failure is indicated by the presence of numerous large pitch tubes on the bark.

Typical Life History. The life histories of dendroctonus beetles vary in detail but are similar in many respects. The adults work in pairs and cut egg galleries in the phloem. Unlike the engravers, the beetles of this genus do not keep the egg galleries clear of frass. Some frass is cast out of the entrance tunnel when the gallery is being started, but by the time oviposition has been completed, most of the egg gallery is packed with frass. This characteristic will usually distinguish the galleries of the dendroctonus beetles from those of the engravers. The larvae work away from the egg tunnels, feeding on the phloem. When full grown, they form cells in either the phloem or the outer bark, where they pupate and transform to adults. The winter is passed in all stages except the pupa. The overwintering brood completes development in the spring, so that the peak of adult emergence occurs in July, although some beetles are flying throughout the season. In the North and at higher elevations, there is usually one generation or one and a partial second, but in warmer localities there are several generations during the season. Table 13 summarizes the characteristics of the more important dendroctonus beetles.

Necessity for Control. In many localities the fate of the existing virgin forests depends upon the ability of the forester to cope with the dendroctonus problem. At times the ravages of the beetles have been so damaging that many timberland operators have felt compelled to liquidate their holdings in the shortest possible time in order to save them from the beetles. Unless these reserve stands are removed over as long a time as possible, we cannot obtain, in the next tree generation, the normal distribution of age-classes so essential to good forest economy. Thus, the beetle hazard has been a threat to sustained yield management.

Forest landowners in the West can be persuaded to practice forestry on a sustained yield basis only if the entomologist can convince them that it is possible to control the dendroctonus beetles. The control measures may be aimed at the prevention of outbreaks or their direct suppression.

Preventive Practices. In the prevention of bark-beetle outbreaks, as discussed in Chap. 14, it was pointed out that tree classifications and risk rating could be used as a guide for the removal of high-risk trees in

TABLE 13   Characteristics of Dendroctonus Beetles

COMMON NAME	SPECIFIC NAME	SIZE AND COLOR OF ADULTS	EGG GALLERIES	LARVAL MINES	PUPAL CELLS	NUMBER OF GENERATIONS	COMMON HOST TREES
Western pine beetle	*brevicomis*	3 to 5 mm Dark brown to black	Winding between bark and wood	In phloem little exposed on inner surface	In outer bark	1 and partial second to 2 and partial third	Ponderosa pine Coulter pine Lodgepole pine (rarely)
Southern pine beetle	*frontalis*	2.2 to 4 mm Brown to black	Winding between bark and wood	Practically all in phloem	Outer bark except thin-barked trees	3 to 5	Shortleaf pine Loblolly pine and other pines and spruce in S.E.
Northwestern pine beetle	*ponderosae*	3.7 to 6.4 mm Brown to black Head with frontal groove	Elongate Usually straight but sometimes sinuous	Grouped alternately on opposit sides of egg gallery. Exposed on inner surface	In phloem Usually exposed on removal of bark	1 and a partial second in northern part of range	Lodgepole pine Sugar pine Western white pine Ponderosa pine White-barked pine Limber pine Engelmann spruce Mexican white pine Pinyon
Douglas-fir beetle	*pseudotsugae*	4 to 7 mm Red to dark brown Hairy	Vertical, sinuous, or straight Usually 12 to 14 in. long. Occasionally 30 in. or very short	Fan-shaped groups Mostly in phloem but may engrave wood. On alternate sides of egg gallery	In phloem May or may not be exposed when bark is removed	1 and a partial second	Douglas fir Western larch Bigcone pine (Usually secondary)
Northern spruce beetle	*obesus*	4.5 to 7 mm Reddish brown to black	Vertical, straight, 6 to 8 in. long	Grouped on opposite sides of egg gallery. First in phloem, later between bark and wood	Between bark and wood. Engraving wood	1 generation or 1 generation in two seasons	Mature Black spruce Red spruce White spruce Engelmann spruce Blue spruce
Red turpentine beetle	*valens*	5.7 to 9.5 mm	Irregular winding or straight gallery at base of tree	Grouped along egg gallery and work in mass formation	Between bark and wood	2 or more	All pines and occasionally spruce, larch, and fir. (Primary on Monterey pine, otherwise secondary)
Black turpentine beetle	*terebrans*	5.0 to 8.0 mm	Elongate gallery parallel to grain	Eggs in groups along gallery and larvae feed in groups	Between bark and wood	2 or more	All southern pines, most serious on loblolly slash longleaf

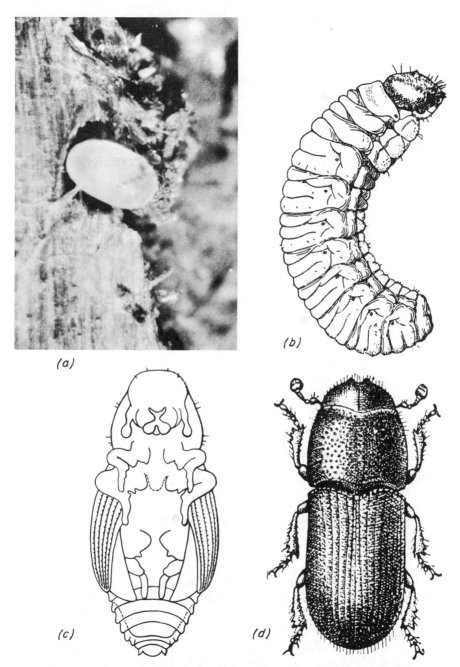

FIGURE 86. The stages of the southern pine beetle. (A) Egg, (B) larva, (C) pupa, (D) adult. (U.S. Dept. Agr. Forest Service.)

the mature forest. This sanitation-salvage cutting can be used success-fully to reduce the hazards from the less aggressive dendroctonus beetles, such as the western pine beetle. It is applicable to overmature stands and to those on relatively poor sites.

Protection of the younger forests from the attack of the more aggressive beetles, such as the northwestern pine beetle, presents problems of control that have not been completely solved. However, under endemic conditions, even these aggressive species prefer dying and decadent trees. Epidemics build up in windfall or fire-killed areas or in forests where the stand is lacking in vigor. Therefore, the prompt utilization of recently

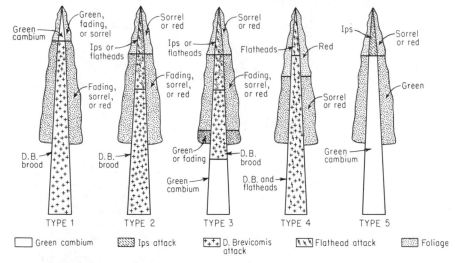

FIGURE 87. Insect attack observed near the base of the tree does not necessarily indicate either the cause or progress of mortality caused by bark beetles. Color phases indicate that death usually progresses from the top of the tree downward and that the initial attack is often by *Ips*. (U.S. Dept. Agr. Forest Service.)

killed or dying timber will often prevent outbreaks. Also the application of practices presented in Chap. 14, designed to maintain thrifty growth, should materially reduce the chance of outbreaks in any stand. It is a desirable practice to leave freshly cut logs on the ground during the beetle flight and, after they are infested, to utilize them as promptly as possible in order to destroy the beetles in them.

When to Use Suppressive Practices. When dendroctonus beetle num-bers continue to increase beyond the endemic level, then direct methods of control must be applied if disastrous outbreaks are to be prevented. The changing complex of bark-beetle populations emphasizes the necessity for the annual detection and evaluation activities discussed in Chap. 6. To decide when control measures should be applied is not always easy and must rest upon the factual foundation provided by the detection and appraisal procedures.

After evaluating the results of many control projects, some effective and some ineffective, Craighead et al. (1931) formulated general rules to use in deciding the desirability of direct control for dendroctonus beetles. They were revised by Keen (1949) insofar as they apply to the Pacific Coast states. These rules cannot be reproduced here in full but may be summarized as follows:

1. Maintenance control, that is, removal of trees as they become infested, is justified only
   a. On high-value recreational or protection forests,
   b. Where individual trees can be utilized profitably.
2. Suppression control is justified
   a. When strong broods in single trees or groups of trees indicate an upward population trend,
   b. When areas are isolated and can be treated completely in a single season,
   c. When infested trees can be salvaged by logging,
   d. When cost of control will not exceed the value of benefits derived therefrom.

Direct control on a maintenance basis may seem a logical procedure to the average forester. Superficially the yearly costs do not seem extreme, the work time can be allotted in the plans for the year, and no severe losses may occur. In the long run, however, such procedures may be far more costly than other methods. Maintenance work is completely needless in years when population trends are downward. Only in years when population trends are upward is direct control of any value. Therefore control should be based on biological and economic analysis rather than on the convenience of planning and application.

Direct control varies greatly with the species. No rule-of-thumb recommendations can be made. In the West, direct control is much more likely to be required in areas infested by the northwestern pine beetle than in those infested by the western pine beetle. This is because of the difference in aggressiveness between these species. Rules for removal of high-risk trees which are so effective in protecting overmature stands from the western pine beetle cannot be applied to the younger stands that characterize the Black Hills and Colorado forests. In general direct control must be based on (1) careful biological evaluations which reveal a serious risk of high continual losses, followed by (2) an economic evaluation showing that benefits of control will exceed the costs.

Detection of Infestations. Recognizing dendroctonus infestations is not always an easy matter, and survey or scouting crews must adapt themselves to using different methods to suit the particular circumstances. Early-season attacks on pine produce easily recognizable color changes in the foliage. The color phases through which infested trees pass are first a slight paling of the needles, followed by fading to a greenish-yellow, and finally turning red. Red tops are obviously the

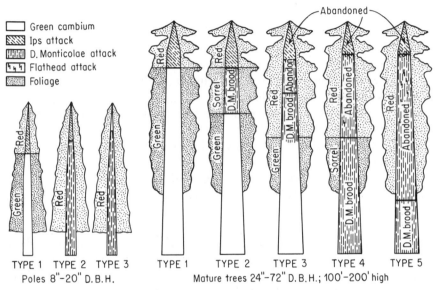

FIGURE 88. Different types of insect attacks observed on ponderosa pine. Color phases indicate the order of attack of the various insects. From these diagrams it is evident that trees apparently killed by *Dendroctonus* may have been previously attacked by other beetles. (U.S. Dept. Agr. Forest Service.)

most conspicuous, but trees showing this characteristic no longer indicate a bark-beetle hazard, because the beetles will have emerged from the trees by that stage. The pale and yellowish tops are signs that indicate the presence of beetles. The red tops are, of course, not marked for treatment, but are an aid in indicating where to look for newly infested trees.

Late summer attacks in pine often cause no distinguishable color changes. Therefore, the presence of late brood can be spotted only by the resinous frass or pitch tubes around the entrance tunnels. Infestations of the northern spruce beetle are especially difficult to detect. Often there is very little color change apparent. In some cases, the needles are shed while the brood is still in the trees. As a result, the ground survey crews must examine each tree with care to determine whether or not it is infested.

Direct Control Procedure. The objective of direct dendroctonus-beetle control is to reduce the population of the beetles in an area to the point of innocuousness. After an infested area has been detected and evaluated by the survey crews, the infested trees are marked for attention and then treated by one of several methods to destroy the infesting

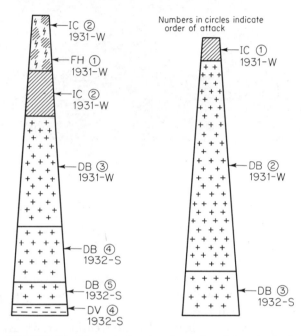

FIGURE 89. Diagram showing the order of insect attack upon two east-side ponderosa pine trees. These trees are typical of many overmature trees in this very susceptible type. IC, *Ips calligraphus;* FH, *Melanophila;* DB, *Dendroctonus brevicomis;* DV, *Dendroctonus valens.* (U.S. Dept. Agr. Forest Service.)

brood. The attacked trees are sacrificed to protect their neighbors. No method has, as yet, been devised to save an attacked tree.

Only those trees that actually contain broods are marked for treatment. An attempt is made to mark every infested tree in a control area. In order to do this, the markers must examine every tree for signs of fading, for active entrance holes indicated by frass or pitch tubes, or for both. In order that no trees will be missed, the area is examined in contiguous strips, each spotter examining and marking for treatment the trees

FIGURE 90. Bark-beetle control projects require much hard work on the ground. Here jeep cans filled with insecticide formulations are brought into remote control blocks on pack animals. (U.S. Dept. Agr. Forest Service.)

on his own strip. The width of the strips will vary, but a common width is 2 chains. The usual procedure is to lay out a grid pattern with string line within which the spotter works.

The spotters are followed by the treating crews. Any season when the beetles are not actively in flight is satisfactory for control. The kind of treatment will depend upon the species of tree and the species of beetle. Owing to increasing labor costs, there is a strong trend away from methods requiring a great amount of labor. Therefore, where chemical control is practicable, penetrating oils are generally used. The most commonly used toxicants are benzene hexachloride, ethylene dibromide, and orthodichlorobenzene. Older methods may still be used. The most effective of these is the cut, deck, and burn method. The least expensive method is to spray standing trees. Large trees must be felled because spray equipment is limited in effective treatment to heights of about 30 to 40 feet.

Cost of Control.   From our discussion it is evident that treatment for destroying beetle brood must be adjusted to the beetle species and to the species and size of the trees involved. The cost of applying the various kinds of treatment varies greatly; even the same treatment will vary in cost, depending upon the size and accessibility of the trees. Therefore, it is impossible to make any generalizations concerning the cost of beetle control. However, it may be expected to vary from slightly more than $1 for a small thin-barked tree to $20 or even more for large trees with thick bark or trees of moderate size in a location difficult of access. Fortunately, this high cost per tree can justifiably be distributed over the entire area of forest protected.

The forest entomologist, through experience, must estimate the cost of control, and the forest owner must then decide whether the protection afforded by the operation and the values involved will justify the expense. The decision cannot always be made in the light of a single ownership, however. Flights of beetles sometimes result in infestation of new areas several miles away from the places where the beetles were reared.

FIGURE 91. A treating crew applies insecticide to an infested spruce. The equipment consists essentially of a jeep can, stirrup pump, and a connecting wand with spray nozzle. (U.S. Dept. Agr. Forest Service.)

Therefore, in the public interest, bark-beetle infestations must often be controlled regardless of ownership. Here is one of the situations where public funds, appropriated under the Forest Pest Control Act or under the various state forest pest laws, can play an important role in forest-insect control. Participation of all parties affected, as provided for under pest control laws, provides the only satisfactory solution of the beetle control problem.

Research on bark beetles has produced many contributions during recent years. These serious pests are being thoroughly investigated. Their life histories are generally well known, and gradually knowledge is being accumulated on their overall relationship in the ecosystems of which they are a part. These studies should lead to the more effective regulation of bark-beetle populations.

BIBLIOGRAPHY CHAPTER 18

Bark beetles in general:

Craighead, F. C., J. M. Miller, J. C. Evenden, and F. P. Keen, 1931. *J. Forestry,* **29:** 1001–1018.

Hopkins, A. D., 1909. *U.S. Dept. Agr. Bur. Entomol. Bull.* 83, pt. 1.

Keen, F. P., 1952. Insect enemies of Western Forests, *U.S. Dept. Agr. Misc. Pub.* 273.

Miller, J. M., and J. E. Patterson, 1927. *J. Agr. Res.,* **34:** 597–613.

Reid, R. W., 1957. *Can. Entomologist,* **89:** 437–447.

Rudinsky, J. A., 1962. *Ann. Rev. Entomol.,* **7:** 327–348.

Thatcher, R. C., 1960. *U.S. Dept. Agr. Southern Forest Expt. Sta. Occasional Paper* 180.

Thomas, J. B., 1957. *Can. Entomologist, Suppl.* 5.

Vité, J. P., and R. I. Gara, 1962. *Contrib. Boyce Thompson Inst.,* **21:** 251–273.

Wood, S. L., 1963. *Great Basin Naturalist,* **23.**

Wygant, N. D., 1959. *J. Forestry,* **57:** 274–277.

Miscellaneous Dendroctonus:

Lee, R. E., and R. H. Smith, 1955. *U.S. Dept. Agr. Southern Forest Expt. Sta. Occasional Paper* 138.

Massey, C. L., 1961. *Ann. Entomol. Soc. Am.,* **54:** 354–359.

Smith, R. H., 1961. *U.S. Dept. Agr. Forest Pest Leaflet* 55.

———, and R. E. Lee, 1957. *U.S. Dept. Agr. Forest Pest Leaflet* 12.

Douglas-fir beetle, *Dendroctonus pseudotsugae* Hopk.:

Bedard, W. D., 1950. *U.S. Dept. Agr. Circ.* 817.

Evenden, J. C., and K. H. Wright, 1955. *U.S. Dept. Agr. Forest Pest Leaflet* 5.

Rudinsky, J. A., 1963. *Contrib. Boyce Thompson Inst.,* **22:** 22–38.

Vité, J. P., and J. A. Rudinsky, 1957. *Forest Sci.,* **3:** 156–167.

Northwestern pine beetle, *Dendroctonus ponderosae* Hopk.:

Beal, J. A., 1939. *U.S. Dept. Agr. Farmers' Bull.* 1824.

Blackman, M. W., 1931. *N.Y. State Coll. Forestry Bull.* IV, no. 4.

Craighead, F. C., 1925. *J. Forestry*, **23**: 340–354.

DeLeon, D., W. D. Bedard, and T. T. Terrell, 1934. *J. Forestry*, **32**: 430–436.

Eaton, C. B., 1956. *U.S. Dept. Agr. Forest Pest Leaflet* 11.

Hay, C. J., 1956. *Ann. Entomol. Soc. Am.*, **49**: 567–571.

Hopkins, A. D., 1905. *U.S. Dept. Agr. Bur. Entomol. Bull.* 56.

Hopping, Ralph, 1921. *Can. Dept. Agr. Entomol. Branch Circ.* 15.

Knight, F. B., 1959. *J. Econ. Entomol.*, **52**: 1199–1202.

———, 1960. *U.S. Dept. Agr. Rocky Mt. Forest Range Expt. Sta. Res. Note* 48.

Massey, C. L., R. D. Chisholm, and N. D. Wygant, 1953. *J. Econ. Entomol.*, **46**: 601–604.

Patterson, J. E., 1930. Control by solar heat, *U.S. Dept. Agr. Tech. Bull.* 195.

Reid, R. W., 1958. *Can. Entomologist*, **90**: 505–509.

Struble, G. R., and P. C. Johnson, 1955. *U.S. Dept. Agr. Forest Pest Leaflet* 2.

Wickman, B. E., and R. L. Lyon, 1962. *J. Forestry*, **60**: 395–399.

Southern pine beetle, *Dendroctonus frontalis* Zimm.:

Beal, J. A., 1933. *J. Forestry*, **31**: 329–336.

Craighead, F. C., 1925. *J. Econ. Entomol.*, **18**: 577–586.

Dixon, J. C., and E. A. Osgood, 1961. *U.S. Dept. Agr. Southeast. Forest Expt. Sta., Sta. Paper* 128.

Gerhart, G. A., and E. E. Ahler, 1941. *J. Forestry*, **47**: 636–640.

Heller, R. C., J. F. Coyne, and J. L. Bean, 1955. *J. Forestry*, **53**: 483–487.

Hopkins, A. D., 1920. *U.S. Dept. Agr. Farmers' Bull.* 1188.

Kowal, R. J., 1960. *U.S. Dept. Agr. Forest Pest Leaflet* 49.

Osgood, E. A., 1957. *U.S. Dept. Agr. Southeast. Forest Expt. Sta., Sta. Paper* 80.

Northern spruce beetle, *Dendroctonus obesus* (Mann.):

Davis, J. M., and R. H. Nagel, 1956. *J. Econ. Entomol.*, **49**: 210–211.

Gobeil, A. R., 1941. *J. Forestry*, **39**: 622–640.

Hopkins, A. D., 1909. *U.S. Dept. Agr. Bur. Entomol. Bull.* 83, pt. 1.

Knight, F. B., 1961. *Ann. Entomol. Soc. Am.*, **54**: 209–214.

Massey, C. L., and N. D. Wygant, 1954. *U.S. Dept. Agr. Circ.* 994.

Swaine, J. M., 1924. *Can. Dept. Agr. n. s. Pamphlet* 48.

Vaux, H. J., 1954. *J. Forestry*, **52**: 506–510.

Western pine beetle, *Dendroctonus brevicomis* Lec.:

Keen, F. P., 1955. *U.S. Dept. Agr., Forest Pest Leaflet* 1.

Miller, J. M., and F. P. Keen, 1960. *U.S. Dept. Agr. Misc. Publ.* 800.

Patterson, J. E., 1927. Slash and infestation, *U.S. Dept. Agr. Tech. Bull.* 3.

Whiteside, J. M., 1951. *U.S. Dept. Agr. Circ.* 864.

ENGRAVER BEETLES

Miscellaneous engravers:

Blackman, M. W., and J. M. Swaine, 1915. *N.Y. State Coll. Forestry Tech. Publ.* 2.

Hopping, G. R., 1963. *Can. Entomologist*, **95**: 508–516.

———, 1961. *Can. Entomologist*, **93**: 1050–1053.

McMullen, L. H., and M. D. Atkins, 1962. *Can. Entomologist,* **94**: 17–25.
Thomas, G. M., and K. H. Wright, 1961. *U.S. Dept. Agr. Forest Pest Leaflet* 60.

Balsam-fir bark beetle, *Pityokteines sparsus* Lec.:
Swaine, J. M., 1919. *Quebec Soc. Protection Plants Ann. Rept.* 11, pp. 46–48.

Elm bark beetle, *Hylurgopinus rufipes* (Eichhoff):
Kaston, B. J., 1939. Morphology, *Conn. Agr. Expt. Sta. Bull.* 420.
Martin, H. M., 1938. *J. Econ. Entomol.,* **31**: 470–477.

Fir engraver, *Scolytus ventralis* Lec.:
Stevens, R. E., 1956. *U.S. Dept. Agr. Forest Pest Leaflet* 13.
Struble, G. R., 1937. *U.S. Dept. Agr. Circ.* 419.
————, 1957. *U.S. Dept. Agr. Forest Serv. Prod. Res. Rept.* 11.

Five-spined engraver, *Ips confusus* (Lec.):
Struble, G. R., 1955. *U.S. Dept. Agr. Forest Pest Leaflet* 4.
————, and R. C. Hall, 1955. *U.S. Dept. Agr. Circ.* 964.
Wood, D. L., 1962. *Can. Entomologist,* **94**: 473–477.
————, 1963. *Univ. Calif. Press* (*Berkeley*) *Publ. Entomol.,* **27**: 241–282.

Hickory bark beetle, *Scolytus quadrispinosus* Say:
Blackman, M. W., 1924. *J. Econ. Entomol.,* **17**: 460–470.
Hopkins, A. D., 1912. *U.S. Dept. Agr. Bur. Entomol. Circ.* 144.

Pine bark beetle, *Ips pini* (Say):
Anderson, R. F., 1948. *J. Econ. Entomol.,* **41**: 596–602.
Clemens, W. A., 1916. *Cornell Agr. Expt. Sta. Bull.* **383**: 287–289.
Thomas, J. B., 1961. *Can. Entomologist,* **93**: 384–390.

Smaller European elm bark beetle, *Scolytus multistriatus* Marsham.:
Anon., 1953. *U.S. Dept. Agr. Leaflet* 185.
Collins, D. L., 1938. *J. Econ. Entomol.,* **31**: 196–200.
Dimond, A. E., et al., 1949. *Conn. Agr. Expt. Sta. Bull.* 531.
Felt, E. P., and S. W. Bromley, 1941. *J. Econ. Entomol.,* **34**: 384–385; 1942, **35**: 170; 1944, **37**: 212.
Norris, D. M., 1961. *The American City,* May.
Watson, W. Y., and W. L. Sippell, 1961. *Can. Entomologist,* **93**: 403–405.
Whitten, R. R., 1942. *U.S. Dept. Agr. Circ.* 647.

PHLOEM WEEVILS

Miscellaneous weevils:
Finnegan, R. J., 1961. *Can. Entomologist,* **93**: 501–502.
————, 1958. *Can. Entomologist,* **90**: 348–354.
Warren, G. L., 1960. *Can. Entomologist,* **92**: 321–341.

Elm snout beetle, *Magdalis barbita* (Say) and *M. armicollis* (Say):
Felt, E. P., 1905. *N.Y. State Museum Mem.* 8, pp. 73–75.
Hubbard, H. G., 1874. *Psyche,* **1**: 5–6.

Poplar-and-willow borer, *Sternochetus* (*Crytorhynchus*) *lapathi* (L.):
Blackman, M. W., and W. O. Ellis, 1915. *N.Y. State Coll. Forestry Bull.* 26, pp. 67–71.
Matheson, Robert, 1915. *J. Econ. Entomol.,* **8**: 522–525.
————, 1917. *Cornell Agr. Expt. Sta. Bull.* 388.

Root collar weevil, *Hylobius radicis* Buch.:

Finnegan, R. J., 1962. *Can. Entomologist*, **94**: 11–17.

————, and K. E. Stewart, 1962. *J. Econ. Entomol.*, **55**: 483–486.

Schaffner, J. V., et al., 1944. *J. Forestry*, **42**: 269–275.

Schenefelt, R. D., 1950. *J. Econ. Entomol.*, **43**: 684–685.

PHLOEM BORERS

Miscellaneous borers:

Morris, R. C., 1955. *Southern Lumberman*, December.

Schopmeyer, C. S., and R. H. Smith, 1955. *AT-FA J.*, **18**: 10–11.

Bronze birch borer, *Agrilus anxius* Gory:

Anderson, Roger F., 1944. *J. Econ. Entomol.*, **37**: 588–596.

Barter, G. W., 1957. *Can. Entomologist*, **89**: 12–36.

————, and W. J. Brown, 1949. *Can. Entomologist*, **81**: 245–249.

Blackman, M. W., and W. O. Ellis, 1916. *N.Y. State Coll. Forestry Bull.* **26**: 46–49.

Britton, W. E., 1922. *Conn. Agr. Expt. Sta. Bull.* 247, pp. 359–361.

Clark, J., and G. W. Barter, 1958. *Forest Sci.*, **4**: 343–364.

Hall, R. C., 1933. *Univ. Mich., School of Forestry Conserv.* (now *Natural Resources*) *Bull.* 3.

Morris, R. F., 1951. *Forestry Chron.*, **27**: 1–16.

Peirson, H. B., 1927. *J. Forestry*, **25**: 68–72.

Slingerland, M. V., 1906. *Cornell Agr. Expt. Sta. Bull.* 234, pp. 65–78.

Smith, S. G., 1949. *Evolution*, **3**: 4.

California flatheaded borer, *Melanophila californica* VanD.:

Lyon, R. L., 1958. *U.S. Dept. Agr. Forest Pest Leaflet* 24.

West, A. S., 1947. *J. Agr. Res.*, **D25**: 97–110.

Dipterous cambium miners:

Burke, H. E., 1905. *U.S. Dept. Agr. Bur. Entomol. Circ.* 61, pp. 1–10.

Green, C. T., 1914. *J. Agr. Res.*, **1**: 471–474.

Douglas-fir pitch moth, *Synthadon novaroensis* (Edw.):

Brunner, Josef, 1915. *U.S. Dept. Agr. Bull.* 255.

Flatheaded apple tree borer, *Chrysobothris femorata* Oliv.:

Brooks, F. E., 1919. *U.S. Dept. Agr. Farmers' Bull.* 1065, pp. 3–12.

Burke, H. W., 1919. *J. Econ. Entomol.*, **12**: 326–330.

Pine pitch-mass borer, *Vespamima pini* Kellicott:

Felt, E. P., 1905. *N.Y. State Museum Mem.* 8, pp. 341–342.

Sugar-maple borer, *Glycobius* (*Plagionotus*) *speciosus* (Say):

Blackman, M. W., and W. O. Ellis, 1916. *N.Y. State Coll. Forestry Bull.* 26, pp. 60–65.

Britton, W. E., 1922. *Conn. Agr. Expt. Sta. Bull.* 247, pp. 351–355.

Kotinski, Jocob, 1921. *U.S. Dept. Agr. Farmers' Bull.* 1167, pp. 53–55.

CHAPTER **19**

PHLOEM–WOOD
INSECTS

The third group of meristem insects are those that attack both phloem and wood. They are commonly called phloem-wood insects. For the most part, these insects are pests of dying trees and freshly cut logs; in some cases, they attack living trees.

PESTS OF LIVING TREES

Some of the outstanding examples of phloem-wood insects that attack living trees are the locust borer, *Megacyllene robiniae;* the poplar borer, *Saperda calcarata;* the carpenterworm, *Prionoxystus robiniae;* the linden borer, *Saperda vestita;* the western cedar borer, *Trachykele blondeli;* and the red oak borer, *Romaleum rufulum.* All the insects in this group work in the phloem for a time after hatching and later penetrate into the wood. Their work in the meristematic tissues is of relatively short duration and is not sufficiently extensive to result in the death of the trees. Therefore, the damage caused by these insects is the reduction in quality resulting from their boring and the weakening of standing trees by their work. In addition to these direct effects, the phloem-wood insects open the way for the attack of fungous infection, thus materially hastening decay. Only a few representative species can be discussed here.

Locust Borer. The locust borer is one of the best-known examples of the phloem-wood insects that attack living trees. It is a member of the family Cerambycidae. At one time the black locust in the eastern United

States was considered to be one of the best trees for posts, poles, and railroad ties because of its rapid growth and the durability of its wood when it is in contact with the ground. Many plantations of this species were set out in Pennsylvania and in the Ohio and Mississippi valleys. Today, a large proportion of these plantations have been abandoned as valueless because of the ravages of the locust borer. Black locust is especially desirable for producing a quick cover on eroded lands and is widely used in plantations for soil protection. As a result of an increasing number of plantings for protection purposes, there has been a corresponding increase in the economic importance of the locust borer.

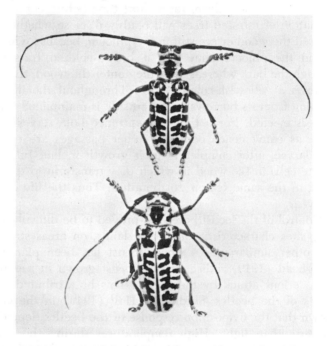

FIGURE 92. Adults of the cottonwood borer, *Plectrodera scalator*. (U.S. Dept. Agr. Forest Service.)

The adults of the locust borer are beautiful black beetles, ½ to ¾ inch in length, with narrow yellow crossbands on the elytra. The beetles emerge in late summer and autumn. They deposit their white eggs singly in cracks and crevices in the rough bark of black locust trees. The numerous moist spots on the bark at points where the newly hatched larvae are working are conspicuous on heavily infected trees in the spring. Young trees under 1½ to 2 inches in diameter and older trees over 5 to 6 inches in diameter appear to be comparatively unsusceptible to attack, although if a tree is once infested, it may remain subject to infestation regardless of size. Thickness and surface character of the bark appear ordinarily to be the factors that determine the susceptibility of the tree to attack. The bark should be sufficiently old to be rough but not so thick that the young larvae cannot bore through it. This limitation of attack to certain specific age-classes aids greatly in formulating plans for the control of this insect.

In a short time after the eggs are deposited, they hatch, whereupon the young larvae cut their way through the bark to the inner phloem. There they feed until cold weather forces them into hibernation. The winter is passed in the larval tunnels. In the spring the larvae continue their work in the phloem for a short time before entering the wood. Examination of infested trees will readily disclose whether the larvae have entered the wood or are still in the phloem, because while they are working in the phloem, they cast a brown-colored frass out of openings through the bark whereas after they enter the wood, they push from their burrows a yellowish-colored frass. Throughout the life of the larva an opening from its burrows to the outside is maintained through which the frass is ejected. For a time the entrance hole serves this purpose, but later, as convenience demands, other passages are cut to the outside. The larvae, after completing their growth in late July and August, excavate cells in the wood in which they transform to the pupal stage and later, in the same season, to the adult. Thus the life cycle is completed in 1 year.

Control of the locust borer has proved to be difficult, especially on the poor sites characteristic of eroded lands, on areas strip-mined for coal, and other similar places where locust has been planted. The work of Craighead (1919) indicated that locust grown in a dense stand is free from serious attack by the borers. This he attributed to the sun-loving habits of the beetles. Studies by Hall (1942) in the Ohio Valley have shown that the oviposition response of the beetles depends more on temperature than light: High temperatures during the oviposition period will result in heavy oviposition within the stand, and cool temperatures will result in heavier oviposition on the outer trees exposed to the sun. The optimum temperature for oviposition is about 70°F. Since oviposition occurs in late summer and fall, there is a tendency toward heavier oviposition on the outer exposed trees. From this it appears that the maintenance of as dense a stand as possible is advantageous but cannot be depended upon to give adequate control.

Hall has also shown that there is a definite correlation between rate of tree growth and the amount of borer injury. Presumably that is due partly to the shorter period during which rapidly growing trees are susceptible to attack and perhaps to an actual resistance to attack exhibited by such trees. One method of encouraging growth rate that appears to offer much promise is to clear-cut hopelessly infested plantations. This results in a dense growth of suckers from the roots and stumps, which grow at an almost unbelievable rate for at least the first few years.

The locust borer is definitely favored by dry weather as evidenced by the heavy infestation and death of very large old locusts in Pennsylvania during a period of excessive drought (Craighead, 1937). Prior to this dry period, these trees had not appeared to be infested.

Wollerman (1962) presents several suggestions for control of the locust borer. Silvicultural methods should be used for control in forested areas. Slow-growing young stands are very susceptible to borer attack. These stands can be cut back before the borers become serious. The vigorous sprouts which follow will generally be less subject to attack. Severely infested stands can also be improved by clear-cutting during the dormant season. The sprouts which follow should be thinned. This procedure has produced good second crops of trees with little injury. Thinning is also beneficial to lightly injured stands on better sites. Removal of infested individuals will reduce the population and help to protect the more desirable residual trees.

Shade or lawn trees can be protected by spraying the trunk and limbs with a DDT emulsion. The proper proportions are 1 gallon of a 25 percent DDT concentrate to 99 gallons of water. This mixture is applied two or three times at 2-week intervals beginning when the goldenrod

FIGURE 93. Stump and roots of a cottonwood infested by the cottonwood borer near the ground line. (U.S. Dept. Agr. Forest Service.)

comes in bloom. Larvae can be killed in their galleries by squirting carbon tetrachloride into the holes and plugging with grafting wax. Another effective method can be applied in the spring when larvae are small. The wet spots which indicate larvae activity may be sprayed in early spring with orthodichlorobenzene emulsion; lindane emulsion should also be effective. These measures are all excessively expensive for forest-tree protection.

Poplar Borer.   Another important phloem-wood beetle is the poplar borer, *Saperda calcarata*. It is distributed throughout the United States and Canada wherever its host trees are found. This insect is injurious to forest trees both directly and indirectly. Directly it reduces the value of the trees it attacks by cutting large tunnels in the wood. When they are numerous the tunnels may so weaken the tree that windbreakage occurs. Occasionally, when extremely numerous, the beetles may kill a few trees, but generally, the poplar borer is not a tree killer.

This beetle does even more important economic damage by its indirect effects than by its direct injury. Other injurious insects are attracted to trees that have been attacked by the poplar borer. For instance, several Buprestidae, such as *Dicera prolongata* and *Poecilonota cyanipes*, deposit their eggs in the old egg scars of the poplar borer. The carpenterworm, *Prionoxystus robiniae*, also finds that the scars made by the poplar borer offer desirable locations for oviposition. Thus this beetle may be the indirect cause of other insect injury. Certain other habits of the poplar borer are conducive to another type of secondary injury. This insect keeps its tunnels comparatively free of frass by pushing this waste material out of openings through the bark. These open tunnels offer a ready means of access deep into the wood for the inoculum of wood-rotting fungi. *Fomes igniarius*, an important heartrot that causes a large proportion of the defects found in aspen and poplar, frequently gains entrance through these openings. In some regions it has been shown that a large proportion of heartrot infections have arisen from insect tunnels. Also in certain years the egg niches provide favorable infection courts for the hypoxylon canker fungus (Graham and Harrison, 1954). Thus the poplar borer and the carpenterworm are indirectly responsible for a great deal of damage that is not ordinarily charged to them.

The adult beetles are rather large, often over 1 inch in length. Their color is gray with yellow markings. Emerging from their pupal cells in late July and August, the female beetles lay their eggs in slits that they gnaw in the bark. The period of incubation is long, 20 to 25 days being required. The larvae, as soon as they hatch, tunnel into the phloem, where they feed until overtaken by cold weather. The following spring they enter the wood, where they spend the remainder of their developmental period tunneling through the wood. In the autumn when full grown, they hollow out a pupal cell in the sapwood. This cell is blocked off by a plug of shredded wood from the tunnel in which the insect previously lived. The winter is passed in the prepupal stage within the pupal cell. Early the following summer the larvae transform to the pupal stage; after 25 to 30 days in that stage, they transform to the adult, cut their way to the surface, and emerge. Thus the normal developmental period is two full years. In Colorado, however, at elevations ranging from 6,000

FIGURE 94. The poplar borer, *Saperda calcarata*. Adults and pupa. (U.S. Dept. Agr. Forest Service.)

to 9,000 feet, this species requires three full years to complete its life cycle. In warmer climates, on the other hand, it is probable that a developmental period shorter than the normal is possible.

Control measures for this insect are usually necessary only on the poorer quality sites. A thrifty closed stand is seldom damaged severely. A severely infested stand can be recognized by the black oval spots on the bark that overgrow the egg niches. These marks last indefinitely.

Red Oak Borer.   There are several important phloem-wood insects in the Southern hardwood forests. One of these, the red oak borer, *Romaleum rufulum,* seriously damages various oaks by creating large, extensive galleries in the wood. Damage can be reduced greatly by proper stand improvement. Most borer larvae die if the host trees to be cut in thinnings are previously poisoned while the larvae are still in the phloem (Hay, 1962).

The red oak borer has a 2-year life cycle with emergence of adults occurring during odd-numbered years in the Central states. Eggs are laid during the summer on the bark of trees over 2 inches in diameter. The young larva spends its first year in the inner-bark region. In July and August of the second year it burrows into the wood through the sapwood and for 6 to 10 inches into the heartwood. Once the larva has started its burrow into the sapwood, it is too late to kill the insect by killing the tree. Thus, trees to be cut should be poisoned between peak emergence in July of odd-numbered years and the first of June of even-numbered years to assure mortality of larvae.

Carpenterworm.   The carpenterworm, *Prionoxystus robiniae,* is one of the common phloem-wood insects that may well be cited as a lepidopterous representative of this group. It is distributed generally throughout the United States and the southern part of Canada. It was first described as a pest of black locust, hence its specific name, but it also feeds on a variety of hardwood species. Some of the trees that are frequently attacked are oaks, elms, and poplars. Although the carpenterworm seldom kills trees, it is nevertheless a primary insect, and most of its damage is done to living trees.

The adults are large gray moths with a wingspread of about $2\frac{1}{2}$ inches. They emerge in early summer and deposit their eggs on the bark of the host tree. Wounds or scars on the trunk or larger branches provide the most attractive oviposition places. The larvae bore into the phloem where they excavate shallow galleries. After a brief period of feeding in the phloem, they penetrate into the sapwood and later into the heartwood. The remainder of the larval life is spent in the wood. The larvae are typical caterpillars in form and are pinkish white in color. Their galleries are long and winding and are kept free of frass so that the larvae can pass freely back and forth. In order to secure free passages, the borings are pushed out through holes in the bark. These holes provide an easy avenue of entrance for the spores of wood-rotting fungi; consequently these organisms are almost always associated with the work of the carpenterworm.

The length of the life cycle is variable (Hay and Morris, 1961), requiring 2 to 4 years depending on location. In the Deep South 2 or 3 years are required, in the Central and Western states 3 years, and in the Northern states and southeastern Canada, 4 years.

At the end of the larval period, a pupal cell is formed in the wood near the surface. Before pupation, a hole is cut almost through the bark, and the tunnel behind the cell is closed with a plug of shredded wood. The larvae then transform to the pupal stage, and later the moths emerge.

Almost all the investigations of this insect have been chiefly concerned with ornamental trees. As a result, although this insect is at times an im-

FIGURE 95. The carpenter moth, *Prionoxystus robiniae*. (A) The life stages; (B) attacks on a Nuttall oak during a drought period. (U.S. Dept. Agr. Forest Service.)

portant forest pest, no control under forest conditions has been perfected. Any silvicultural treatments that will stimulate growth should be helpful, since slow-growing trees are most subject to attack. Shade trees may be protected by painting injuries with wound dressings or spraying with a residual emulsion insecticide.

PESTS OF DYING TREES AND LOGS

Representatives of phloem-wood insects that attack only dying trees or freshly cut logs are important because of the loss which they cause in both logs and pulpwood, in the former by reducing the grade and in the latter the volume. Some of them also cause indirect injury aiding infection by wood-rotting fungi. Craighead estimates that the loss in grade due to the activities of these insects amounts to about 5 percent of the value of the annual cut. The most important of these insects belong to the coleopterous families Cerambycidae and Buprestidae.

The few species that will be discussed here should not be taken as an indication that there are not many more species that damage dying trees and logs. There are many species of phloem-wood insects in this category. Gardiner (1957) made an intensive survey of the wood-boring beetles causing deterioration of fire-killed pine in Ontario. Following this single fire he observed 17 species of Cerambycidae that were attacking the fire-damaged trees. In addition numerous examples of other families were also present.

Flatheaded Apple Tree Borer.   One of the many buprestids that feed on the phloem and wood is the flatheaded apple tree borer, *Chrysobothris femorata*. This insect attacks numerous species of forest trees and also a great variety of orchard trees. Some of its hosts are walnut, pecan, hickory, poplar, willow, beech, oak, elm, hackberry, and many others. Because of its importance as a pest of apple trees, this insect is called the flatheaded apple tree borer. Because it is a pest of orchards as well as forests, it has received more attention from entomologists than if its activities had been confined to forest trees alone. As a result, its habits are well known, and it will serve well as an illustration of the phloem-wood buprestids.

The flatheaded apple tree borer lies in the middle ground between the primary and the secondary insects. It apparently cannot attack successfully a vigorous, healthy tree but attacks trees that are on the decline. The adult females are attracted for oviposition not only to the subnormal trees but also to healthy trees in sunny locations. The eggs hatch and the young larvae bore into the bark, but they do not enter the phloem while the tree is in a thrifty condition. If, however, such a tree should decline in health, the larvae will promptly penetrate into the phloem and kill it. If, on the other hand, the tree remains in good health, the young larvae will remain in the bark for at least 1 year before they succumb to starvation. This habit has been observed in other species of the same genus, for example, *Chrysobothris dentipes*, a flatheaded borer of pine. When bark-infested trees are cut, the larvae are then able to attack the phloem and later the sapwood; thus they are able to complete their normal development in the logs.

The adults of the flatheaded apple tree borer are short, broad, flat beetles about ½ inch long. In color they vary from dark brown to black on the top, with grayish spots and bands, while the ventral side and the legs are bronze. They emerge from their pupal cells in early spring and are on the wing for about 1 month. The beetles are active only on warm, sunny days; at other times they remain quiescent, hidden away beneath bark scales or in other suitable places. In warm weather, they are very active, flying and running about. Experiments have shown that beetles of this genus are very resistant to heat and can endure a temperature as high as 52°C. The larvae also are heat resistant and are able to live on the hot upper side of logs lying in the sun, where no other insect life can exist.

The adult beetles feed on the foliage of hardwood trees and sometimes become so numerous that they cause appreciable defoliation. The female beetles deposit their eggs in crevices in the bark of the host trees. These eggs are pale yellow, flattened, and about $\frac{1}{20}$ inch in diameter. The young larva, after an incubation period of 15 to 20 days, bores through the underside of the egg and into the bark. This habit is true of all buprestids.

The thoracic region of these larvae is greatly enlarged transversely and flattened dorsoventrally. The head is invaginated into this enlarged thorax so that only the mouth parts protrude. On casual inspection, the thorax appears to be the head of the grub, thus the name flatheaded borer. The larvae are helpless when removed from their burrow. Unless they have convenient surfaces against which they can expand the enlarged thorax, they are unable to move; therefore they can move about only in a tunnel that fits their bodies. Thus, if a larva should cut through some portion of the egg shell that was not in contact with the bark, it would be unable to progress further.

If on boring through the bark the larvae find conditions are favorable, they will construct broad feeding tunnels in the phloem and outer sapwood. They grow rapidly and in late summer are ready to bore into the solid sapwood; there they form their pupal cells in which they pass the winter. In the South the pupal cell is sometimes formed between the bark and the wood, but this condition has never been observed in the North. The winter is passed in the larval stage within the pupal cell, and pupation takes place early in the following spring.

Thrifty trees are not susceptible to injury by this borer; therefore, it is a pest only of overmature, decrepit, or dying forest trees. Like many other members of this genus, it does not penetrate deeply into the heartwood and, therefore, is not so injurious to logs as are some other buprestids and cerambycids. It does, however, loosen the bark and make openings through which decay-causing organisms may enter, and it may tunnel to a considerable extent the outer inch of wood.

Some of the other buprestids that feed first in the phloem and later in the wood are *Chalcophora virginiensis,* and *Chalcophora angulicollis.* The first is an eastern species and the second a western species, both attacking pines and firs. Several species of the genus *Dicerca* are common phloem-wood borers that may at times cause considerable injury to the wood of dying trees and freshly cut logs (Chamberlin, 1949).

The best way to prevent injury from these insects is prompt utilization. If this is impossible, water treatment is the next best procedure. Heavy shading of logs left in the woods will give reasonable but not perfect protection. Rustic work may be effectively protected by using benzene hexachloride or pentachlorophenol in oil solution.

White-spotted Sawyer. Numerous phloem-wood insects refuse to attack standing trees until they have been severely injured or killed by some other agency. Of these the white-spotted sawyer, *Monochamus scutellatus,* is a good example. This secondary insect is one of the most common wood-boring insects in the coniferous forests of the Northeast. It infests and reduces the value of freshly cut logs and of trees that have been severely injured or killed by fire or by other insects. This insect is so abundant in most localities that practically every log or newly killed tree that is left in the woods over the summer is almost certain to be infested.

FIGURE 96. Adult *Monochamus oregonensis* emerging from wood of Pacific Coast silver fir. (Weyerhaeuser Company.)

The habits and life history of this species are very similar to those of other closely related species of *Monochamus.* The adult insects are somewhat elongate, cylindrical black beetles about 1 inch long with very long filiform antennae. The antennae of the male are twice as long as the body, whereas those of the female are only slightly longer than the body. The adult beetles emerge in spring and early summer. During the flight period, they feed upon the green bark of pine twigs. Sometimes, when the beetles are abundant, numerous pine tips may be girdled and killed as a result of this feeding activity. After feeding for a brief period, the beetles deposit their eggs in slits that they cut with their mandibles in the bark of logs and recently killed trees. Oviposition continues throughout the summer season but usually reaches its height before mid-summer.

The larvae hatch from the eggs and tunnel at first in the inner phloem. They are legless, cylindrical white grubs with powerful mandibles. At first, they excavate broad, shallow galleries in the phloem, but as they increase in size, their phloem galleries include not only the green tissues of the inner bark but also the surface of the wood. Later the larvae penetrate into the sapwood and sometimes into the heartwood. When growth is completed, they cut a pupal cell in the sapwood and transform to the pupal stage. The length of the development varies greatly. Under favorable conditions of temperature and moisture, a single year is sufficient, but under less favorable conditions, the life cycle may require 3 years or possibly longer. The larvae of this species, like those of the poplar borer and the carpenterworm, always keep at least a part of their tunnels clear of frass and chips. Thus the pine sawyer maintains ideal conditions for the infection of the log with wood rots. These organisms are usually associated with monochamus work.

This insect tunnels primarily in the peripheral layer of a tree or log. It is in this layer that the most valuable high-grade wood occurs. Thus, in clear logs the insect may reduce the grade of lumber sawed from infested parts from a select grade to a number 3 grade; this means a reduction in the retail value of from 50 to 75 percent.

Control of the white-spotted sawyer may be accomplished in a variety of ways. Fire-killed trees should be utilized promptly or cut and kept wet with water. Prompt utilization is the best way to handle the borer problem. Water storage of freshly cut material, either by emponding or by sprinkling, is the next best solution. If neither of these methods is feasible, barking will prevent infestation by destroying the necessary green food for the young larvae. Spraying with BHC has been recommended. Where no other method of control can be used, experiments indicate that a heavy shade of brush, piled over logs left in the woods during the summer, will afford some protection from this insect. This cannot be recommended if other methods can be used because of the inferior quality of protection afforded.

This and several other species of *Monochamus* have at times caused considerable damage in lumber that has been freshly sawn but not edged. The insects lay their eggs in the bark-covered edges of the boards, and the larvae work first in the phloem and then into the wood, sometimes to a depth of several inches. Still other cerambycids may cause similar injury. For instance, *Callidium antennatum* has attacked piled lumber in

California. Edging the lumber when it is sawed will prevent such injury as this.

BIBLIOGRAPHY CHAPTER 19

General:

Bletchly, J. D., 1961. *Ann. Appl. Biol.*, **49:** 362–370.

Chamberlin, W. J., 1949. O.S.C. Cooperative Association, lithographed.

Bark loosener, *Callidium antennatum* Casey:

Miller, J. M., 1943. *U.S. Dept. Agr., Bur. Entomol. P. Q.*, E599.

Carpenterworm, *Prionoxystus robiniae* (Peck):

Burke, H. E., 1921. *J. Econ. Entomol.*, **14:** 369–372.

Felt, E. P., 1905. *N.Y. State Museum Mem.* 8, pp. 79–84.

Hay, C. J., and R. C. Morris, 1961. *U.S. Dept. Agr. Forest Pest Leaflet* 64.

Packard, A. S., 1890. *Entomol. Comm. Rept.* 5, 53–58.

Cottonwood borer, *Plectrodera scalator* Fabr.:

Milliken, F. B., 1916. *U.S. Dept. Agr. Bull.* 424.

Deterioration of dead timber:

Furniss, R. L., 1937. *Timberman*, **39:** 11–13.

Gardiner, L. M., 1957. *Can. Entomologist*, **89:** 241–263.

Ross, D. A., 1960. *Forestry Chron.*, **36:** 355–361.

Wright, E., W. K. Coulter, and J. J. Gruenfeld, 1956. *J. Forestry*, **54:** 322–325.

Dogwood borer, *Thamnosphecia scitula* (Harr.):

Schread, J. C., 1956. *Conn. Agr. Expt. Sta. Circ.* 199.

Hickory spiral-borer, *Agrilus arcuatus* Say:

Brooks, F. E., 1926. *J. Agr. Res.*, **33:** 331–338.

Leopard moth, *Zeuzera pyrina* (Linn.):

Britton, W. E., and G. A. Cromie, 1911. *Conn. Agr. Expt. Sta. Bull.* 169, pp. 3–24.

Howard, L. O., and F. H. Chittenden, 1916. *U.S. Dept. Agr. Farmers' Bull.* 708.

Linden borer, *Saperda vestita* Say.:

Felt, E. P., and L. H. Joutel, 1904. *N.Y. State Museum Bull.* 74, pp. 54–58.

Locust borer, *Megacyllene robiniae* (Forst.):

Craighead, F. C., 1919. *U.S. Dept. Agr. Bull.* 787, pp. 1–12.

———, 1937. Drought, *J. Forestry*, **35:** 792–793.

Hall, R. C., 1942. *U.S. Dept. Agr. Circ.* 626.

———, 1937. *J. Forestry*, **35:** 721–727.

St. George, R. A., and J. A. Beal, 1932. *J. Econ. Entomol.*, **25:** 713–721.

Wollerman, E. H., 1962. *U.S. Dept. Agr. Forest Pest Leaflet* 71.

Oak sapling borer, *Goes tesselatus* Hald.:

Brooks, F. E., 1919. *J. Agr. Res.*, **26:** 313–317.

Poplar borer, *Saperda calcarata* Say.:

Felt, E. P., and L. H. Joutel, 1904. *N.Y. State Museum Bull.* 74, pp. 39–44.

Graham, S. A., and R. P. Harrison, 1954. *J. Forestry*, **52:** 741–743.

Hofer, George, 1920. *U.S. Dept. Agr. Farmers' Bull.* 1154, pp. 3–11.

Red oak borer, *Romaleum rufulum* (Hald.):

Hay, C. J., 1962. *U.S. Dept. Agr. Central States Forest Expt. Sta. Sta. Note* 154.

Sawyer beetles, *Monochamus* spp.

Gardiner, L. M., 1954. *Can. Entomologist,* **86:** 465–470.

Parmalee, F. T., 1941. *J. Econ. Entomol.,* **34:** 377–380.

Rose, A. H., 1957. *Can. Entomologist,* **89:** 547–553.

Swaine, J. M., 1917. *Ontario Entomol. Soc. Rept.* 471, pp. 96–97.

Tothill, J. D., 1923. *New Brunswick Land Dept. Ann. Rept.* 63, pp. 86–87.

Western cedar borer, *Trachykele blondeli* Mars.:

Burke, H. E., 1928. *U.S. Dept. Agr. Tech. Bull.* 48.

CHAPTER **20**

WOOD
DESTROYERS

Although most borers require green meristematic tissues for food during at least a part of the developmental period, certain species are able to develop from egg to adult in wood alone. These wood destroyers are chiefly secondary pests, attacking forest products, but some of them may attack and injure the wood of standing green timber. Some require unseasoned wood, for example, the horntails; others, such as the powder-post beetles, work only in thoroughly seasoned wood; still others, for instance, the carpenter ants, are less exacting in their requirements.

The separation of wood-destroying species into clear-cut ecological groups is not easy because of the variations in habits. For example, certain insects may be found in fire scars on living trees but occasionally they may attack flooring in houses, some which usually attack only the sapwood of freshly felled trees may occasionally be found attacking seasoned material under some special conditions simulating those that are characteristic of the freshly cut tree, or some moisture-loving species may tunnel into dry wood and maintain the necessary moisture conditions by keeping contact with moist wood in the soil or by air-conditioning their nests with moisture evaporated from their bodies. The subdivisions into which these wood-destroying insects have been divided are, therefore, somewhat arbitrary. Each insect is discussed under the group most typical for the species, and in the discussion exceptions to the general rule will be pointed out. Following are the arbitrary groups: (1) those attacking the wood of living trees, (2) those attacking freshly cut or dying trees, (3) those attacking moist seasoned wood, (4) those attacking dry seasoned wood.

The preceding paragraphs should not be interpreted to imply that all wood destroyers are insects. There are a few other groups of animals that are wood borers. The most destructive of these are the marine borers. Because their activities are very similar to those of wood-destroying insects and because they are frequently confused with insects in popular discussion, they will be included in this chapter.

ATTACKING WOOD OF LIVING TREES

Although most of the wood-destroying insects attack after the trees are felled, there are a few that infest standing timber. Many of these enter through injured areas such as fire scars, logging scars, or other spots where the bark is broken. A few gain entrance through the unbroken bark.

Western Cedar Borer.   The western cedar borer, *Trachykele blondeli,* is a beautiful metallic emerald-green buprestid which is very injurious, especially to western red cedar in certain localities (Burke, 1928; Hopping, 1932). This is one of the species that gains entrance into the wood through the unbroken bark. The adults lay their eggs in crevices on the branches of living trees, and the larvae bore their long flattened tunnels in both the sapwood and the heartwood until they are fully grown. This requires several years, during which time they leave the branches and work in the tree trunk, sometimes extensively. When fully grown, they return to the branch to pupate. There the pupal cell is constructed within $\frac{1}{2}$ inch of the surface. Transformation to the pupa occurs in midsummer and to the adult stage about 3 weeks later. These adults remain in the pupal cells until the following spring, at which time they emerge, feed on the foliage, mate, and oviposit.

The kind of injury caused by this insect is objected to by consumers of posts and poles, but actually it causes little if any reduction in the usefulness of these materials (Chamberlin, 1949). On the other hand, it ruins the wood for shingles, siding, boat planking, and other uses where tightness is essential. No control for the western cedar borer in the forest has been developed. The habits of oviposition are such that the adults or eggs are difficult to reach with an insecticide. The fact that certain stands are more severely injured than others indicates that ultimately silvicultural control may be possible. Burke (1928) suggests that the disposal of branches following logging might be helpful in reducing the beetle population. By using infested materials for posts and poles and reserving the uninfested trees for shingles, siding, and similar purposes, the economic losses caused by this insect might be materially reduced.

It must be admitted, however, that such practice would not appeal to companies in the pole business.

Other Buprestid Borers. Among a number of other buprestid borers that attack the wood of living trees is the golden buprestid *Buprestis aurulenta*. This western species attacks the pitchy wood in fire scars, lightning scars, and injuries caused by logging machinery. The galleries are filled with pitchy frass. Repeated attacks may completely destroy the wood, weakening the trees so that they may be easily wind-thrown (Chamberlin, 1949). Keen (1952) reports that this buprestid occasionally attacks lumber and unpainted flooring.

A similar species, the turpentine borer, *Buprestis apricans,* formerly was a serious pest in stands of southern pines used for the production of naval stores (Beal, 1932). Deep chipping of the faces, burning, and subsequent checking of the wood created conditions favorable for oviposition by the beetles. Repeated attacks so weakened the trees that they were subject to breakage by windstorms.

Modern turpentining practice has practically eliminated serious injury by this borer. It still may be found in fire scars and other injuries that kill the bark and expose the bare wood at the base of standing trees, but in turpentine orchards where modern methods are used, it is practically nonexistent.

Instead of the narrow, deeply chipped faces, usually four on a tree, and frequently scorched by fire, the modern face is somewhat wider, no more than two to a tree, and the chipping is shallow, each strip being little deeper than the bark. The gum flowing down the face is drained into a container through metal troughs attached to the tree. These are fastened with double-headed nails that can easily be pulled out of the wood when the trough is removed. In this way the face is continuously covered by a coating of gum which prevents checking, and no nails are left in the face after the gum harvest is completed, usually after 5 years.

Previously the nails left in the faces made the butt section of a turpentined tree unmerchantable. Therefore, that section, usually infested by borers, was left in the woods. Today the butt section is utilized along with the rest of the tree. Modern methods thus largely eliminate places suited for oviposition by the beetles and also remove from the woods parts of the trees that previously were a hazard.

ATTACKING WOOD OF DYING OR RECENTLY CUT TREES

Most insects that attack wood prefer dying trees or trees that have been cut recently. Usually, after the wood has been cut for a season or more, it becomes unattractive to the insects. This is apparently because of changes in moisture conditions or in the physical and chemical conditions within the wood. What these physical and chemical changes are has never been determined. Probably they are the result of slow oxidation processes. There is indication that some insects may be attracted to freshly killed or cut wood by products of fermentation that disappear as the wood seasons or as organisms of decay gain a predominant position in the wood. The fact that ambrosia beetles are not attracted to all wood, even though moisture conditions are favorable, but are in rare instances attracted to and attack wine casks containing wine in storage suggests that the presence of an alcohol or some other product associated with fermentation may determine where the beetles will attack. More information on why wood is or is not attractive to certain insects would almost certainly lead to the development of better control measures than those now used.

Of the insects that attack the wood of dying, recently killed, or recently cut trees, two groups will be discussed: the ambrosia beetles and the horntails. Although both attack the same sort of material, their habits and the character of their work are very different.

Ambrosia Beetles. Ambrosia beetles are chiefly pests of green wood, although occasionally they may attack other wood, such as the wine casks,

FIGURE 97. Ambrosia beetle tunnels and associated black stain of *Platypus compositus* in pecan. (U.S. Dept. Agr. Forest Service.)

mentioned above, in which conditions are somewhat similar to those found in freshly cut wood. With the exception of the genus *Platypus*, which belongs to the family Platypodidae, these insects are all members of the family Scolytidae. Although they belong to the same family as the bark beetles, their habits are very different. Nevertheless, they have many points in common. They are small, dark-colored insects, more or less cylindrical in form. Instead of working in the phloem, they cut their tunnels into green wood. The tunnel entrances resemble those of bark beetles, but because the beetles tunnel into the wood, the frass which they cast out is light-colored instead of brown. Although they bore in

FIGURE 98. Ambrosia beetles. The numerous piles of frass are an indication of a heavy infestation in this black gum log. (U.S. Dept. Agr. Forest Service.)

wood, they are not wood eaters; instead, they feed upon a fungus growing on their tunnel walls. This type of fungus is always associated with ambrosia beetles, each group of beetles having its own specific fungus. Whenever the wood ceases to be suitable for the fungus, the beetles must leave. When departing, they unwittingly carry the sticky spores or the mycillium either adhering to their bodies or in special structures in the head or thorax (Finnegan, 1963). Having sought out a suitable freshly cut tree or stump, they proceed to bore directly into the wood. For a short time they are without food, but soon the spores that they brought with them germinate and grow on the walls of the new tunnels.

This apparent cultivation of food by an insect has caused some observers to ascribe a high degree of intelligence to these beetles. However, the facts do not justify such a conclusion. It is, nevertheless, an interesting example of an effective symbiotic relationship between a fungus and an insect: the beetle depending upon the fungus for food and the fungus depending upon the insect for transportation from an old host to a new one.

There are numerous species of ambrosia beetles, most of them belonging to one of the following genera: (1) *Platypus,* (2) *Anisandrus,* (3) *Xyleborus,* (4) *Gnathrotrychus,* (5) *Pterocyclon,* (6) *Trypodendron,* (7) *Xyloterinus.* Some of them are confined to a single species of tree, whereas others may be found in a number of species. Inasmuch as the beetles do not eat the wood but simply use it as a place in which to construct their nests, the specificity of the beetles for certain trees is the direct result of the specific requirements of their particular fungus.

The arrangement of tunnels varies greatly with different species of ambrosia beetles. *Xyleborus xylographus* constructs simple branching galleries in which the eggs, larvae, and pupae are all found together. Species of *Pterocyclon* excavate several secondary tunnels branching in a horizontal plane from the main entrance tunnel, which is widened to form a nuptial chamber. Along the secondary tunnels, chambers called larval cradles are excavated both above and below and parallel with the grain of the wood. Certain others, species of *Trypodendron,* for example, construct compound tunnels, the main gallery being cut directly into the wood in a generally radial direction and the secondary galleries being cut in the same horizontal plane but in a tangential direction. In the case of *Gnathotrychus materiarius* the secondary tunnels usually follow an annual ring, and the larval cradles are cut in a series both above and below the main and secondary galleries. With such species the entire developmental period of a beetle is passed in a cradle. In species where no cradles are formed, the larvae shift for themselves, feeding on the ambrosia fungus growing on the tunnel walls. In some species the larvae, immediately prior to pupation, cut pupal cells similar to the cradles. The adults of at least some ambrosia beetle species hibernate in the litter and duff of the forest floor. Beetles of the genus *Trypodendron* are among those that hibernate in such locations (Dyer and Kinghorn, 1961).

The ambrosia beetle colonies are constantly faced with two problems: (1) the selection of trees in which conditions are suitable for the growth of the fungus upon which they feed and (2) protection for themselves against the growth of the fungus itself. When conditions for the growth of the fungus are not right, the larvae will starve and the adults will be forced to seek other trees. If conditions are favorable for the fungus but the beetles do not multiply rapidly enough to consume their food as fast as it grows, the rank growth of the fungus may block the tunnels, thus smothering the beetles in their food.

The injury to logs and recently killed trees by ambrosia beetles results in a decided loss in quality of the lumber and other products cut therefrom. This type of injury is serious in lumber because of the resultant reduction in grade, but it is of even greater consequence in other classes of material, for example, stave bolts and wood for furniture. With such materials, pinhole injury may render the product valueless.

In certain cases, however, ambrosia beetle tunnels cannot be considered as serious defects. In oak flooring, for instance, style may demand a few knots and a few wormholes. These defects are said to lend character to a floor, and in some high-class homes this onetime low-grade flooring is now being used. In most cases, however, beetle tunnels constitute a defect that decidedly reduces the value of any forest product so injured.

Some of the greatest losses occasioned by these insects occur in the South, where the long growing seasons permit the beetles to remain active during a greater part of the year than in the North. As a result the number of broods is greater and the problem of preventing damage by ambrosia beetles is correspondingly increased.

In the North, the beetles have but one or at the most two generations, and the long winters and short summers permit logging while the beetles are dormant, thus eliminating much of the injury in the woods.

The control of ambrosia beetles is difficult and, in many instances, entails considerable expense. They can, however, be held in check in several ways. The prompt sawing of logs followed by kiln drying provides the best and most certain protective measure. When storage space and expense permit, sun-curing is an effective means of controlling these and other wood borers. By being placed on long sloping skids, the logs may be turned from time to time with a minimum of effort, exposing all sides to the effect of the sun. However, sun-curing in this way is applicable only to logs that are stored in localities where sunny days prevail. In cool, cloudy localities solar treatment is useless.

Debarking agents are now commonly used in some localities. The trees are treated with a chemical the season before logging. If the treatment is successful, the bark is loosened and falls from the trees when they are felled. If a poison such as sodium arsenite is used as the debarking agent, we may logically expect that damage to the trees by ambrosia beetles and other wood borers might be reduced. If, however, one of the debarking agents of the growth-hormone type is used, no such effect could be expected. In fact such debarking agents would probably be conducive to injury by ambrosia beetles. No research that we know of has tested these effects of debarking, but in some localities they should be important considerations. Either debarking treatment or girdling prior to logging should be done in late summer or the fall, after the flight of the beetles is over, in order to reduce to the minimum the opportunity for infestation. It has also been suggested that the inferior trees may be used for traps, felling or girdling them in early spring when the beetles are in flight. Later, after the trap material has been infested, it can be destroyed by burning or placing in water. One of the best and most effective methods of preventing attack is by the water treatment, already considered in Chap. 11. Some recent experiments in the South, the results of which are still unpublished,[1] indicate that keeping freshly cut logs continuously wet produces inconsistent control. The best results in the North have been obtained when logs have been kept wet by use of a continuously operated sprinkler system. Logs floating in water may sometimes be attacked on the upper side unless they are rolled over from time to time. Furthermore, short water treatment does not give permanent immunity. Ambrosia beetles sometimes attack lumber sawn from freshly felled logs, especially large-dimension stock, before it has had time to dry. Careful piling so as to provide for good circulation of air through and around the piles will shorten the period of susceptibility, but of course, kiln drying is preferable, since it gives absolute protection.

Horntails. The horntails, another important group of borers that attack recently killed trees or fresh logs, belong to the family Siricidae of the order Hymenoptera. They are very common insects and are responsible for more damage to logs than is usually ascribed to them. Although many species are known to science, little detailed information is known concerning their life histories and habits. Unlike the ambrosia beetles, the horntails are wood-eating insects (xylophagous). They work in solid wood, maintain no opening to the outside, and apparently are not necessarily associated with any fungi. One of the largest and best-known members of this group is said to be an exception to the above rule in that it bores only in decaying wood. This is the species known as the pigeon tremex, *Tremex columba.*

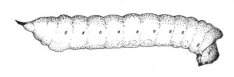

FIGURE 99. Horntail larvae. Although the group name was presumably derived from the conspicuous ovipositor of the adult female, it is, nevertheless, equally appropriate for the larvae with their hornlike caudal appendage. (U.S. Dept. Agr. Forst Service.)

The adults are thick-waisted wasplike insects. They vary greatly in size, some being less than ½ inch in length whereas others are more than 2 inches long. Black is the predominant color, but nearly all species have markings of yellow or orange. Projecting beyond the end of the abdomen, the female bears a hornlike projection from which the group name is derived. This is the ovipositor sheath. The larvae are white legless grubs,

[1] H. R. Johnston, personal conversation.

cylindrical in form and armed with a dark-colored spine on the end of the abdomen.

The adults of most species fly in spring and early summer. The females, by means of their long ovipositors, insert their eggs into solid wood. This is no mean feat when we consider the flexibility of the ovipositor and the solidity of the wood. Sometimes a female may get her ovipositor wedged into the wood so that she is unable to extricate herself. Horntails are particularly abundant and especially injurious in fire-killed forests. The scorched trees seem to be especially attractive to the adults. Trees killed by spring fires are much more subject to attack by these insects than are trees killed at other seasons of the year.

The horntail larvae tunnel through the wood and cut burrows just large enough for their bodies. The wood passes through their digestive tracts and is packed behind them as they advance. The length of the larval stage appears to be variable, even with the same species, and depends upon conditions of temperature and moisture. With most species the larval stage requires one or two seasons. When growth is completed, the larvae cut their pupal chambers in the peripheral layers of the sapwood. In logs the pupal cells are usually constructed on the upper side so that, although the larval tunnels may be distributed throughout the log, the majority of exit holes are on top.

Water treatment and prompt utilization are the best ways to prevent injury by these insects. A residual spray applied during early summer should prevent oviposition but would not kill larvae already in the wood. These borers may continue to work in lumber sawed from infested logs. Kiln drying gives good control of larvae in sawed materials.

ATTACKING MOIST SEASONED WOOD

Insects in the moist-wood group attack the moist heartwood of living trees or wood that has been cut or dead for at least a year but is partially moist as a result of contact with the ground or other moist material. These insects are usually associated with protozoa, fungi, and bacteria, organisms which aid the insects by converting the indigestible cellulose and lignin into materials that are more digestible. Because of the microorganisms present in it, moist and decaying deadwood provides very suitable food conditions for its insect inhabitants. Indirect proof of this is found in the fact that moist and decaying deadwood is attacked directly by many insects, even more than those gaining a living in green wood. The dietetic relationship of insects with these microorganisms offers a fertile field for future investigations. Some of the moist-wood insects may be found in scars in the sapwood and the heartwood of living trees, but they are usually pests of forest products in contact with the ground. Some of these wood borers, such as the carpenter ant, do not obtain their food within the wood but use their tunnels in log or tree for a sheltered base from which to conduct foraging expeditions and for a nursery for their young. The carpenter bees, the leafcutter bees, and the carpenter ants are common examples of insects that make nests in wood but obtain their food from outside the nest. None of them are very exacting in their moisture requirements, but they are nearly always found in moist wood. Their chief requirement, however, seems to be softness. For this reason, they are likely to be associated with decaying wood.

The leafcutter bees, although common, are not usually of economic importance because they work singly. The carpenter bees, on the other hand, commonly work in groups, maintain moisture conditions to their liking, and by their combined activities seriously injure the wood attacked. Their nests are often found in wooden pillars and rails. They may easily be controlled in such situations by injecting an oil solution of DDT or benzene hexachloride into the tunnels.

Carpenter Ants. The carpenter ants, the commonest species of which is *Camponotus pennsylvanicus,* are widely distributed in the United States and Canada. They are large black ants, sometimes ½ inch or more in length. They build their nests in soft or decaying wood, and there they rear their young well protected from the attack of enemies. They are social insects, living together in large colonies. These ants do not have as many castes as do the termites, which will be discussed later, but there is a distinct division of labor within the nest. Three castes are recognized: the kings and the queens, which are the true males and females, and the workers, which are sexually imperfect females. Although the workers are all similar in appearance, each has her own work to do. As in the honeybee hive, some of the workers care for the young, others care for the queen, while still others collect food. Like many other ants, the carpenter ant may care for aphids and, by husbanding these noxious insects, may be indirectly responsible for their damage.

The life history of the carpenter ant is very interesting. In brief, it is as follows: In early summer the young males and females leave the nest. Being winged at that time, they fly in all directions; sometimes the air is filled with these flying ants emerging simultaneously from many nests. This is known as the swarming period, but unlike the bees, in swarming, the young males and females leave the nest at the same time, unattended by workers. It would be much better to call this the mating flight, for that is really what it is.

Shortly after mating, the males die while the young females may either be taken into old-established colonies to replace a decrepit queen or each may establish a new colony. In the latter case, the young queen seeks out a small cavity in a tree or piece of timber and there makes up her brood cell by completely enclosing the cavity, leaving no exit or entrance. She then breaks off her wings, for they are no longer of any use to her. After sealing herself in, she does not feed again until her first brood of young is mature (Wheeler, 1910). She deposits only a few eggs in the brood cell. When they hatch, the larvae are fed a material secreted from the salivary glands of the female. The young then complete their larval development, spin their cocoons, pupate, and emerge as adults, without any other food than that furnished by the mother from her own body. The ants of the first brood are workers of very small size. As soon as they are mature, they take over the work of the nest. They cut approximately parallel, concentric galleries running longitudinally through the wood to accommodate the enlarging colony and bring the organic food on which they live into the nest through openings cut to the outside, sometimes called windows. The young workers feed the queen and care

FIGURE 100. This carpenter-moth gallery has been kept open by carpenter ants for 30 years. (U.S. Dept. Agr. Forest Service.)

for the eggs that she lays and the larvae that hatch from these eggs. They feed the young, after the first brood, upon secretions from their mouths. The nurses carry both the larvae and pupae from place to place in the nest in an effort to keep them under the most favorable conditions; also, when the young adults are fully developed, they are assisted from the cocoon and treated with the greatest consideration. As the colony grows, more galleries are cut in the wood in order to enlarge the nest.

Carpenter ants build their nests in a great variety of places. They may attack the dead moist heartwood of living trees, or they may hollow out logs, house timbers, or almost any wood materials that are soft. It has been stated frequently that these insects attack only decaying wood. This is not entirely true, although the original attack is usually in a decayed spot. In trees having hard wood, the work is confined to decayed wood; in trees having soft wood such as cedar, the nests are often constructed in solid wood. The chief requirement is that the wood be soft and relatively moist. The carpenter ant does its greatest economic injury to house timbers in contact with the ground, in the basal portion of poles, and in standing trees with moist soft wood. Eastern white cedar is especially susceptible to injury by these insects; in fact attack by ants is one of the most frequent causes of defect in that species. In some places 20 percent of the trees that are cut show ant injury. The nests are usually built near the base of the tree where the wood is moist, the highest being not much more than 8 or 10 feet above the ground. The exact location of a nest can be determined by the position of the windows, openings through which the ants enter and leave the nests.

Much unavoidable loss is occasioned by injury caused by ants to eastern white cedar. In trees grown on swampy ground there is an average unavoidable loss of about 3 feet from the butt of every ant-infested cedar whereas on higher ground the average is estimated to be almost 6 feet. A part of this is, of course, due to butt rot. However, an average loss of about 2 feet from the butt of every ant-infested tree is a conservative estimate.

Control of these insects may be accomplished in several ways. The simplest method is to inject an insecticide into the nest through the entrance hole. Several of the synthetic organics, especially DDT, benzene hexachloride, and chlordane in oil solution, are suitable for this purpose. If buildings are set upon stone or concrete foundations, they will be dry and will not usually provide suitable nesting places for these insects. Poles treated full length with pentachlorophenol are not subject to attack. In the forest the ants gain entrance to the trees only through injuries. Therefore, surface injuries such as axe marks, fire scars, and logging injuries should be kept to the minimum in order to avoid infestation by ants.

Chestnut Pole Borer.   The chestnut pole borer, *Parandra brunnea*, is another insect that is a frequent pest of wood that is not too dry. It is widely distributed, probably occurring in all hardwood areas in the

United States and Canada. The larvae are elongate, cylindrical grubs, like the other roundheaded borers. The adults are glossy, chestnut-brown beetles about ¾ inch in length.

This insect attacks posts, poles, and the moist dead heartwood of standing trees of many different hardwood species. It was so common in chestnut, especially in trees killed by the chestnut blight, that it has been called the chestnut pole borer. Even though it attacks living trees, it cannot be regarded as a primary insect, since it can gain entrance into the tree only through a wound and then works in the moist dead heartwood. Thus a tree is in very little danger of attack as long as it is not injured in such a way that the heartwood is exposed. The chestnut pole borer usually confines its activities to the lower parts of the tree trunks or to the portion of a post or a pole near the ground line.

The adults emerge in late July and August and soon thereafter begin to oviposit. The females place their eggs in niches cut in the surface of deadwood or in the walls of old galleries. One egg is laid in each niche. In from 2 to 3 weeks the larvae hatch and take up their labors as wood borers. They tunnel through the heartwood and to a lesser degree in the sapwood, making irregular tortuous galleries that may be several feet in length. As they progress through the wood, they pack the frass behind them in the gallery. Many larvae work together in a limited area, with the result that the entire heart of the tree, at the point of attack, may be destroyed. Soon organisms of decay join the borer in its pernicious work, and the pole becomes weakened and breaks off. It is probable that the larvae require 3 years for their full development. On reaching full growth, they hollow out cells in the wood, where they transform to pupae and later to adults. The adults then cut their way to the outside.

The attack of this insect can be prevented by the usual kinds of preservative treatment. Full-length treatment is best, but if the poles or posts are given a butt treatment that extends at least 1 foot above the ground, they will be reasonably well protected.

Subterranean Termites. Among the wood destroyers the termites comprise a most important group. These insects may be separated into three divisions on the basis of their habits: the moist-wood termites, the subterranean termites, and the dry-wood termites. The first group is relatively unimportant economically, since it is usually confined to wood that is largely buried in the ground, and therefore these termites seldom attack materials of value. Members of the second group are by far the most important and widely distributed and will be discussed in this section. The third group are more restricted in distribution but are destructive in localities where they occur. They will be discussed in the section on dry-wood insects.

The subterranean termites make their nests in wood buried in the ground where the required moisture conditions prevail, but unlike the moist-wood termites, they are able to work out from the nest and invade wooden structures aboveground. They must, however, always maintain moist conditions in their tunnels aboveground. To do this their aboveground activities must be connected with the subterranean nest. It is for this reason that these insects are discussed in this section.

FIGURE 101. Termites *Reticulitermes virginicus*. (A) Alate queen; (B) dealate queen; (C) worker; (D) soldier; (E) secondary reproductive. (U.S. Dept. Agr. Forest Service.)

The termites are especially injurious in tropical parts of the world. In temperate lands, however, their activities are serious enough to cause concern as far north as Massachusetts, southern Michigan, southern Minnesota, and the north Pacific Coast states. Their greatest damage is to wooden buildings, posts, poles, and railroad ties. In a building that is not properly constructed, their attack may so weaken the structure as to cause collapse.

The termites, like other insects that eat wood, are faced with a difficult nutritional problem. The material that they eat is chiefly cellulose, one of the most difficult of organic substances to digest. The relation between wood-eating insects and fungi has already been mentioned, and it seems probable that fungi may also be helpful in termite nutrition. Studies of termites have shown that these insects are provided with an intestinal fauna of protozoans that is directly responsible for the digestion of the cellulose eaten by the insects. Without these symbiotic helpers, the termites would starve, even though they continued to ingest wood. How general such relations are among wood-boring insects is not known, but it is reasonable to suspect that they are common.

Subterranean termites are social insects somewhat antlike in appearance and live in colonies composed of a number of castes. Each caste has a more or less specific function to perform, and each will be mentioned in the following discussion of their biology. The primary reproductives, usually called kings and queens, are the only members of the colony that at any time have functional wings. These dark-colored long-winged males and females swarm out of the nest at certain seasons of the year for the purpose of mating and establishing new colonies. The common termite of the eastern United States, *Reticulitermes flavipes*, swarms early in the spring. After a brief flight period, they break off their wings and the pairs that survive their hazardous expedition seek suitable locations for new nests in wood buried in the soil. Eggs are deposited, and the first broods of young are cared for by the young queen. Later she devotes her efforts entirely to egg production. The nymphs develop in such a manner that each becomes adapted for special duties. Some become workers, some soldiers, some primary reproductives, and some secondary or supplementary reproductives. The last develop when the true king or queen dies or when the colony becomes very large. Most of the nymphs develop into wingless workers, which comprise the laboring class, or into large-mandibled soldiers. These two castes form the major part of the colony. A smaller proportion of the nymphs develop wing pads and later become winged males and females. In addition to the nymphs that develop into winged adults, there are others with shorter wing pads or without wing pads, which may develop into the supplementary reproductives. According to Pickens (Kofoid, 1934), these supplementary reproductives in the case of the western subterranean termite, *Reticulitermes hesperus*, develop more rapidly than the primary reproductives; they are at least as prolific individually and may live peaceably together several in a cell. Thus their presence speeds up materially the growth of a colony. He points out that the growth of the primary colony is very slow and accounts for the rapid infestation of buildings by the combination of several primary colonies, the elimination of all but one pair of primary reproductives, and the development of many supplementary reproductives.

FIGURE 102. Termite damage and colony. *Reticulitermes virginicus* in southern pine. (U.S. Dept. Agr. Forest Service.)

Termites may sometimes be in a building a long time before making their presence known by swarming or by the failure of the timbers weakened by their mining. Their activities are mostly within the wood, but careful inspection will often reveal the presence of exploratory or bridging passages.

The subterranean termites always enter wooden structures from the ground, where the nest is located. The nest may be in a tree stump, in pieces of waste wood buried near the foundation or under the building, or in other similar wood materials. From these nests the termites construct tunnels through the ground and covered passages over foundation walls and other objects too hard for them to tunnel. Thus their injurious work may be some distance from the nest, but they must, as we have said, maintain a continuous contact with the soil. The loss of such contact is fatal.

Therefore, the best way to protect wooden structures from the attack of subterranean termites is to build in such a manner as to separate effectively the untreated wood from the soil by solid good-quality concrete or metal. Detailed specifications for the termite-proofing of buildings will be found in references cited in the bibliography. In general, the following points should be observed:

1. Clean up all waste wood under and about buildings and remove all tree stumps before grading.

2. Set buildings on concrete foundations at least 18 inches above the ground, using a good cement mix either for a poured wall or for laying up a stone or block wall.

3. Capping foundations with a metal termite shield with tight joints between sections will prevent the insects from entering the building through cracks in the foundation.

4. Use a good cement mix for basement floors and close expansion joints with pitch or metal.

5. Keep all untreated wood away from contact with the ground.

The best time to control termites in a building is at the time of construction. If, however, a building becomes infested, steps must be taken to construct a physical or chemical barrier, or both, between the nest and the infested wood. Also nests and potential nesting places near the building should be destroyed.

It is advisable although not essential to use sills that have been effectively treated against termites or sills of resistant species such as redwood, southern cypress, the heartwood of longleaf pine, western red cedar, Monterey cypress, or western white cedar. Snyder (1948) lists several other less common North American woods that proved resistant during a 5-year test in infested ground. Some resistant tropical woods are, according to Snyder, teak, sal, camphorwood, and cypress pine.

A number of materials may be used in treating wood to protect it against the attack of termites. One of the most satisfactory and effective methods is pressure treatment with creosote or pentachlorophenol. Brush treatments give some protection but are by no means so certain as the pressure method.

With the advent of modern synthetic insecticides, especially the chlorinated hydrocarbons, the use of chemical barriers for preventing access of termites to buildings received a great impetus. For many years tests have been conducted at the Gulfport laboratory of the U.S. Forest Service, Southern Forest Experiment Station, to determine the effectiveness and longevity of various chemicals (Johnston, 1963). The following substances have been tested as soil poisons against termites for varying lengths of time with the following results.

SUBSTANCE	FAILED AFTER	EFFECTIVE AFTER
Aldrin, 0.5% (actual) in water emulsion	. . . .	13 years
Chlordane, 1.0% (tech) in water emulsion	. . . .	14 years
Dieldrin, 0.5% (actual) in water emulsion	. . . .	13 years
Heptachlor, 0.5 %(actual) in water emulsion	. . . .	10 years
Benzene hexachloride, 0.8%	12 years*	7 years
DDT, 8.0% (tech) in oil	14 years*	5 years

* Less than 50 percent effective.

Chemical barriers are usually applied to the soil outside foundation walls at the rate of 4 gallons per 10 lineal feet for surface treatment when the foundation is solid concrete without cracks. If the foundation is not solid, the treatment should be made to the depth of the footings, the above lineal dosage for each foot of depth. Under a concrete slab the recommended dosage is 4 gallons per 10 square feet for overall treatment.

Termites seem to be increasing in abundance in the north and central parts of the United States, and it is often felt that they are extending their range northward. Modern styles in residence architecture that demand very low foundations may be a stimulus to the multiplication of these insects. Another factor of importance in causing these insects to increase may be indirectly associated with the use of steam shovels for basement excavations. This method of excavation usually leaves a large space in the ground outside the foundation wall into which wood waste inevitably falls during construction. There is a tendency on the part of builders not only to leave this wood in the trench but also to throw in other waste material, knowing that it will be effectively hidden by grading. In this way ideal conditions for termites are created.

Several states and many individual communities have incorporated into their building codes the minimum protective practices that should always be employed in localities where termites are serious pests (Chamberlin, 1949). Such regulations provide for approval by building inspectors and appear to be the only way to ensure satisfactory construction. When buildings become infested and control becomes necessary, the objective will be to destroy the colony or colonies or, if this is impossible, to place a barrier between the colony and the infested building.

ATTACKING DRY SEASONED WOOD

In the preceding sections of this chapter, those insects that usually attack moist wood have been studied. Now we come to a group of insects that are able to attack sound dry wood. There are comparatively few groups of insects that are able to live throughout their entire developmental period in this medium. It has been a constant question to entomologists how any insect can digest sterile wood. This has now been explained for the termites, as we have already seen, by the presence of an intestinal fauna capable of digesting cellulose, but it has not been demonstrated for most other wood eaters. It seems likely that this symbiotic relationship may be characteristic of most, if not all, of the dry-wood insects.

Powderpost Beetles.   The name powderpost beetle is applied to representatives of several small families of the Coleoptera that feed upon dry wood. The two families that contain most of the powderpost species are the Bostrychidae and the Lyctidae. In America, the species of the genus *Lyctus* are the most common insects of this group. *Lyctus planicollis*, *Lyctus parallelopipedus*, and *Lyctus cavicollis* are three common species of these beetles.

These beetles are called powderpost beetles because of their effect upon the wood in which they work. They may reduce the entire interior of a piece of wood to a fine, flourlike powder, leaving only the exterior shell intact. These beetles are pests of the sapwood of broad-leaved species. Wood of oaks, hickories, ash, and poplars is most frequently injured. Since the heartwood is immune, the injury is always confined to the sapwood.

The powderpost beetles feed only in dry well-seasoned wood. As a rule, a full year of air drying is required before the wood becomes suitable to the taste of these beetles, although small pieces may dry out more rapidly and become susceptible to attack in 8 months after cutting. Kiln-dried material is susceptible to attack as soon as it leaves the kiln.

One full year is required to complete the life cycle of these insects. The adults emerge in early spring, and it is at that time that the injurious work of these pests is most likely to be noticed. It is not at all uncommon during the spring months for dealers in such hardwood products as handles and furniture or specialty stock to discover suddenly that they have been harboring these unwelcome guests. Sometimes when infestation is severe, a merchant's entire supply of axe and shovel handles may be destroyed before he realizes that the insects are present. Occasionally, infested flooring may be laid and finished without anyone realizing that the wood is not perfectly sound, and it is not until the beetles emerge in the spring that their presence is recognized. Even furniture may be infested. When this occurs, it usually happens before the wood has been finished. After the insects emerge, the wood may be peppered with the small round, exit holes.

FIGURE 103. Bostrychid tunnels in eucalyptus. The larvae of this insect, *Scobicia declivis*, pack the frass in the tunnels as they bore through the wood. This habit is characteristic of most bostrychids.

During the brief period of flight, mating takes place and the females seek out suitable places for oviposition. The eggs of the lyctus powder-post beetles are laid in pores of the sapwood. When the young larvae hatch, they find themselves in a desirable location and immediately proceed to make the best of their opportunities. Their first meal consists of the remains of the eggs from which they hatched, but from then on they find sustenance in the solid dry wood. The larvae cut irregular winding galleries in the wood, packing behind them, as they progress, the finely pulverized frass. The winter is passed in the larval stage. In early spring the transformation, first to pupae and next to adults, takes place within the wood. The adult beetles then cut their way to the outside.

Prevention is the keynote of powderpost beetle control, because after wood is once infested by these insects, it is usually fit for nothing except firewood. In lumberyards and manufacturing plants where large quantities of hardwood stock must be kept on hand, thorough inspection of wood more than 1 year old should be made annually for the purpose of eliminating any stock that may have become infested. The best time for inspection is in the winter months. Infestation is usually indicated by small quantities of fine borings that sift out of infested pieces. Infested pieces break easily, exposing the powder-filled tunnels to view.

FIGURE 104. Handle stock infested by lyctus powderpost beetles. Observe that only the sapwood is mined, although emergence tunnels may perforate heartwood. (U.S. Dept. Agr. Forest Service.)

In order to simplify inspection, heartwood and sapwood stock should not be piled together. The heartwood is not susceptible and need not be inspected. Wood in storage should be classified according to age because the oldest wood is most likely to be infested. All new stock should be carefully inspected to prevent introducing the beetle into uninfested sheds and storehouses. Any suspicious material should be kept under observation for several months.

Rapid utilization will greatly reduce the chance of infestation in storage sheds inasmuch as wood that is less than 1 year old is never a menace. Woodworking industries should always utilize the oldest stock first. All waste sapwood should be burned or hauled away from woodworking establishments; under no circumstances should it be allowed to accumulate or else powderpost beetles may become established in these waste piles and from there infest the stock piles.

Ordinarily the safest course of procedure in dealing with infested material is to burn it. Sometimes, however, a part of the stock that has not

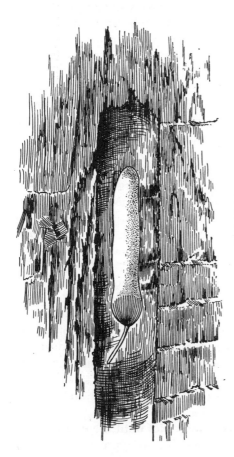

FIGURE 105. Egg of a lyctus powderpost beetle inserted in a pore in a piece of hardwood. (U.S. Dept. Agr. Forest Service.)

been too heavily injured may be saved if the insects working in it can be killed. To accomplish this, the dipping of infested wood in kerosene, an oil solution of DDT, or orthodichlorobenzene has been recommended. Repeated applications of any of these materials to infested wood, by means of a brush or a spray, will kill the insects. These materials will evaporate and leave the wood unstained. In using hot inflammable oils such as kerosene, it should be borne in mind that to heat liquids of this sort over an open flame is to invite disaster. Inflammable oils should always be heated by steam coils arranged in the bottom of the dipping vat.

One of the most effective means of protecting susceptible wood from the attacks of powderpost beetles is by treatment with a sealer such as boiled linseed oil, varnish, or paint. It will be remembered that the lyctus powderpost beetles deposit their eggs only in open pores of wood. Treatment with any of the materials mentioned above will close the pores and prevent oviposition by the beetles. In many lumberyards it is customary to paint the end of hardwood lumber to prevent checking. This treatment also protects the wood against end attack by powderpost beetles. It does not, however, prevent side attack.

Dry-wood Termites. The dry-wood termites are limited in their distribution in the United States to a belt along the Atlantic Coast and the Gulf Coast from Virginia to Texas and thence westward along the Mexican border into California. In California they are found as far north as San Francisco. They attack buildings, posts, poles, fences, and other structures of seasoned wood (Snyder, 1958).

In many respects the life cycle and the nest organization of the dry-wood termites are similar to those of the subterranean termites. In other respects they are quite different. For example, the dry-wood termites require no contact with the ground; therefore, the new attack may be at any point where the newly mated insects can find unpainted wood in a protected situation.

Unlike the subterranean termites, the dry-wood termite colony is composed chiefly of nymphs. Some of these, immediately after hatching, are soldiers with long mandibles designed for purposes of defense, but most of them are workers that carry on the regular duties of the colony while they are growing to maturity. Some of the nymphs develop into primary winged sexuals, while others may become secondary sexuals without wings.

The winged primary sexuals attack exposed wood in pairs. Open checks or cracks provide favorable locations for these primary attacks. At first the new colony grows very slowly. Not until the elapse of several years would a single primary attack develop to appreciable proportions. Nevertheless buildings, especially those that are not painted, become heavily infested in a season or two. This condition can be explained only by multiple attack. Many pairs may start primary colonies close together. Soon their tunnels coalesce and appear to be a single large colony. Then, supplemented by secondary sexuals, the combined colonies grow rapidly.

When infestation occurs, treatment may be made, using the chemicals discussed in Chaps. 9 and 10. The insecticide should be injected into holes bored into the infested wood. Badly damaged timbers will, of course, have to be replaced. Since such control work is always expensive and usually not permanent, preventive practices are far more desirable. Good construction, with tight joints and with all pieces nailed firmly into place, is the first step in protection against dry-wood termites. This should be followed by thorough painting of all exposed surfaces. Moreover all painted surfaces should be repainted often enough to maintain a protective covering over the wood. Back painting of siding and wood trim with a priming coat of paint or a wood preservative is excellent practice. Finally, watchfulness is of prime importance if infestations are to be detected at an early stage when they can be most effectively treated.

FIGURE 106. The old-house borer, *Hylotrupes bajulus,* causes structural damage to dry pine timbers. (U.S. Dept Agr. Forest Service.)

The Old-House Borer. The old-house borer, *Hylotrupes bajulus,* is a cerambycid beetle that has been introduced into the United States from Europe. It seems to be spreading and becoming more and more abundant in the eastern half of this country. It infests seasoned lumber, mostly pine and spruce. Its common name arises from its prevalence in old houses in Europe. This name is not so appropriate in this country because here it is more common in newer houses.

The adults emerge from infested wood during the summer and deposit their eggs in checks, nail holes, and other openings in the wood surface. The length of the larval period varies greatly. If the wood is very dry and temperature is predominantly cool, the development may extend for many years. If conditions are more favorable, the larval period may be completed within a few years.

The same timbers are attacked generation after generation until the sapwood is honeycombed with tunnels. The timbers become weakened and must be replaced.

In accessible timbers brush treatment or spraying with DDT or another chlorinated hydrocarbon can, if thoroughly done, bring an infestation under control. One should bear in mind that some of these materials are highly toxic to man and precautions in their use must be observed. The use of benzene hexachloride and chlordane should be avoided in closed inhabited spaces. Endrin should never be used inside buildings. DDT is probably safest of the chlorinated hydrocarbons.

DDT combined with pentachlorophenol is excellent for treating infested materials but should be used only when ventilation is good. In inaccessible timbers only fumigation can control an infestation. Such treatment should be entrusted only to an experienced operator. Methyl bromide is a most effective fumigant but must be used with caution (McIntire, 1961).

MARINE WOOD BORERS

The wood-boring insects are so numerous and their work is so conspicuous and so familiar to everyone that we are sometimes prone to think only of insects when we consider wood-boring organisms. As a matter of fact, however, wood provides food or shelter for many other forms of life. Among the most important of these from the economic standpoint are the marine borers. In the strictest interpretation of the scope of forest entomology, these organisms would be excluded, but inasmuch as they are often thought to be insects by the layman and are responsible for tremendous losses wherever wood is used in salt water, it seems appropriate that at least a brief discussion of them should be included here. The most destructive of the marine wood borers are the bivalve mollusks called shipworms. Much damage also results from the activities of several genera of marine crustaceans called wood lice. The most common genus of these crustaceans is *Limnoria*. Each of these groups will be considered in turn.

Shipworms. The shipworms belonging to the genera *Bankia* and *Teredo* have been known to maritime peoples since the dawn of history and have been studied periodically from earliest times. When we consider the time that has been spent upon the study of these creatures by investigators in centuries past, it is surprising that we know so little about them. The imperfect state of our knowledge concerning this group is emphasized by the statement of Bartsch, published in 1922, to the effect that ". . . the complete life history of not a single species is known today." Although much more information has been accumulated since this statement was made, much remains to be learned. It is not surprising, therefore, that methods used in the control of these pests are not entirely successful.

In the past, it was thought that there were only a few species of shipworms and that these were practically universal in their distribution. It has now been shown that many species exist and that, for the most part, each one is definitely limited geographically, just as terrestrial organisms are limited to definite ranges by ecological factors. Bartsch, in his "Monograph of American Shipworms," lists 30 distinct species that inhabit the waters of the Western Hemisphere.

FIGURE 107. On the left, teredo marine borer tunnels in a piece of piling. Each tunnel is lined with a smooth calcareous material secreted by the borer. On the right is a piece of piling infested heavily with wood lice. Neither of these organisms is insects.

Shipworms attack all kinds of wood. Very hard woods are somewhat resistant but are by no means immune to attack. It is said that very soft, porous woods, like palmetto, are also not very attractive to shipworms but nevertheless are attacked. In fact, shipworms will attack any wood that is submerged in salt water. The greatest damage is done to piling. The replacement cost of piling destroyed annually by these animals is tremendous. Table 14 gives some idea of the rapid destruction of piling that may occur in warm salt water. It indicates that injury by shipworms is greater in warm water than in cold. On the Atlantic Coast, the pest is not serious north of the Chesapeake Bay, although some species are able to live as far north as the Maine coast. On the Pacific Coast, the warm waters of the Japan current make conditions favorable as far north as

Alaska. Temperature, however, is not the only limiting factor in the life of these animals; salinity of the water has an influence upon them. Fresh water is decidedly detrimental; this probably explains the comparatively long life of piling at Norfolk, Virginia.

The shipworms in early life are free-swimming organisms and are provided with a bivalve shell. After certain stages have been passed in the water, the young mollusks attach themselves to submerged wood. They then bore into the wood leaving very small openings to the outside. Under favorable developmental conditions, a pile may be attacked by thousands of these tiny creatures. Once inside the wood, they grow rapidly and enlarge the tunnel to suit their increased size. The shell is used as a boring

TABLE 14   Life of Pine Piling in Different Localities*

LOCALITY	LENGTH OF LIFE, MONTHS	
	AVERAGE	MINIMUM
Colon, Panama	10	
Norfolk, Va.	60	12
Newport News, Va.	24	
Hampton Roads, Va.	18	
St. Andrews, Fla.	30	
Pensacola, Fla.	30	12
Fort Morgan, Ala.	..	12
West Pascagoula, Miss.	30	12
Texas City, Tex.	12	1
Galveston, Tex.	18	5
Aransas Pass, Tex.	12	3
Puget Sound, Wash.	12	
Klawak, Alaska	36	18

* Smith, *U.S. Dept. Agr. Forest Serv. Circ.* 128.

tool and is no longer needed for protection of the body. The animal, in its burrow, is elongate and soft-bodied, with the small chisel-like shell at the anterior end of the body and, at the posterior end, two tubes that are the exhalant and inhalant siphons. Some of the larger species of shipworms may attain a length of 4 feet under favorable conditions, while other species may never exceed 5 inches in length. As the shipworm develops within its tunnel, it secretes a calcareous, shell-like material, which is used to line the burrow. This lining is thicker in soft porous woods and thinner in harder woods.

Considerable diversity of opinion has been expressed concerning the food of the shipworms. Some authorities maintain that the wood passes unchanged through their digestive tract and that their entire food consists of plankton drawn in through the inhalant siphon. Several investigators have demonstrated, however, that this is not altogether true. Although plankton probably forms a considerable part of the shipworm's diet, about 80 percent of the cellulose and from 15 to 16 percent of the hemicelluloses contained in a Douglas-fir pile are lost during the passage of the wood through the digestive tract of *Teredo navalis*. Also, the proportion of reducing sugars is found much higher in the caecum of *Bankia setacea* than in the original wood (Dove and Miller, 1923; Miller and Boynton, 1926). From these observations, we must conclude that at least a part of the wood that passes through the digestive tract of these animals is digested and assimilated.

Owing to the fact that the entrance hole into the wood is very small and inconspicuous, there is usually little indication externally of the presence of the borers. More than one-half of the volume of a pile might easily be destroyed without any evidence of injury being apparent on the surface. Only by cutting into the pile can its condition be ascertained. The portion of a pile that is most susceptible to shipworm injury is that between mean tidewater mark and about 4 feet below low water. The entrance holes are usually in this portion of the pile, although active boring may extend several feet above or below the point of entry.

Control of shipworms is theoretically a simple matter, but practically, it is anything but simple. Protecting the susceptible parts of piling with any sort of covering will prevent the attack of these pests. Metal sheathing of copper or any other metal is effective but expensive and not very durable owing to the corroding action of salt water. Cement casings of various kinds have been suggested and experimented with but have not proved satisfactory because of cracks that are almost certain to develop as the result of expansion and contraction or of wave action or the battering of driftwood. Likewise, coatings of tar, asphalt, pitch, and other similar materials give protection while they remain intact, but a single blow from a piece of floating debris may easily open the way for infestation. Unbarked piling is not susceptible to shipworm attack while the bark remains intact, but it is next to impossible to find a pile with no break in the bark. The success of all these mechanical-barrier methods of protection depends upon the maintenance of an unbroken covering, for the smallest break opens the wood to an attack that may easily result in the complete destruction of the pile. The only really successful method of protecting piling against shipworms that has been developed so far is impregnation with creosote or other suitable preservative. Surface treatment is not sufficient. Only by pressure treatments or by alternate hot- and cold-bath treatment can the wood be sufficiently impregnated to resist attack. Satisfactory impregnation is impossible to obtain with dense hardwoods; therefore only pine, Douglas fir, or other porous softwoods should be used.

Movable structures and boats may be protected by an unbroken covering of paint. When borers have gained entrance into wooden vessels, they can be killed by running the boats into fresh water.

Wood Louse.   The wood louse, *Limnoria,* is another of the marine borers that does considerable damage along the Atlantic Coast. It is confined to clear salt water and cannot endure fresh or turbid water. Its temperature range is much greater than that of the shipworms, and as a result, it is found much farther north. It is very common along the New England coast and in the Bay of Fundy.

The wood louse is a crustacean only about ⅛ inch long and suggests in form a very small sowbug. *Limnoria* is gregarious and attacks piling and other structures in large numbers, usually near low-water mark. As a general rule, the greater the difference between high and low tide, the greater will be the vertical distribution of these organisms.

Limnoria finds both food and shelter in the wood that it attacks. Each individual gallery is short, about ½ inch in length, and penetrates directly into the wood. When large numbers attack a pile, their tunnels almost touch, so that the thin walls between them are quickly worn away by wave action, leaving a new surface of wood ready for reinfestation. The progress of this injury is slower but more easily seen than the work of the shipworms. Heavily infested piling may lose 1 inch a year in diameter as a result of *Limnoria* attack. The control of *Limnoria* may be accomplished by impregnating wood exposed to salt water with creosote or other suitable preservative.

LOOKING AHEAD

In concluding a book of this sort, we may be permitted to look toward the future for some indication of what may be in store for the forest entomologist. Forest entomology, as it is actually applied in the field, is becoming more and more a part of forestry. The young forest entomologist in his first job is likely to be assigned to survey work. He may be surprised to find himself using a compass, an axe, a diameter tape, and a tally sheet more often than a microscope or pinning forceps. If he cannot use the ordinary tools of the forester, many jobs in forest entomology will be closed to him. He will be called upon to evaluate insect injury, and as soon as he has shown sufficient competence and judgment, he will be expected to advise forest managers on the practical problems of control and to direct control operations.

Increasing Interest.   These practical demands upon the forest entomologist have arisen as a result of increasing interest on the part of forest managers in the damage that insects are causing. They are beginning to realize that insects have been killing more timber than man has been utilizing and that much of this damage is unnecessary because many of these pests can be controlled. Some forest managers still wait until an insect outbreak gets under way before calling for help, but most of them are beginning to realize that they themselves can do much to prevent losses due to insects. Many of them are beginning to recognize that forests differ in their degree of susceptibility to insect attack and are taking these differences into consideration when acquiring forest properties. Furthermore, they have learned that, by certain forest practices, they can do much to reduce the danger of excessive insect multiplication, and when indirect methods fail, they are applying the various methods of direct control.

Some companies are now employing technically trained forest entomologists to apply both preventive and corrective forest-insect control. These men are expected to adapt known control practices to the specific conditions existing on the company's lands and to instruct woods foremen in when and how to apply certain practices.

Shift in Emphasis. All this increased interest in forest entomology has resulted in a shift of emphasis from taxonomy and natural history to control, both preventive and corrective. Henceforth, the forest entomologist not only must know forest insects and their habits but must have a practical understanding of forestry and forest-insect control practices. The adoption of the Forest Pest Control Act was an outgrowth of increased interest and has contributed greatly toward the shift of emphasis toward control.

In the eastern United States we have seen the passing of the virgin forests and their replacement with second-growth stands and plantations. As a result, the emphasis has shifted from insects affecting mature trees to those attacking young forests. Similarly in the West, a shift of emphasis is evident. As the virgin forest is being replaced with younger stands, there is developing an increasing interest in defoliators, plantation insects, and other pests of the younger trees. Thus it seems certain that in the future bark beetles will assume a position of lesser importance than is the case today. Large-scale control projects for the fir tussock moth and the spruce budworm indicate that the shift of emphasis away from bark beetles is already well under way.

Looming Dangers. Large-scale spraying operations in the forest represent the beginning of a movement, the end of which is difficult to prophesy. It seems evident, however, that, unless these operations are carefully supervised and regulated, they constitute a serious threat to biotic control agencies. Useful as spraying may be in the right place and at the right time, it can never profitably replace natural control. Forest entomologists recognize these hazards, but some forest operators do not. Interest in keeping their equipment busy and their staffs employed will prompt those offering spraying services to search vigorously for spraying jobs. The ready availability of spraying services and fears of some operators may easily lead to spraying projects which are not only unnecessary but actually harmful. Pressure of this sort has already resulted in some areas being sprayed contrary to the advice of competent forest entomologists. This trend constitutes a real danger that cannot be disregarded.

The Forest Pest Control Act, desirable as it is in most respects, carries with it certain potential dangers. The availability of Federal funds to aid states and private industry to control forest pests will doubtless encourage some unwise expenditures. Courage on the part of forest entomologists will be required to prevent the initiation of unnecessary or undesirable projects. A second danger is that such a large proportion of trained manpower will be employed on actual control projects that other essential activities may suffer. If these dangers are recognized, they can be avoided.

Another development in forest practice that should cause concern to the forest entomologist is the trend toward single-species culture, especially in the South. The financial attractiveness of single-species row forestry is so great that even competent forest entomologists may fail to weigh the advantages against the long-term disadvantages. The increased risk of disastrous insect outbreaks entailed by monoculture must not be disregarded. This has been discussed in Chap. 14 but by way of conclusion deserves special mention here. Unless he warns loudly against dangerous practices, the forest entomologist must accept the blame for financial losses attributable thereto.

Some Requirements.   The forest entomologist must realize that, in making decisions concerning control precedures and practices, he is compelled to assume a heavy responsibility. The correct decision may mean the saving of tremendous values in timber, perhaps millions of board feet. The wrong decision may result in correspondingly great losses or unnecessary expense. Therefore, it is never safe to make these decisions blindly. The stakes are too high to permit avoidable gambling.

Conclusions.   The apparent trends and the dangers inherent in them indicate an increasing need for well-trained forest entomologists. The finest type of personnel will be needed in this growing field. It is essential that the forest entomologist be broadly trained not only in insect biology and ecology but also in silvics, silviculture, and forest management. He must learn to be cooperative, and he must be taught how to convey his information to forest operators and other interested people with such effectiveness that they will trust and follow his advice.

Although the great majority of future forest entomologists will be engaged in control activities, there will always be need for some who are especially trained in the field of research and teaching. Through the activities of the researcher, we shall gain a better understanding of the complex forces that determine the rise and fall of insect populations, we shall learn new methods of forest-insect control, and we shall gain new insight into the multiplicity of other forest-insect problems. These research men must receive even broader basic training than the man engaged chiefly in control. Not every forest entomologist will be adapted to doing research work. The researcher, in addition to the expected qualities of intelligence and training, must have imagination, patience, and a high degree of intellectual honesty: imagination to visualize possible solutions of his problems, patience to perform the drudgery of collecting and analyzing data, and intellectual honesty to prevent him from arriving at unjustified conclusions. Some researchers must also be teachers who devote their energies toward training men needed for control, research, and other forest entomological work.

If our schools of forestry can turn out forest entomologists with the sort of training described above and likewise forest managers and silviculturists equipped by training to cooperate with these entomologists, forests in the future will have a chance of avoiding many of the terrific insect losses suffered in the immediate past. If knowledge and cooperation go hand in hand, the outlook for effective forest-insect control is bright.

BIBLIOGRAPHY CHAPTER 20

Ambrosia beetles:
   Dyer, E. D. A., 1963. *Can. Entomologist,* **95:** 624–631.
   ———, and J. M. Kinghorn, 1961. *Can. Entomologist,* **93:** 746–759.
   Felt, E. P., 1905. *N.Y. State Museum Mem.* 8, pp. 289–293.
   Finnegan, R. J., 1963. *Can. Entomologist,* **95:** 137–139.
   Hopkins, A. D., 1905. *U.S. Dept. Agr. Bur. Entomol. Circ.* 82, pp. 1–4.
   Hubbard, H. G., 1897. *U.S. Dept. Agr. Div. Entomol. n. s. Bull.* 7.
   Johnson, N. E., 1958. *J. Forestry,* **56:** 508–511.
   Kinghorn, J. M., and J. A. Chapman, 1959. *Forest Sci.,* **5:** 81–92.
   Prebble, M. L., and K. Graham, 1957. *Forest Sci.,* **3:** 90–112.
   St. George, R. A., 1941. *U.S. Dept. Agr. Farmers' Bull.* 1582.
Buprestid dry-wood borer, *Chrysophana placida* Lec.:
   Burke, H. E., 1917. *J. Econ. Entomol.,* **10:** 406–407.
   Keen, F. P., 1952. *U.S. Dept. Agr. Misc. Publ.* 273.
Carpenter ant, *Camponotus pennsylvanicus* (DeGeer):
   Friend, R. B., and A. B. Carlson, 1937. *Conn. Agr. Exp. Sta. Bull.* 403.
   Graham, S. A., 1918. *Minn. State Entomol. Rept.* 17, pp. 32–40.
   Wheeler, W. M., 1910. "Ants: Their Structure, Development, and Behavior."
   Sanders, C. J., 1964. *Can. Entomologist,* **96:** 894–909.
Carpenter bee, *Xylocopa virginica* (Drury):
   Nininger, H. H., 1916. *J. Entomol., Zoöl.,* **8:** 157–166.
Horntails:
   Felt, E. P., 1905. *N.Y. State Museum Mem.* 8, pp. 667–669.

Harrington, W. H., 1883. *Ontario Entomol. Soc. Rept.* 14, 40–42.

Riley, C. V., 1888. *Insect Life*, 1: 168–179.

Marine borers:

Bartsch, Paul, 1922. *Smithsonian Inst. U.S. Natl. Museum Bull.* 122.

Calman, W. T., 1919. *Brit. Museum (Nat. Hist.), Econ. Ser.* 10.

Clapp, W. F., 1951. American Wood Preservers Association.

Dove, W. H., and R. C. Miller, 1923. *Univ. Cal. Pub. Zoöl.*, **22**: 383–400.

Hill, C. L., and C. A. Kofoid, 1927. San Francisco Bay marine piling committee representative. National Resources Council and American Wood Preservers Association.

Lane, C. E., 1961. *Sci. Am.*, **204**: 132–140, 142.

Miller, R. C., and L. C. Boynton, 1926. *Science, n. s.*, **63**: 524.

Ray, D. E., 1959. University of Washington Press.

Sigerfoos, C. P., 1907. *U.S. Bur. Fish Bull.* 27, pp. 191–231.

Smith, S. C., 1907. *U.S. Dept. Agr. Forest Serv., Circ.* 128, pp. 3–15.

Old-house borer, *Hylotrupes bajulus* (L.):

McIntyre, T., 1961. *U.S. Dept. Agr. Northeast Forest. Expt. Sta. Leaflet* 501.

Parandra borer, *Parandra brunnea* Fabr.:

Brooks, F. E., 1915. *U.S. Dept. Agr. Bull.* 262, pp. 1–7.

Snyder, T. E., 1910. *U.S. Dept. Agr. Bur. Entomol. Bull.* 94, pp. 1–11.

————, 1911. *U.S. Dept. Agr. Bur. Entomol. Circ.* 134.

Powderpost beetles:

Anon., 1954. *U.S. Dept. Agr. Leaflet* 358.

Blake, E. G., 1925. "Enemies of Timber: Dry Rot and the Death-watch Beetle."

Gerberg, E. J., 1957. *U.S. Dept. Agr. Tech. Bull.* 1157.

Johnston, H. R., 1955. *Southern Lumberman*, March.

St. George, R. A., 1943. *U.S. Dept. Agr. Farmers' Bull.* 1582.

Snyder, T. E., 1916. *J. Agr. Res.*, **6**: 273–276.

Wright, C. G., 1959. *Ann. Entomol. Soc. Am.*, **52**: 632–634.

Termites, Isoptera:

Anon., 1949. *U.S. Dept. Agr. Farmers' Bull.* 1911.

Berger, B. G., 1947. *Illinois Nat. Hist. Surv. Circ.* 41.

Emerson, A. E., 1926. *Zoologica (N.Y. Zool. Soc.)*, **7**: 69–100.

Hetrick, L. A., 1950. *J. Econ. Entomol.*, **43**: 57–59.

Johnston, H. R., 1963. *Pest Control Mag.*, February.

Kofoid, C. A. (ed.), et al., 1934. University of California Press, Berkeley, Calif.

McCauley, W. E., and W. P. Flint, 1938. *Illinois Nat. Hist. Surv. Circ.* 30.

St. George, R. A., H. R. Johnston, and R. J. Kowal. *U.S. Dept. Agr. Home Garden Bull.* 64.

Snyder, T. E., 1926. *Quart. Rev. Biol.*, **1**: 522–552.

————, 1948. Revised ed. *U.S. Dept. Agr. Leaflet* 101.

————, 1958. *U.S. Dept. Agr. Farmers' Bull.* 218.

Turner, N., and J. F. Townsend, 1936. *Conn. Expt. Sta. Bull.* 382.

Wolcott, G. N., 1949. *J. Econ. Entomol.*, **42**: 273–275.

Turpentine borer, *Buprestis apricans* Herbst:
  Beal, J. A., 1932. *U.S. Dept. Agr. Circ.* 226.
  Clements, R. W., 1960. *U.S. Dept. Agr. Southeast. Forest Expt. Sta.* (Turpenting Methods) *Manual.*
Western cedar borer, *Trachykele blondeli* Mars.:
  Burke, H. E., 1928. *U.S. Dept. Agr. Tech. Bull.* 48.
  Chamberlin, W. J., 1949. O.S.C. Cooperative Association, lithographed.
  Hopping, G. R., 1932. *Can. Entomologist,* **64:** 189–190.

Page numbers for bibliography references are given in **boldface** type.